INTELLIGENT KNOWLEDGE-BASED SYSTEMS

BUSINESS AND TECHNOLOGY IN THE NEW MILLENNIUM

VOLUME 2
INFORMATION TECHNOLOGY

INTELLIGENT KNOWLEDGE-BASED SYSTEMS

BUSINESS AND TECHNOLOGY IN THE NEW MILLENNIUM

VOLUME 2
INFORMATION TECHNOLOGY

Edited by

CORNELIUS T. LEONDES
University of California, Los Angeles, USA

KLUWER ACADEMIC PUBLISHERS
BOSTON/DORDRECHT/LONDON

Distributors for North, Central and South America:
Kluwer Academic Publishers
101 Philip Drive
Assinippi Park
Norwell, Massachusetts 02061 USA
Telephone (781) 871-6600
Fax (781) 871-6528
E-Mail <kluwer@wkap.com>

Distributors for all other countries:
Kluwer Academic Publishers Group
Post Office Box 322
3300 AH Dordrecht, THE NETHERLANDS
Telephone 31 78 6576 000
Fax 31 78 6576 474
E-Mail <orderdept@wkap.nl>

Electronic Services <http://www.wkap.nl>

Library of Congress Cataloging-in-Publication Data

Intelligent knowledge-based systems : business and technology in the new millennium. / edited by Cornelius T. Leondes.

Includes bibliographical references and index.
Contents: v. 1. Knowledge-based systems—v. 2. Information technology—
v. 3. Expert and agent systems—v. 4. Intelligent systems—
v. 5. Neural networks, fuzzy theory and genetic algorithms.
ISBN 1-40207-746-7 (set)—ISBN 1-40207-824-2 (v.1)—ISBN 1-40207-825-0 (v.2)—
ISBN 1-40207-826-9 (v.3)—ISBN 1-40207-827-7 (v.4)—ISBN 1-40207-828-5 (v.5)
ISBN 1-40207-829-3 (electronic book set)

(LOC information to follow.)

Printed on acid-free paper.
Printed in the United States of America.

CONTENTS

FOREWORD

Almost unknown to the academic world, and to the general public, the application of intelligent knowledge-based systems is rapidly and effectively changing the future of the human species. Today, human well-being is, as it has been for all of history, fundamentally limited by the size of the world economic product. Thus, if human economic well-being (which I personally define as the bottom centile annual per capita income) is ever soon to reach an acceptable level (e.g., the equivalent of $20,000 per capita per annum in 2004), then intelligent knowledge-based systems must be employed in vast quantities. This is primarily because of the reality that few humans live in efficient societies (such as the United States, Canada, Japan, the UK, France, and Germany, for example) and that inefficient societies, many of which are already large, and growing larger, may require many decades to become efficient. In the meantime, billions of people will continue to suffer economic impoverishment—an impoverishment that inefficient human labor cannot remedy. To create the extra economic output so urgently needed, we have only one choice: to employ intelligent knowledge-based systems in great numbers, which will produce economic output prodigiously, but will consume hardly at all.

This multi-volume major reference work, architected by its editor, Cornelius T. Leondes, provides a wealth of 'case studies' illustrating the state of the art in intelligent knowledge-based systems. In contrast to ordinary academic pedagogy, where 'ivory tower' abstraction and elegance are the guiding principles, practical applications require detailed relevant examples that can be used by practitioners to successfully innovate new operational capabilities. The economic progress of the species depends upon the flow of these innovations, which requires multi-volume major reference works with carefully selected, well-written, and well-edited 'case studies.' Professor Leondes knows these realities well, and the five volumes in this work resoundingly reflect his success in achieving their requirements.

Volume 1 addresses Knowledge-Based Systems. These eleven chapters consider the basic question of how accumulated data and staff expertise from business operations can be abstracted into valuable knowledge, and how such knowledge can then be applied to ongoing operations. Wide and representative situations are considered, ranging from product innovation and design, to intelligent database exploitation, to business model analysis.

Volume 2, Information Technology, addresses in ten chapters the important question of how data should be stored and used to maximize its overall value. Case studies consider a wide variety of application arenas: product development, manufacturing, product management, and even product pricing.

Volume 3 addresses Expert and Agent Systems in ten chapters. Application arenas considered include image databases, business process monitoring, e-commerce, and production planning and scheduling. Again, the coverage is designed to provide a wide range of perspectives and business-function concentrations to help stimulate innovation by the reader.

Volume 4, Intelligent Systems, provides nine chapters considering such topics as mission-critical functions, business forecasting, medical patient care, and product design and development.

Volume 5 addresses Neural Networks, Fuzzy Theory, and Genetic Algorithm Techniques. Its ten chapters cover examples in areas including bioinformatics, product life-cycle cost estimating, product development, computer-aided design, product assembly, and facility location.

The examples assembled by Professor Leondes in this work provide a wealth of practical ideas designed to trigger the development of innovation. The contributors to this grand project are to be congratulated for the major efforts they have expended in creating their chapters. Humans everywhere will soon benefit from the case studies provided herein. Intelligent Knowledge-Based Systems: Business and Technology in the New Millennium, is a reference work that belongs on the desk of every innovative technologist.

It has taken many decades of experience and unflagging hard work for Professor Leondes to accumulate the wisdom and judgment reflected in his editorial stewardship of this reference work. Wisdom and judgment are rare—but indispensable—commodities that cannot be obtained in any other way. The world of innovative technology, and the world at large, stand in his debt.

Robert Hecht-Nielsen
Computational Neurobiology
Institute for Neural Computation
Department of Electrical and Computer Engineering
University of California, San Diego

PREFACE

At the start of the 20th century, national economies on the international scene were, to a large extent, agriculturally based. This was, perhaps, the dominant reason for the protraction, on the international scene, of the Great Depression, which began with the Wall Street stock market crash of October, 1929. After World War II the trend away from agriculturally based economies and toward industrially based economies continued and strengthened. Indeed, today, in the United States, approximately only 1% of the population is involved in the agriculture requirements of the US and, in addition, provides significant agriculture exports. This, of course, is made possible by the greatly improved techniques and technologies utilized in the agriculture industry.

The trend toward industrially based economies after World War II was, in turn, followed by a trend toward service-based economies. In the United States today, roughly over 70% of the employment is involved with service industries—and this percentage continues to increase. Separately, the electronic computer industry began to take hold in the early 1960s, and thereafter always seemed to exceed expectations. For example, the first large-scale sales of an electronic computer were of the IBM 650. At that time, projections were that the total sales for the United States would be twenty-five IBM 650 computers. Before the first one came off the projection line, IBM had initial orders for over 30,000. That was thought to be huge by the standards of that day, and today it is a very miniscule number, to say nothing of the fact that its computing power was also very miniscule by today's standards. Computer mainframes continued to grow in power and complexity. At the same time, Gordon Moore, of "Moore's Law" fame, and his colleagues founded INTEL. Then around 1980 MICROSOFT was founded, but it was not until the early 1990s, not that long ago, that WINDOWS were created—incidentally, after the APPLE computer family started. The first browser was the NETSCAPE browser, which appeared in 1995, also not that long ago. Of course, computer networking equipment, most notably CISCO's, also appeared about that time. Toward the end of the last century the "DOT COM bubble" occurred and "burst" around 2000.

Coming to the new millennium, for most of our history the wealth of a nation was limited by the size and stamina of the work force. Today, national wealth is measured in intellectual capital. Nations possessing skillful people in such diverse areas as science, medicine, business, and engineering produce innovations that drive the nation to a higher quality of life. To better utilize these valuable resources, intelligent, knowledge-based systems technology has evolved at a rapid and significantly expanding rate, and can be utilized by nations to improve their medical care, advance their engineering technology, and increase their manufacturing productivity, as well as play a significant role in a very wide variety of other areas of activity of substantive significance.

The breadth of the major application areas of intelligent, knowledge-based systems technology is very impressive. These include the following, among other areas.

Agriculture	Electronics
Business	Engineering
Chemistry	Environment
Communications	Geology
Computer Systems	Image Processing
Education	Information
Management	Military
Law	Mining
Manufacturing	Power Systems
Mathematics	Science
Medicine	Space Technology
Meteorology	Transportation

It is difficult now to imagine an area that will not be touched by intelligent, knowledge-based systems technology.

The great breadth and expanding significance of such a broad field on the international scene requires a multi-volume, major reference work to provide an adequately substantive treatment of the subject, "Intelligent Knowledge-Based Systems: Business and Technology of The New Millennium." This work consists of the following distinctly titled and well integrated volumes.

Volume I.	Knowledge-Based Systems
Volume II.	Information Technology
Volume III.	Expert and Agent Systems
Volume IV.	Intelligent Systems
Volume V.	Neural Networks

This five-volume set on intelligent knowledge-based systems clearly manifests the great significance of these key technologies for the new economies of the new millennium. The authors are all to be highly commended for their splendid contributions, which together will provide a significant and uniquely comprehensive reference source for research workers, practitioners, computer scientists, students, and others on the international scene for years to come.

Cornelius T. Leondes
University of California, Los Angeles
January 5, 2004

CONTRIBUTORS

VOLUME 1: KNOWLEDGE-BASED SYSTEMS

N. Bassiliades
Department of Informatics
Aristotle University of Thessaloniki
Thessaloniki
GREECE
Chapter 6. Aggregator: A Knowledge-Based Comparison Chart Builder for eShopping

Peter Bernus
Griffith University
School of CIT
Nathan
Queensland
AUSTRALIA
Chapter 10. Business Process Modeling and Its Applications in the Business Environment

Mariano Corso
Department of Management Engineering
Polytechnic University of Mailand
Milano
ITALY
Chapter 2. Knowledge Management Systems in Continuous Product Innnovation

Eugenio di Sciascio
Dipartimento Elettrotecnica ed Elettronica
Politecnico di Bari
Bari
ITALY
Chapter 11. Knowledge-Based Systems Technology and Applications in Image Retrieval

Francesco M. Donini
Università della Tuscia
Viterbo
ITALY
Chapter 11. Knowledge-Based Systems Technology and Applications in Image Retrieval

Janis Grundspenkis
Faculty of Computer Science and Information Technology
Riga Technical University
Riga
LATVIA
Chapter 7. Impact of the Intelligent Agent Paradigm on Knowledge Management

P. Humphreys
Faculty of Business and Management
University of Ulster
Northern Ireland
UNITED KINGDOM
Chapter 4. Knowledge-Based Systems Technology in the Make-or-Buy Decision in Manufacturing Strategy

Brane Kalpic
ETI Elektroelement Jt. St. Comp.
Izlake
SLOVENIA
Chapter 10. Business Process Modeling and Its Applications in the Business Environment

Marite Kirikova
Faculty of Computer Science and Information Technology
Riga Technical University
Riga
LATVIA
Chapter 7. Impact of the Intelligent Agent Paradigm on Knowledge Management

F. Kokkoras
Department of Informatics
Aristotle University of Thessaloniki

Thessaloniki
GREECE
Chapter 6. Aggregator: A Knowledge-Based Comparison Chart Builder for eShopping

Shian-Hua Lin
Department of Computer Science and Information Engineering
National Chi Nan University
Taiwan
REPUBLIC OF CHINA
Chapter 5. Intelligent Internet Information Systems in Knowledge Acquisition: Techniques and Applications

Antonella Martini
Faculty of Engineering
University of Pisa
Pisa
ITALY
Chapter 2. Knowledge Management Systems in Continuous Product Innovation

R. McIvor
Faculty of Business and Management
University of Ulster
UNITED KINGDOM
Chapter 4. Knowledge-Based Systems Technology in the Make-or-Buy Decision in Manufacturing Strategy

István Mezgár
CIM Research Laboratory
Computer and Automations Research Institute
Hungarian Academy of Sciences
Budapest
HUNGARY
Chapter 9. Security Technologies to Guarantee Safe Business Processes in Smart Organizations

Marina Mongiello
Dipartimento di Elettrotecnica ed Elettronica
Politecnico di Bari
Bari
ITALY
Chapter 11. Knowledge-Based Systems Technology and Applications in Image Retrieval

Ralf Muhlberger
University of Queensland
Information Technology & Electrical Engineering

Queensland
AUSTRALIA
Chapter 10. Business Process Modeling and Its Applications in the Business Environment

Cezary Orlowski
Gdansk University of Technology
Gdansk
POLAND
Chapter 8. Methods of Building Knowledge-Based Systems Applied in Software Project Management

Emilio Paolucci
Department of Operation and Business Management
Polytechnic University of Turin
Torino
ITALY
Chapter 2. Knowledge Management Systems in Continuous Product Innovation

Luisa Pellegrini
Faculty of Engineering
University of Pisa
Pisa
ITALY
Chapter 2. Knowledge Management Systems in Continuous Product Innovation

Ram D. Sriram
Design and Process Group
Manufacturing Systems Integration Division
National Institute of Standards and Technology
Gaithersburg, Maryland
USA
Chapter 1. Platform-Based Product Design and Development: Knowledge Support Strategy and Implementation

Nikos C. Tsourveloudis
Department of Production Engineering and Management
Technical University of Crete
Chania, Crete
GREECE
Chapter 3. Knowledge-Based Measurement of Enterprise Agility

I. Vlahavas
Department of Informatics
Aristotle University of Thessaloniki

Thessaloniki
GREECE
Chapter 6. Aggregator: A Knowledge-Based Comparison Chart Builder for eShopping

Xuan F. Zha
Design and Process Group
Manufacturing Systems Integration Division
National Institute of Standards and Technology
Gaithersburg, Maryland
USA
Chapter 1. Platform-Based Product Design and Development: Knowledge Support Strategy and Implementation

VOLUME 2: INFORMATION TECHNOLOGY

Aleš Brezovar
Faculty of Mechanical Engineering
University of Ljubljana
Ljubljana
SLOVENIA
Chapter 4. Techniques and Analysis of Sequential and Concurrent Product Development Processes

Chris R. Chatwin
School of Engineering and Information Technology
University of Sussex
Brighton
UNITED KINGDOM
Chapter 3. Modeling Techniques in Integrated Operations and Information Systems in Manufacturing

Ke-Zhang Chen
Department of Mechanical Engineering
The University of Hong Kong
HONG KONG
Chapter 5. Design and Modeling Methods for Components Made of Multi-Heterogeneous Materials in High-Tech Applications

Adrian E. Coronado
Management School
The University of Liverpool
Liverpool
UNITED KINGDOM
Chapter 2. Information Systems Frameworks and Their Applications in Manufacturing Systems

Xin-An Feng
School of Mechanical Engineering
Dalian University of Technology
Dalian
CHINA
Chapter 5. Design and Modeling Methods for Components Made of Multi-Heterogeneous Materials in High-Tech Applications

Janez Grum
Faculty of Mechanical Engineering
University of Ljubljana
Ljubljana
SLOVENIA
Chapter 4. Techniques and Analysis of Sequential and Concurrent Product Development Processes

George Hadjinicola
Department of Public and Business Administration
School of Economics and Management
University of Cyprus
Nicosia
CYPRUS
Chapter 9. Product Design and Pricing in Response to Competitor Entry: A Marketing-Production Perspective

Jared Jackson
IBM Almaden Research Center
San Jose, California
USA
Chapter 7. Web Data Extraction Techniques and Applications Using the Extensible Markup Language (XML)

D. F. Kehoe
Management School
The University of Liverpool
Liverpool
UNITED KINGDOM
Chapter 2. Information Systems Frameworks and Their Applications in Manufacturing Systems

Andreas Koeller
Department of Computer Science
Montclair State University
Upper Montclair, New Jersey
USA
Chapter 6. Quality and Cost of Data Warehouse Views

K. Ravi Kumar
Department of Information and Operations Management
Marshall School of Business
University of Southern California
Los Angeles, California
USA
Chapter 9. Product Redesign and Pricing in Response to Competitor Entry: A Marketing-Production Perspective

Janez Kušar
Faculty of Mechanical Engineering
University of Ljubljana
Ljubljana
SLOVENIA
Chapter 4. Techniques and Analyses of Sequential and Concurrent Product Development Processes

Henry C. W. Lau
Department of Industrial and Systems Engineering
The Hong Kong Polytechnic University
Hunghom
HONG KONG
Chapter 10. Knowledge Discovery by Means of Intelligent Information Infrastructure Methods and Their Applications

Amy Lee
The Ohio State University
Columbus, Ohio
USA
Chapter 6. Quality and Cost of Data Warehouse Views

Choon Seong Leem
School of Computer and Industrial Engineering
Yonsei University
Seoul
KOREA
Chapter 1. Techniques in Integrated Development and Implementation of Enterprise Information Systems

A. C. Lyons
Management School
The University of Liverpool
Liverpool
UNITED KINGDOM
Chapter 2. Information Systems Frameworks and Their Applications in Manufacturing Systems

Jussi Myllymaki
IBM Almaden Research Center
San Jose, California
USA
Chapter 7. Web Data Extraction Techniques and Applications Using the Extensible Markup Language (XML)

Anisoara Nica
Sybase Incorporated
Waterloo, Ontario
Canada
Chapter 6. Quality and Cost of Data Warehouse Views

Jörg Niemann
IFF University of Stuttgart
Fraunhofer IPA
Stuttgart
GERMANY
Chapter 8. Product Life Cycle Management in the Digital Age

Andrew Ning
Department of Industrial and Systems Engineering
The Hong Kong Polytechnic University
Hunghom
HONG KONG
Chapter 10. Knowledge Discovery by Means of Intelligent Information Infrastructure Methods and Their Applications

Elke A. Rundensteiner
Department of Computer Science
Worcester Polytechnic Institute
Worcester Massachusetts
USA
Chapter 6. Quality and Cost of Data Warehouse Views

Marko Starbek
Faculty of Mechanical Engineering
University of Ljubljana
Ljubljana
SLOVENIA
Chapter 4. Techniques and Analyses of Sequential and Concurrent Product Development Processes

Jong Wook Suh
School of Computer and Industrial Engineering
Yonsei University

Seoul
KOREA
Chapter 1. Techniques in Integrated Development and Implementation of Enterprise Information Systems

Qian Wang
School of Engineering and Information Technology
University of Sussex
Brighton
and
Department of Mechanical Engineering
University of Bath
Bath
UNITED KINGDOM
Chapter 3. Modeling Techniques in Integrated Operations and Information Systems in Manufacturing Systems

Engelbert Westkämper
IFF University of Stuttgart
Fraunhofer IPA
Stuttgart
GERMANY
Chapter 8. Product Life Cycle Management in the Digital Age

Christina W. Y. Wong
Department of Industrial and Systems Engineering
The Hong Kong Polytechnic University
Hunghom
HONG KONG
Chapter 10. Knowledge Discovery by Means of Intelligent Information Infrastructure Methods and Their Applications

R. C. D. Young
School of Engineering and Information Technology
University of Sussex
Brighton
UNITED KINGDOM
Chapter 3. Modeling Techniques in Integrated Operations and Information Systems in Manufacturing Systems

VOLUME 3: EXPERT AND AGENT SYSTEMS

Dimitris Askounis
Institute of Communications & Computer Systems
National Technical University of Athens

Athens
GREECE
Chapter 2. Expert Systems Technology in Production Planning and Scheduling

G. A. Britton
Design Research Center
School Of Mechanical and Production Engineering
Nanyang Technological University
SINGAPORE
Chapter 1. Techniques in Knowledge-Based Expert Systems for the Design of Engineering Systems

Jing Dai
School of Computing
National University of Singapore
SINGAPORE
Chapter 9. Finding Patterns in Image Databases

Robert Gay
Institute of Communication and Information Systems
School of Electrical and Electronic Engineering
Nanyang Technological University
SINGAPORE
Chapter 6. Agent-Based eLearning Systems: A Goal-Based Approach

Angela Goh
School of Computer Engineering
Nanyang Technological University
SINGAPORE
Chapter 4. The Knowledge Base of a B2B eCommerce Multi-Agent System

Ivan Romero Hernandez
Technological University of Grenoble
LCIS Research Laboratory
Valence
FRANCE
Chapter 5. From Roles to Agents: Considerations on Formal Agent Modeling and Implementation

Tu Bao Ho
Japan Advanced Institute of Science and Technology
Ishikawa
JAPAN
Chapter 7. Combining Temporal Abstraction and Data-Mining Methods in Medical Data Analysis

Wynne Hsu
School of Computing
National University of Singapore
SINGAPORE
Chapter 9. Finding Patterns in Image Databases

Chun-Che Huang
Department of Information Management
National Chi Nan University
Taiwan
REPUBLIC OF CHINA
Chapter 3. Applying Intelligent Agent-Based Support Systems in Agile Business Processes

K. Karibasappa
Department of Electronics and Telecommunication Engineering
University College of Engineering, Burla
Sambalpur, Orissa
INDIA
Chapter 10. Cognition Techniques and Their Applications

Nelly Kasim
Singapore-MIT Alliance
National University of Singapore
SINGAPORE
Chapter 4. The Knowledge Base of a B2B eCommerce Multi-Agent System

Saori Kawasaki
Japan Advanced Institute of Science and Technology
Ishikawa
JAPAN
Chapter 7. Combining Temporal Abstraction and Data-Mining Methods in Medical Data Analysis

Jean-Luc Koning
Technological University of Grenoble
LCIS Research Laboratory
Valence
FRANCE
Chapter 5. From Roles to Agents: Considerations on Formal Agent Modeling and Implementation

Si Quang Le
Japan Advanced Institute of Science and Technology
Ishikawa

JAPAN
Chapter 7. Combining Temporal Abstraction and Data-Mining Methods in Medical Data Analysis

Mong Li Lee
School of Computing
National University of Singapore
SINGAPORE
Chapter 9. Finding Patterns in Image Databases

Antonio Liotta
Center for Communication Systems Research
University of Surrey
Guildford, Surrey
UNITED KINGDOM
Chapter 8. Distributed Monitoring: Methods, Means, and Technologies

Kostas Metaxiotis
Institute of Communications & Computer Systems
National Technical University of Athens
Athens
GREECE
Chapter 2. Expert Systems Technology in Production Planning and Scheduling

Chunyan Miao
School of Computer Engineering
Nanyang Technological University
SINGAPORE
Chapter 4. The Knowledge Base of a B2B eCommerce Multi-Agent System

Yuan Miao
Institute of Communication and Information Systems
Nanyang Technological University
SINGAPORE
Chapter 6. Agent-Based eLearning Systems: A Goal-Based Approach

Trong Dung Nguyen
Japan Advanced Institute of Science and Technology
Ishikawa
JAPAN
Chapter 7. Combining Temporal Abstraction and Data-Mining Methods in Medical Data Analysis

Srikanta Patnaik
Department of Electronics and Telecommunication Engineering
University College of Engineering, Burla

Sambalpur, Orissa
INDIA
Chapter 10. Cognition Techniques and Their Applications

John Psarras
Institute of Communications & Computer Systems
National Technical University of Athens
Athens
GREECE
Chapter 2. Expert Systems Technology in Production Planning and Scheduling

Zhiqi Shen
Institute of Communication and Information Systems
School of Electrical and Electronic Engineering
Nanyang Technological University
SINGAPORE
Chapter 6. Agent-Based eLearning Systems: A Goal-Based Approach

S. B. Tor
Singapore-MIT Alliance
Nanyang Technological University
SINGAPORE
Chapter 1. Techniques in Knowledge-Based Expert Systems for the Design of Engineering Systems

W. Y. Zhang
Design Research Center
School of Mechanical and Production Engineering
Nanyang Technological University
SINGAPORE
Chapter 1. Techniques in Knowledge-Based Expert Systems for the Design of Engineering Systems

VOLUME 4: INTELLIGENT SYSTEMS

Cheng-Leong Ang
Singapore Institute of Manufacturing Technology
SINGAPORE
Chapter 4. An Intelligent Hybrid System for Business Forecasting

Sistine A. Barretto
Advanced Computing Research Centre
The University of South Australia
Adelaide

AUSTRALIA
Chapter 6. Techniques in the Utilization of the Internet and Intranets in Facilitating the Development of Clinical Decision Support Systems in the Process of Patient Care

Billy Fenton
International Test Technologies
and
University of Ulster
Letterkenny, Donegal
IRELAND
Chapter 5. Intelligent Systems Technology in the Fault Diagnosis of Electronic Systems

Robert Gay
Institute of Communication and Information Systems
School of Electrical and Electronic Engineering
Nanyang Technological University
SINGAPORE
Chapter 4. An Intelligent Hybrid System for Business Forecasting

Victor Giurgiutiu
Mechanical Engineering Department
University of South Carolina
Columbia, South Carolina
USA
Chapter 8. Mechatronics and Smart Structures Design Techniques for Intelligent Products, Processes and Systems

Marc-Philippe Huget
Leibnitz Laboratory
Grenoble
France
Chapter 9. Engineering Interaction Protocols for Multiagent Systems

Richard W. Jones
School of Engineering
University of Northumbria
Newcastle upon Tyne
England
UNITED KINGDOM
Chapter 2. Intelligent Patient Monitoring in the Intensive Care Unit and the Operating Room

Jean-Luc Koning
Technological University of Grenoble
LCIS Research Laboratory

Valence
FRANCE
Chapter 9. Engineering Interaction Protocols for Multiagent Systems

Xiang Li
Singapore Institute of Manufacturing Technology
SINGAPORE
Chapter 4. An Intelligent Hybrid System for Business Forecasting

Liam Maguire
Department of Informatics
University of Ulster
Derry
NORTHERN IRELAND
Chapter 5. Intelligent Systems Technology in the Fault Diagnosis of Electronic Systems

T. M. McGinnity
Department of Informatics
University of Ulster
Derry
NORTHERN IRELAND
Chapter 5. Intelligent Systems Technology in the Fault Diagnosis of Electronic Systems

Tolety Siva Perraju
Verizon Communications
Waltham, Massachusetts
USA
Chapter 3. Mission Critical Intelligent Systems

Mauricio Sanchez-Silva
Department of Civil and Environmental Engineering
Universidad de los Andes
Bogotá
COLOMBIA
Chapter 7. Risk Analysis and the Decision-Making Process in Engineering

Garimella Uma
South Asia International Institute
Hyderabad
INDIA
Chapter 3. Mission Critical Intelligent Systems

James R. Warren
Advanced Computing Research Centre
The University of South Australia

Mawson Lakes
AUSTRALIA
Chapter 6. Techniques in the Utilization of the Internet and Intranets in Facilitating the Development of Clinical Decision Support Systems in the Process of Patient Care

Xuan F. Zha
Design and Process Group
Manufacturing Systems Integration Division
National Institute of Standards and Technology
Gaithersburg, Maryland
USA
Chapter 1. Artificial Intelligence and Integrated Intelligent Systems: Applications in Product Design and Development

VOLUME 5: NEURAL NETWORKS, FUZZY THEORY AND GENETIC ALGORITHM TECHNIQUES

Kazem Abhary
School of Advanced Manufacturing and Mechanical Engineering
University of South Australia
Mawson Lakes
AUSTRALIA
Chapter 8. Assembly Sequence Optimization Using Genetic Algorithms

F. Admiraal-Behloul
Division of Image Processing
Leiden University Medical Center
Leiden
THE NETHERLANDS
Chapter 4. Fuzzy Rule Extraction Using Radial Basis Function Neural Networks in High-Dimensional Data

Kemal Ahmet
Faculty of Creative Arts and Technologies
University of Luton
Luton
UNITED KINGDOM
Chapter 1. Neural Network Systems Technology and Applications in CAD/CAM Integration

Carl K. Chang
Department of Computer Science
Iowa State University
Ames, Iowa
USA
Chapter 7. Genetic Algorithm Techniques and Applications in Management Systems

Lian Ding
Faculty of Creative Arts and Technologies
University of Luton
Luton
UNITED KINGDOM
Chapter 1. Neural Network Systems Technology and Applications in CAD/CAM Integration

Shing-Hwang Doong
Department of Information Management
Shu-Te University
Yen Chau
TAIWAN
Chapter 10. Computational Intelligence for Facility Location Allocation Problems

Yujia Ge
Department of Computer Science
Iowa State University
Ames, Iowa
USA
Chapter 7. Genetic Algorithm Techniques and Applications in Management Systems

Andrew Kusiak
Department of Mechanical and Industrial Engineering
University of Iowa
Iowa City, Iowa
USA
Chapter 5. Fuzzy Decision Modeling of Product Development Processes

Chih-Chin Lai
Department of Information Management
Shu-Te University
Yen-Chau
TAIWAN
Chapter 10. Computational Intelligence for Facility Location Allocation Problems

Wen F. Lu
Product Design and Development Group
Singapore Institute of Manufacturing Technology
SINGAPORE
Chapter 6. Evaluation and Selection in Product Design for Mass Customization

Lee H. S. Luong
School of Advanced Manufacturing and Mechanical Engineering
University of South Australia

Mawson Lakes
AUSTRALIA
Chapter 8. Assembly Sequence Optimization Using Genetic Algorithms

Romeo Marin Marian
CSIRO Manufacturing & Infrastructure Technology
Woodville North, SA
AUSTRALIA
Chapter 8. Assembly Sequence Optimization Using Genetic Algorithms

Stergios Papadimitriou
Department of Information Management
Technological Education Institute of Kavala
Kavala
GREECE
Chapter 9. Kernel-Based Self-Organized Maps Trained with Supervised Bias for Gene Expression Data Mining

Johan H. C. Reiber
Division of Image Processing
Department of Radiology
Leiden University Medical Center
Leiden
THE NETHERLANDS
Chapter 4. Fuzzy-Rule Extraction Using Radial Basis Function Neural Networks in High-Dimensional Data

Kwang-Kyu Seo
Division of Computer, Information and Telecommunication Engineering
Sangmyung University
Chungnam
KOREA
Chapter 2. Neural Network Systems Technology and Applications in Product Life–Cycle Cost Estimates

Joaquin Sitte
Faculty of Information Technology
Queensland University of Technology
Brisbane
AUSTRALIA
Chapter 3. Neural Network Systems Technology in the Analysis of Financial Time Series

Renate Sitte
Faculty of Engineering and Information and Technology
Griffith University
Queensland
AUSTRALIA
Chapter 3. Neural Network Systems Technology in the Analysis of Financial Time Series

Ram D. Sriram
Design and Process Group
Manufacturing Systems Integration Divison
National Institute of Standards and Technology
Gaithersburg, Maryland
USA
Chapter 6. Evaluation and Selection in Product Design for Mass Customization

Fu J. Wang
Design and Process Group
Manufacturing Systems Integration Division
National Institute of Standards and Technology
Gaithersburg, Maryland
USA
Chapter 6. Evaluation and Selection in Product Design for Mass Customization

Juite Wang
Department of Industrial Engineering
Feng Chia University
Taichung, Taiwan
REPUBLIC OF CHINA
Chapter 5. Fuzzy Decision Modeling of Product Development Processes

Chih-Hung Wu
Department of Information Management
Shu-Te University
Yen Chau
TAIWAN
Chapter 10. Computational Intelligence for Facility Location Allocation Problems

Yong Yue
Faculty of Creative Arts and Technologies
University of Luton
Luton
UNITED KINGDOM
Chapter 1. Neural Network Systems Technology and Applications in CAD/CAM Integration

Xuan F. Zha
Design and Process Group
Manufacturing Systems Integration Divison
National Institute of Standards and Technology
Gaithersburg, Maryland
USA
Chapter 6. Evaluation and Selection in Product Design for Mass Customization

VOLUME II. INFORMATION TECHNOLOGY

TECHNIQUES IN INTEGRATED DEVELOPMENT AND IMPLEMENTATION OF ENTERPRISE INFORMATION SYSTEMS

CHOON SEONG LEEM AND JONG WOOK SUH

1. INTRODUCTION TO THE INTEGRATED METHODOLOGY FOR ENTERPRISE INFORMATION SYSTEMS

Information technology is the important weapon to improve and keep an enterprises' competitiveness in ever-changing business environment. It is a systematic methodology that is mostly required as a supporting tool achieving complicated activities connected with introduction of information systems. The information systems embodied to be impertinent can be wasting enterprise resources and weakening enterprise's competitiveness.

Therefore, many consulting corporations have developed and applied various commercial methodologies in order to provide systematic guide on the construction of enterprise information systems. Methodology must integrate each kinds of theory and tools scattered and support that all of the users may utilize it easily. Thus, related methodology research has to connect each kind of theory and tools in synthetic viewpoint to satisfy efficient and effective construction of information systems. Also, previous researches show that enterprises which have systematic methodology construct information systems more effectively.

Most research works and commercial products, however, are lack of the architectural integrity and functional applicability to meet these sophisticated needs of enterprises. Lack of the architectural integrity is caused by two factors: the absence of customizable architecture regarding inner environment and natural culture of enterprises, and the non-integrated framework to manage engineering tools and output data used and generated during development and implementation of information systems. Lack of the functional applicability is caused by three factors: broken bridge linking business strategy with information strategy in rational manner, the absence of economic justification and management systems, and unreliable mechanism for analysis and evaluation about level of enterprise information systems. This chapter introduces a new integrated methodology for successful development and implementation of the enterprise information systems.

1.1. Development of information systems

The development methodology of information system considers the life-cycle of information system and additional elements. At large, the whole life-cycle of information system are like the SDLC (System Development Life Cycle). The life-cycle of information system is composed planning, analysis design, implementation, and maintenance

- Planning: The necessity and purpose of system, validity check, cost/benefit analysis
- Analysis: Investigation on the organizational environment, systems, user requirement, and configuration of the system functions based on user requirement
- Design: Logical system design, design of new system structure, business process, and input-output, file/database design, application coding, software development
- Implementation: Purchasing hardware, installing systems, user training
- Maintenance: System performance evaluation, User feedback, system upgrade, continuous support.

In Addition, IS package introduction and implementation, IS outsourcing, economic justification and measurement of IS, analysis of enterprise competency, and administration of IS projects which are recently applied to the enterprise are included in the integrated methodology.

1.2. Previous research

Methodology in the enterprise informatization and information engineering plays a role in establishing framework to manage the project, defining operations, setting up the goals and procedures of project, identifying the required resources during project, and assigning the responsibility. Moreover, it creates the baseline of project, monitors the executed operations, and evaluates the result of project. Finally it helps to check the parts to be improved for the next businesses.

Methodology is generally composed of systems development life-cycle above mentioned. There are several development methodologies like IDEF (US Air force) and ARIS (Scheer) that can support the enterprise process and data modeling, and Rose (Rational corporation) which support UML. However, these methodologies are not classified as IS development methodology because they cannot cover the whole range of enterprise.

There are some information system development methodologies focused on the development of IS and promotion of informatization. Until by now, the recent information systems development methodologies have been led by IT consulting firms

Table 1 Major information system development methodologies

Methodology	Characteristics
Information Engineering (James Martin)	It develops the information systems with enterprise model, data model, and process model in the knowledge base.
Navigator (Ernst & Young)	It takes the IE (information engineering)-based approach that is composed of planning, analysis, design, construction/acquisition, and evolution of IS.
Method/1 (Accenture)	It has been applied to many projects, and revised and extended periodically
ASAP (SAP)	ASAP (accelerate SAP) helps company to implement SAP R/3 by reducing the time and cost.

which have provided the consulting services and implemented information system to many enterprises. Table 1 is summary of major information system development methodologies.

1.3. Overview of the integrated methodology for enterprise information systems

The integrated methodology for enterprise information systems is the methodology to help the enterprises to construct the information systems. Using this methodology, the ones who implement IS execute the works through the roadmaps suggested in this methodology and store outputs in the repository which is one of the component of this methodology.

Applied subjects are in a larger sense than in general, which is the enterprise includes company, government, university and other organizations.

Framework of the integrated methodology for enterprise information systems

The integrated methodology is composed of pattern & scenario, roadmaps, components and repository as following figure 1.

-Patterns & Scenario

The integrated methodology for enterprise information systems has several development paths. These paths are able to be applied to the peculiar characteristics of enterprises. Besides, this integrated methodology offers the scenarios which can be applied originally using the components.

Figure 2 shows the relations between the roadmaps and patterns. The patterns suggested in the integrated methodology have the meanings as follows.

They are classified into higher and lower patterns by the in/out state of the enterprises for users to apply this methodology easily. The higher patterns have development/package introduction in development method and traditional/radical approach in development velocity. The lower patterns are classified by industry, size and development range.

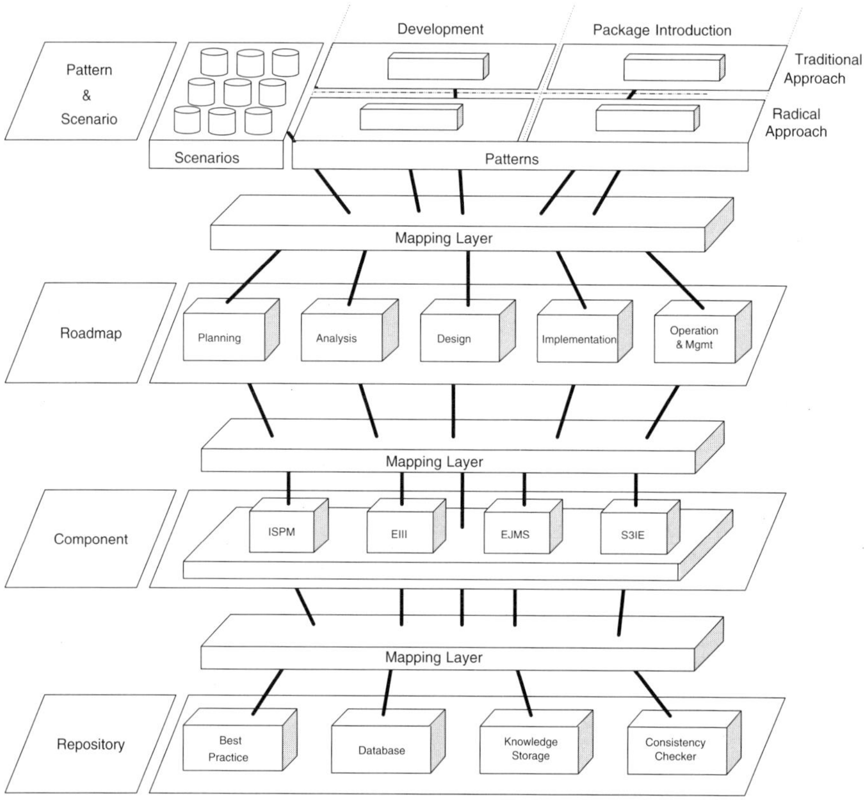

Figure 1. Concept of the integrated methodology for enterprise information systems.

-Roadmap

Each patterns and scenarios has own roadmaps and is supported by the components which are applied to each roadmaps.

-Component

There are five components in the integrated methodology.

A. Information Strategic Planning Methodology (ISPM): is composed of strategic management planning, information strategy, information systems execution planning, and is related and with information strategy and management strategy systemically.
B. Economic Justification and Measurement Systems (EJMS): supports accurate and effective investment decisions by quantitating the economic investment effects of information systems

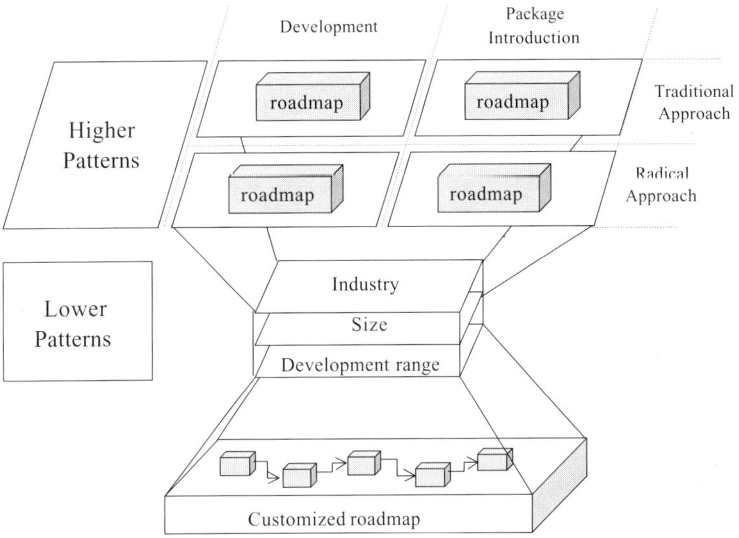

Figure 2. Roadmaps and patterns.

C. Evaluation Indices of Industrial Informatization (EIII): evaluates the state of enterprise taking the objects of information systems implementation and all the circumstances related to information systems into consideration
D. Unified Modeling Technique (UMT): is a modeling tool supporting integration of outputs through entire life-cycle of implementation of information systems. User requirements are reflected by UMT effectively and make it easy to implement information systems by connecting modeling outputs to system deign and analysis of linkage among modeling.
E. Support Systems for Solution Introduction & Evaluation (S3IE): helps decision making of enterprise executives to plan package introduction strategy, to evaluate each package and select one.

These five components support the roadmaps described above continuously. Moreover, they can be used independently in the roadmaps which are supported by scenarios.

-Repository

The outputs created in application of methodology are stored in repository. Repository consists of not only database which has role of storage house of output, but best practice, knowledge coordinator, and knowledge storage.

The features of the integrated methodology for enterprise information systems

The integrated methodology for enterprise information systems supports the whole life-cycle (planning, analysis, design, construction, and operation) and has consistent

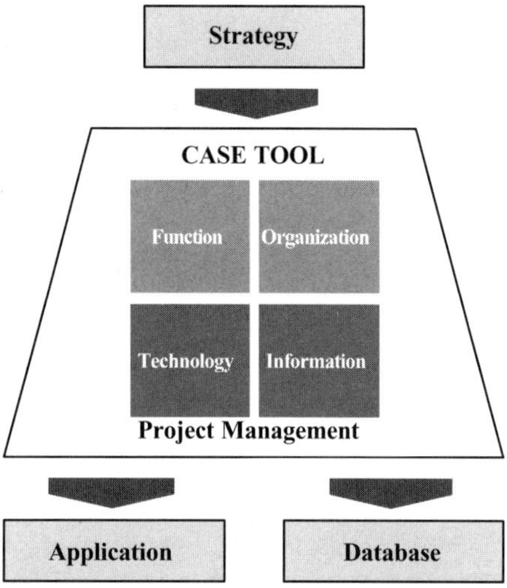

Figure 3. Four models in enterprise model.

approaches through the entire stages. This methodology lets the enterprises use the suitable components to their states of business. This methodology has the architecture which is composed of Milestone, Phase, Activity, Task, and Subtask.

Moreover, the quantitation of the analyzed results and elimination of the irregular factors in the integrated methodology helps the user to implement information systems using case tools easily in this methodology not depending on consultants' ability. And, it is easy to connect qualitative analysis results closely with modeling and guarantees good adaptability to user in the various states. Finally, it provides the results of evaluation in various viewpoints.

The approach of the integrated methodology for enterprise information systems

The integrated methodology supports the consistency from planning to construction by enterprise models. These four models are function, organization, information, and technology model. The enterprise models represent and record the companies or organizations using simple terms and symbols. They are useful tools to presuppose the figures of information systems which will be constructed and to estimate the justification, cost, and time.

Fig. 3 shows the conversion of the strategy to the applications and databases through the integrated methodology. The integrated methodology is supported by four models, case tools and management methods.

Process of the integrated methodology for enterprise information systems

Roadmaps in the integrated methodology have the procedures for the implementation of information systems from information systems planning to construction and maintenance by relating the tasks in each phase of methodology. Besides, roadmaps are sets of action for achieve the goal that is enterprise informatization under the consideration of environment and strategy. Hence, roadmaps in the integrated methodology have several paths.

2. TECHNIQUES OF INFORMATION STRATEGIC PLANNING

2.1. Overview

ISPM (Information Strategic Planning Methodology) plays a role in the integrated methodology for enterprise information systems to establish the Information Strategic Planning (ISP). ISP is defined as the process of defining the business application portfolio and the planning which has goal to achieve the competency in business using the information systems in innovative ways.

Therefore, ISPM means the methodology that makes the requirements of business clear, converts them to into requirement in systems and supports the process to implement information systems.

2.2. Previous researches

The role and functions of IS in organization have been dramatically changed in recent years. Most of all, IS has been the critical value creator nowadays, not just business supporter. Thus, numerous researches on ISP have been conducted.

In 1970, Zani defined ISP as a top down plan concentrating on the alignment business strategy with information system plan, which is considered as the foundation of ISP research. Afterwards there are various researches and corresponding definitions on ISP. King (1994) defined ISP as all planning activities that are directed toward identifying opportunities for using information technology to support the organization's strategic business plans and to maintain an effective and efficient IS function. Lederer and Sethi (1996) defined ISP as the process of identifying a portfolio of computer-based application that will assist an organization in executing its business plans and realizing its business goals. Baker (1995) defined ISP as the identification of prioritized information systems that are efficient, effective and/or strategic in nature together with the necessary resources (human, technical, financial), management of change considerations, control procedures and organizational structure needed to implement IS. However, many definitions confine ISP to a kind of plan for the IS portfolio, while the scope of ISP needs to expand as the role of IS/IT in 21st century expands. In this integrated methodology, ISP is defined as follow. ISP is all planning activities to identify strategic information requirements and business strategies related to IS/IT, and to support information system development, business transformation and education.

Typical objectives of ISP are summarized as below:

- aligning investments in IS with business goals,
- directing the efficient and effective management of IS function and IS resource,
- identifying information requirements and priorities of IS,
- deriving the top executive's participation and supporting to develop IT,
- reducing the implementation and management cost of IS,
- supporting the execution of business plans through IT.

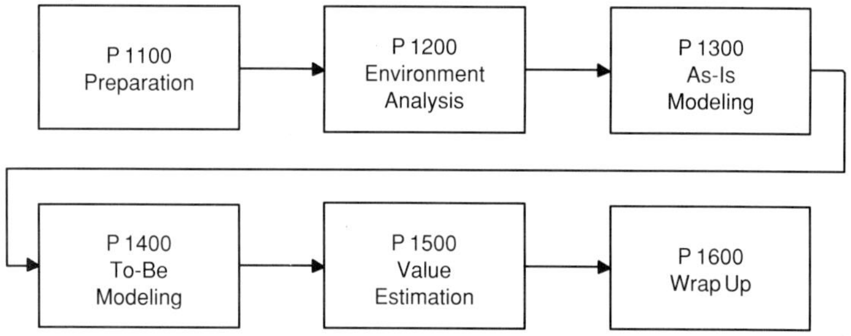

Figure 4. Main flow of ISPM.

In order to achieve objectives of ISP, crucial factors to influence the developing process of ISP should be studied. One of the best-known studies in this field is Lederer and Sethi's. They defined factors influencing ISP as follows: the proliferation and maturity of IT in the company, the complexity of business plan, the scope of ISP, and the involvement of IS organization in developing business plans. Organizational factors such as the scale of organization, the role of top management, the duration of decision making also were considered as major factors.

2.3. Information Strategic Planning Methodology (ISPM)

Objectives of ISPM

Success of Information Strategy Planning (ISP) depends on the linkage between business strategy and information strategy. ISP consists of strategic management planning, strategic information system planning and execution planning of information systems. Control and management of changes must be conducted to feedback ISP to business strategy. Figure 4 shows the main flow of ISPM.

Key features of ISPM

First, requirement analysis via reviews on documents and interviews, and evaluation of existing information systems are conducted in preparation phase.

Second, environment analysis phase executes analysis of enterprise status, business goals which decide enterprise strategy, technical environment, rival company's systems and related information technologies. It estimates enterprise's competitiveness and level of information systems. At last, it sets up key strategic points of information systems.

Third, as-is modeling phase models enterprise in four modeling elements of technology, organization, information and function with simplified terms and symbols to grasp full states of an enterprise. It verifies the integrity of integrity and analyzes consistency of the models with business strategy. Finally, it generates improvement processes and examines improvement possibility.

Fourth, to-be modeling phase models will be enterprise architecture based on improvement process drawn from as-is modeling. It models goals in four modeling

Table 2 The framework for evaluation of ISP

	ISPM-E1 (Information Strategic Methodology—Evaluation 1)	ISPM-E2 (Information Strategic Methodology—Evaluation 2)
Objective	– check the authority of ISP processes, completeness of outputs and their relation	– verify the agreement and possibility to be realized
Role	– evaluate the reliableness of ISP – analyze the competency of To-BE model – analyze the IS performance of To-BE model – analyze economic justification of ISP	– compare the constructed information system with ISP

elements of technology, organization, information and function. After modeling of each model, it sets up strategies for implementation of four models and integrates these strategies.

Fifth, value estimation phase executes estimation on consistency and robustness to judge how faithfully former phases follow methodology in terms of outputs and their formality. It estimates achieved competitiveness, level of information systems and economic values of information strategy planning from to-be modeling.

Sixth, wrap-up phase gets the final confirmation of information strategy planning and endorsement of system users. It includes training plans for newly adopted systems and maintenance plans for information strategy planning.

2.4. Framework for evaluation of ISP

The objective of evaluation of ISP is to reduce the reworks and development time through early adjustment, to establish ISP suitable for the enterprises, and leads the board of directors to take part in IS projects by providing the necessary information in decision making. The framework for evaluation of ISP considered in ISPM is divided into ISPM-E1 and ISPM-E2 as following table 2.

Information Strategic Methodology—Evaluation 1 (ISPM-E1)

The evaluation of ISP establishment has four major roles. First, the reliableness check of ISP evaluates the authority of ISP processes. Second, economic justification of ISP compares the cost with benefit of To-Be enterprise models. Third, analysis of IS performance of To-Be models evaluates the potential level of the state of IS in enterprise. Finally, the assessment of competency in IS shows the latent IS competitiveness of To-Be enterprise models.

Information Strategic Methodology—Evaluation 2 (ISPM-E2)

The evaluation on execution of ISP is achieved by improvement of IS performance, uplift of IS competitiveness, benefit-cost analysis and administration in IS process as shown in fig. 5.

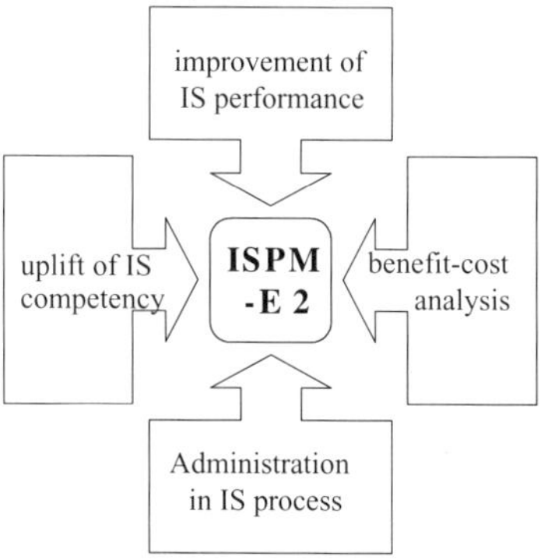

Figure 5. The evaluation on execution of ISP.

3. TECHNIQUES FOR THE EVALUATION OF INDUSTRIAL INFORMATION SYSTEMS (EIII)

3.1. Overview

Recently, the importance of IS (Information Systems) is being rapidly increased as a key strategic mean promoting the efficiency of enterprise activity. According to dramatic progresses of info-technology, the typical users of IS are expected to use various applications in dynamic enterprise environments. Furthermore, most enterprises pursue the renovation of business process and strategies through IS.

In order to adequately response these trends, enterprises have to establish comprehensive concepts and goals based on evolutionary characteristics of IS and to identify their objectives from the continuous evaluation of current IS conditions by a scientific and systemic methodology.

This paper examines the evaluation issues of enterprise IS performance dealing with: (1) suggestion for the performance improvement model based on the evolutionary characteristics of IS, (2) development of an integrated evaluation system based on the improvement model, and (3) verification of efficiency and applicability of the evaluation system.

3.2. Previous researches

This work focuses on improvement of IS performance by systematic evaluation methodology. Previous researches can be classified into two types regarding improvement models and evaluation models of IS performance. Moreover, the researches related to the evaluation models concern three kinds of topic which are evaluation model, evaluation fields, and evaluation items of IS performance.

Previous researches on the improvement model of IS performance

There are two types of researches related to improvement of IS performance. The one is on improvement processes and the other is on improvement stages of IS performance.

Table 3 Researches on important processes of IS performance

Title	Improvement processes	Focus
PDCA	Plan – Do - Check – Act	Product quality improvement
QIP	Characterize the environment - Set goals-Choose and tailor a process model – Execute the process – Analyze the collected data – Learn and feedback	S/W quality improvement
IDEAL	Initiating – Diagnosing - Establishing - Acting – Leveraging or Learning	Process improvement
Kaizen	Contact - Awareness - Understanding – Evaluation – Trial Use – Adoption – Institutionalization	New technology adoption

PDCA (Plan-Do-Check-Act), IDEAL (Initiating-Diagnosing-Establishing-Acting-Learning), and QIP (Quality Improvement Paradigm) are typical researches on improvement process. The PDCA initialized by Shewhart (1931) and generalized by Deming (1986) after World War II is the improvement process of product quality based on feedback cycle that can optimize unit production process. The QIP by NASA Software Engineering Laboratory is the improvement process of software quality based on the meta-lifecycle model to improve long term quality. This process has several functions; packing, assessing, and increasing comprehension of development experience for software. The IDEAL by SEI (Software Engineering Institute) in the Carnegie Mellon University is the process improvement model focused on project management. This model is composed of five steps that are continuously and recursively performed (McFeeley, 1996). The Kaizen model to improve the process performance has been applied to the ESPRIT project. The basic concept of this model is called 'adoption curve' to take up new technology which is proposed by Conner and Patterson. Table 3 briefly summarize these researches (Renaissance Consortium, 1997).

This work focuses on improvement of IS performance by systematic evaluation methodology. Previous researches can be classified into two types regarding improvement models and evaluation models of IS performance. Further, the researches related to the evaluation models concern three kinds of topic which are evaluation model, evaluation fields, and evaluation items of IS performance.

There are several researches on improvement stages of IS performance. Nolan and Wetherbe (1980) suggested six maturity stages of IS focused on data, and Venkatraman (1997) also proposed a five stage model focused on structure innovation of organization by IS. Vernadat (1996) presented a three stage model of systems integration according to expansion of the CIM (Computer Integrated Manufacturing) integration range. The CMM (Capability Maturity Model) by SEI (software engineering institute) is composed of five stages derived from the degree of process maturity (Bate, 1995). The ISM (Information Systems Management) model by Tan (1999) is based on balance between organizational structure and IT components. This model is originated from MIT90s framework that is composed of the levels of IT-enabled business reconfiguration by Venkatraman. In this model, IS fields are divided into three parts which are external environments, organization environments, and IS environments. Table 4 shows the researches related to improvement stages of IS performance.

Table 4 Researches on improvement stages of IS performance

Title	Improvement stages	Focus
Nolan	Initiation – Contagion - Control - Integration – Data Administration – Maturity	Data
CIM	Physical System Integration - Application Integration – Business Integration	System
ISM	Functional Integration - Cross-functional Integration – Process Integration – Business Process Redesign – Business Redesign or Business Scope Redefinition	Business
CMM	Performed Informally (Initial) - Planned & Tracked - Well-defined – Quantitatively Controlled – Continuously Improving	Process

Previous researches on the evaluation model of IS performance

The evaluation diagnoses the current condition, and utilizes its results for future plans, so that the organization could get the better performance. For instance, the Japanese Deming prize, USA's Malcolm Baldrige Award called 'criteria for performance excellence', and European's 'Business Excellence model' are known to significantly contribute to quality improvement of products and process. Also, USA, UK, Japan, and OECD are continuously working out the national IS indices, so as to gradually increase the level of IS performance (Jeong, 1996).

In the research related to the evaluation model of IS, the DeLone and McLean's IS success model (1992) has been referred by many researchers, which was based on the works by Shannon & Weaver (1949) and Mason (1978). This model is examined and improved by Seddon and Kiew (1994) which suggests the measures of six fields and proves their appropriateness. Since the IS model did not cover the appropriate measures coincided with the characteristics of organization, Saunders and Jones (1992) developed the 'IS Function Performance Evaluation Model' which encompasses a selection method of appropriate measures corresponding to organization features. Myers, Kappelman, and Prybutok (1997) worked out the 'Comprehensive IS Assessment Model' that expanded the six evaluation fields of DeLone and McLean's model into eight fields and combined these fields into organizational and external environments. Also, Goodhue and Thompson (1995) and Goodhue (1998) proposed the TPC (Task- to-Performance Chain) model based on a fitting technique into individual performance. The focus of the model is to apply the technique to individual tasks to calculate their positive impact upon individual performance. Additionally, there are several researches related to IS framework. Tan (1999) suggested the 'Consistency Model' composed of seven components that expanded the MIT90s model and SEI also proposed a framework composed of seven evaluation fields (Bergey, 1997).

As researches related to identification of the evaluation items, the GQM (Goal-Question- (indicator)-Measures) methodology was introduced by Basili and Rombach (1988), refined by AMI (1992), Pulford (1996) in ESPRIT project, and was applied to the goal-driven software evaluation by Park (1996) in SEI. Especially, Mondonqa (1998) converted the GQM (Goal-Question-(indicator)-Measures) to another GQM (Goal-Question-Metric) for improvement of evaluation processes. Sometimes researches related to the evaluation model of IS performance.

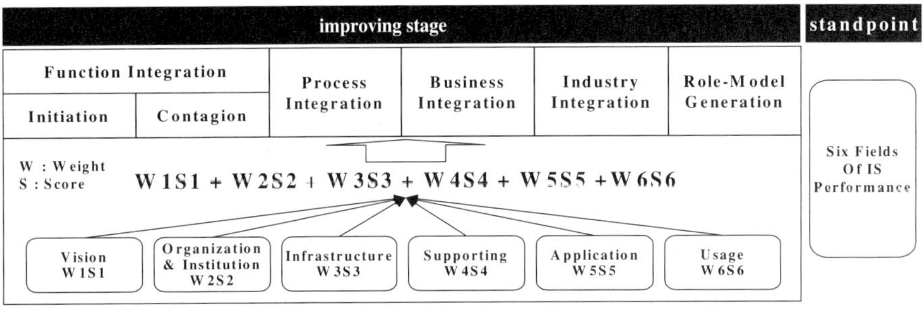

Figure 6. Five improvement stages of IS performance.

3.3. The improvement model of IS performance

'IS (Information Systems)' is able to be defined as integrated systems that collect data, analyze that, generate the new useful information, transmit it and use information related with business activities in organizations, typically business process in enterprises.

'The IS performance' that is usually divided into several stages is defined as the degree of effectiveness and efficiency in business goal accomplishment by IS. The 'Improvement of IS performance' implies that the IS performance is improved to become flexibly commensurate with changes in internal and external environments and various requirements of users, so that the IS performance can be optimized with activities in organization.

'The improvement model of IS performance' is a representation of their relationships and the improvement model of IS performance, which consists of improvement stages and cycles.

Improvement stage of IS performance

The improvement stage of IS performance plays major role in overall evaluation of IS performance. The improvement stage is suggested to consist of five stages and figure 6 shows them.

As shown in figure 6, the five improvement stage of IS performance in this research are function integration, process integration, business integration, industry integration, and role-model generation. The level of the stage can be determined by the six comprehensive fields of IS performance which are vision, organization & institution, infrastructure, supporting, application, and usage of IS. The 'function integration' represents to computerize the individual tasks within isolated systems The 'process integration' combines the individual processes and functions into corresponding working group via IS. The 'business integration' is defined to integrate the working groups into the level of entire organization, and the 'industry integration' should be cover up to partner companies and, individual customers, outside the organization. In the 'role-model generation' stage, the organization can flexibly accommodate to new external environment by itself and naturally create new business models by accumulated information and updated IS.

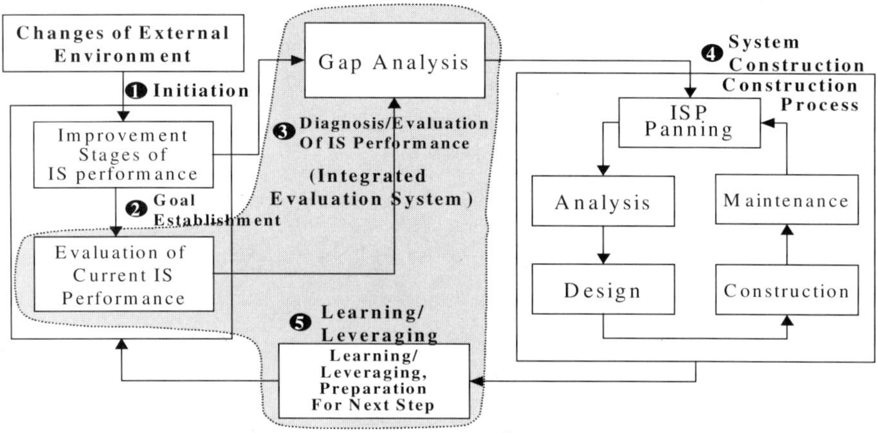

Figure 7. Improvement cycles of IS performance.

The improvement stage of IS performance has important meanings that can quantitatively represent the current IS status and target IS status in future. Seeing that the IS environments have many diverse qualitative factors and these factors are tangled with each other, it is very difficult for organization to decide level of the stages for current IS status or target IS status. Therefore, in order to decide the stage correctly, these stages should be characterized and explained by various factors. This paper suggests these decision factors based on the IS framework that are divided into six fields; IS vision, IS organization & institution, Infrastructure, supporting, application, and usage.

Improvement cycle of IS performance

The improvement model of IS performance in this paper consists of three components: improvement stages, integrated evaluation system, and construction process, and should be applied by five continuous and circular cycles; initiation, goal establishment, diagnosis and evaluation of IS performance, construction process, and leveraging and learning. Figure 7 shows the cycle.

As shown in Figure 7, the improvement of IS performance can be achieved by five processes. First, the motive to improve IS performance is triggered by stimulus originated from changes in internal and external environment. Second, the organization should establish the goal (IS vision) that can flexibly cope with the trends of IS environment. Third, the organization should evaluate the current IS status, identify future objectives, and analyze the gap through the comparison between goal states and current states. Fourth, detailed problems in current states should be considered in planning and construction of IS projects. Finally, information and knowledge acquired from previous processes should be utilized with recursive iterations of the cycle, the IS environments can be continuously reconciled with management environments of the organization.

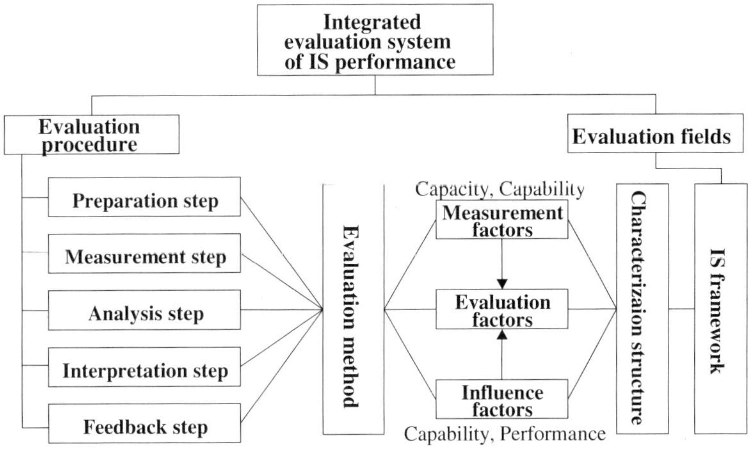

Figure 8. Integrated evaluation system of IS performance.

3.4. Framework for the evaluation of IS performance

The integrated evaluation system of IS performance is designed to diagnose the current IS status, and identify the deficiencies of current status for target systems by gap analysis. This system consists of three parts; evaluation procedures, evaluation fields, and evaluation methods. The evaluation procedures can be decomposed into five steps; preparation, measurement, analysis, interpretation, and feedback. The evaluation fields which are originated from IS framework can be decomposed into three parts; measurement factors, influence factors, and evaluation factors. The measurement factors mean the static standpoint of IS framework, the influence factors mean the dynamic standpoint that represents the relationship between subject and object in IS framework, and the evaluation factors are considered to supply useful information to decision-makers. These factors are measured, analyzed, and interpreted by various evaluation methods. Figure 8 shows a schematic diagram of the integrated evaluation system of IS performance.

4. TECHNIQUES OF IS ECONOMIC JUSTIFICATION AND MEASUREMENT

4.1. Overview

Investment of information system for achieving business goals must be an investment that can achieve the maximum effectiveness from limited resources. Thus, IS economic justification and measurement has the goal to supply quantification methodology and procedure about the effectiveness of information systems investment. Usual investment propriety analysis on information systems consists of economical propriety analysis, technological propriety analysis and operational propriety analysis. But, technological propriety analysis and operational propriety analysis is not so important because most information strategic planning are based on existing information technology and inner resources. IS economic justification and measurement just focuses on economical propriety analysis.

IS economic justification and measurement are used individually or for the purpose of calculating the enterprise competency indices in the integrated methodology for enterprise information systems.

In the case of individual usage, it helps to compares the estimated effectiveness of all alternatives and to selects one. Further, it examines whether or not the estimated effectiveness is made.

When it is applied as a part of the integrated methodology for enterprise information systems, it decides whether ISP or IS are executed in-house developed or outsourced. Besides, the effectiveness estimation of IS projects and cost/benefit analysis are performed after IS project is over.

4.2. Previous researches

Bacon (1992) found that the criteria such as the support of explicit business objectives and response to competitive systems are important in IS investment decision-makings.

Theo and Berghout (1997) discerned four basic approaches such as financial approach, multi-criteria approach, ratio approach, and portfolio approach and group evaluation approach into four classifications: economic appraisal techniques, strategic approaches, analytical appraisal techniques, and integrated approaches. Economic appraisal techniques are structured in nature, and include those traditionally used by accountants. They are based on the assignment of cash values to tangible cost and benefit but largely ignore intangible factors. Strategic approaches are less structured in nature but combine tangible and intangible factors. Analytical appraisal techniques are highly structured in design but subjective in nature, with their use often including tangible and intangible factors. Finally, integrated approaches combine subjectivity with a formal structure. These approaches integrate the financial and non-financial dimensions together, through the acknowledgement and the assignment of weighting factors.

4.3. Framework for economic justification and measurement system (EJMS)

Framework for economic justification and measurement system (EJMS) is classified into cost factors, effectiveness factors, classifying scheme for enterprise features, procedure, and techniques for using.

Cost factors

Cost is divided into investment cost and maintenance cost. They mean the resources which are invested to equipments, time, manpower, and so on. Besides, they are easy to be measured numerically. However, because the identification of the actual IS investment is difficult, the basic guideline must be provided to extract cost factors of IS project.

Cost factors are classified into 12 constructions by periods and items. Periods are subdivided into construction and maintenance. Items are subdivided into service, labor, overhead cost, hardware, software and conversion. Table 5 shows the cost factors of EJMS.

Table 5 Cost factors of EJMS

	Service	Labor	Overhead cost	Hardware	Software	Conversion
Construction	Application development cost	Employment cost Training cost	Communication cost Public charge Equipment cost Space cost	Server cost PC cost N/W cost Peripheral equipment cost	O/S cost DBMS cost Application cost	Loss of work during information systems introduction Inefficient work during the first state
Maintenance	Application development cost Consulting cost	Employment cost Training cost	Communication cost Public charge Equipment cost Space cost	Articles of consumption Machine parts Exchange cost Upgrade cost	Upgrade cost	

Table 6 Benefit factors of EJMS

	Factor	Measurement index
Operational benefits	Cost saving	Logistics cost saving, Operation cost saving, Marketing and sales cost saving, Service cost saving, Firm infrastructure cost saving, Labor cost saving, Technology development cost saving, Procurement cost saving
	Added profitability	Increase of sales, Increase of profitability
	Reduced decision making	Time reduction, Enhanced quality
	Enhanced business function	Enhanced flexibility, Enhanced usability, Enhanced credibility
Strategic benefits	Reduced threat of rivalry	Differentiation, Cost advantage
	Enhanced supplier relationship	Increased supplier, Enhanced supplier manipulation
	Enhanced customer relationship	Increased customer, Enhanced service

Benefit factors

Benefits are divided into three according to their characteristics. One is the economic factor, which is measured and evaluated by monetary terms. Others are the numerical factor, which are measured and evaluated by number or volume. The others are the qualitative factor.

Benefits are divided into operational benefits and strategic benefits. Operational benefits mean the enhanced efficiency of firm operations. They consist of cost saving, added profitability, enhanced decision-making, and enhanced business function.

Strategic benefits mean enhanced competitive advantages. According to Porter (1979)'s five competitive forces model, there are five threats such as the threat of new entrants, the power of suppliers, the threat of substitute products, and the rivalry among existing competitors. Table 6 shows the effectiveness factors of EJMS.

Benefit is divided into three according to their characteristics. One is the economic factor, which is measured and evaluated by monetary terms. Others are the numerical factors which are measured and evaluated by number or volume. The others are the qualitative factors.

Benefit can be classified into easy-quantified benefit and hard-quantified benefit. Easy-quantified benefit is monetary benefit like the reduction of fixed charges and cost reduction. Hard-quantified benefit s is abstract benefit like improvement of service quality, management efficiency, consumer's recognition, enterprise competency, and so on. The techniques which are able to compare each benefit to estimate and qualify the integrated benefit of IS project are need.

Classification of enterprise features

Same investment on IS project doesn't always make same results in enterprises. It is caused by the different features and competency of each enterprise.

EJMS considers the type of industry, size, business process quality, alignment with business strategy, and external factors such as industry types, and competition

Table 7 Processes of EJMS

Phase	Content
Preparation	▪ Analysis of investment objective and background ▪ Determination of evaluation scope and depth ▪ Establishment of evaluation organization and schedule
Analysis	▪ Analysis of organization and business ▪ Analysis of information systems ▪ Analysis of users
Evaluation	▪ Establishment of cost/effectiveness factors ▪ Measurement of cost/effectiveness factors ▪ Evaluation of cost/effectiveness factors
Reporting	▪ Comprehensive evaluation ▪ Report of evaluation results

environment. The enterprise sizes is divided into large enterprises and medium and small-sized enterprises. The industries are sorted in EJMS into the manufacturing industry, finance business, the distribution industry, and service industry. The features of enterprise are applied with the weight for the economic evaluation in EJMS.

Process of EJMS

EJMS makes progresses through four phases: (1) Preparation, (2) Analysis, (3) Evaluation, and (4) Reporting. Detail descriptions are like Table 7.

Methods using in EJMS

Evaluation of economic effectiveness or numerical effectiveness is somewhat easy. Enhanced productivity could be measured by increased amount of task numbers. It also could be measured by changes of task structure. Hedonic wage model could be applied. A task is organized by different value added subtasks. If a high value added subtask is expanded, profitability is grown.

It is hard to evaluate qualitative effectiveness. AHP could be used. IT includes three major steps: identifying and selecting criteria, weighting the criteria and building consensus on their relative important, and evaluation the IS using weighted criteria.

The methods can be classified by their features into measurement methods for the qualification of the tangible value, estimation methods for the quasi-tangible value, and substitution methods for the intangible value.

5. OTHER TECHNIQUES

5.1. Techniques of requirements analysis

Despite the necessity of strategic IS planning, the process is difficult and replete with opportunities for failure. Many strategic planning efforts produce plans that are never implemented. Cerpa and Verner (1998) presented 5 key issues in ISP as follows:

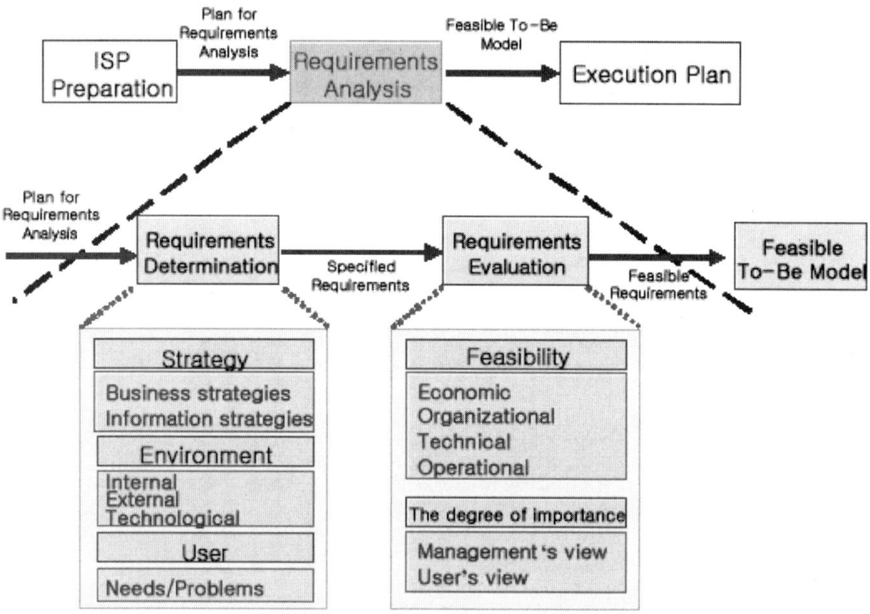

Figure 9. Framework of requirement analysis.

- The involvement and commitment of senior management is essential to the success of the IS plan. It does not matter how good the plan is, if the involvement and commitment of senior management is absent.
- Linking IS to business goals is the heart of IS planning, and without this link, the IS function will not have major relevance for the organization.
- Choosing the right planning methodology depends on the current use and spread of technology within the organization and the importance of the current systems. Available resources (staff, skills, CASE tool, and so on) will also impact this process. It appears that the use of more than one methodology should be recommended.
- While new technology can be advantageous, it can also pose severe problems if the right skills and expertise are not available to use it properly.
- On-going evaluation of the IS strategic plan to ensure that the plan is implemented correctly and the expected results are being obtained.

If requirements analysis is effective and systematic, the alignment of business strategies and information strategies, the evaluation of ISP, and the implementation of ISP will be achieved efficiently. Thus requirements analysis is much important procedure in developing ISP.

Requirements analysis for developing ISP is divided by two domains. One is requirements determination, and the other is requirements evaluation. First, requirements are determined in the area of strategy, environment and user, and supportive tools for users

Table 8 Sub-domain and its supportive tools in requirements determination

Domain	Sub-domain	Supportive tools
Strategy	business strategy	Business strategy statements, SWOT analysis
	information strategy	Information Strategy statement, SWOT analysis, Statement of relationship between information strategy and business strategy
Environment	internal	General environment analysis, Porter's five forces model, statement of evaluation of competitive environment, Portfolio analysis
	external	Value chain analysis, Organization chart RAEW matrix, ERD, DFD, FDD, CRUD matrix
	technological	Information intensity analysis, Strength and weakness analysis of IT, IT environment analysis, IS structure, IT trend analysis, IT in value chain analysis
User	needs/problems	User requirements analysis

are suggested to help them to draw requirements with ease. Last, requirements evaluation also has two domains, one is that of feasibility and the other is that of importance. Checkpoints for each evaluation are suggested to evaluate determined requirements. The evaluation of feasibility has four views, economic, organizational, technological, and operational.

The evaluation of importance considers two perspectives, that of users and that of management. Figure 9 show the framework of requirement analysis.

Requirements determination

Requirements determination for requirements analysis is divided by 3 domains. Those are strategy, environment, and user. They have also sub-domains. Business strategy and information strategy for strategy, internal, external and technological are for environment, and needs/problems are for user. Each sub-domain and its supportive tools in requirements determination are shown in table 8.

Requirements evaluation

Requirements determination for requirements analysis is divided by 2 domains, that of feasibility and that of degree of importance. The former is to check if determined requirements form various analyses are feasible practically and it has 4 domains. ; economic, organizational, technical, and operational. The latter is to find higher prioritized ones among feasible requirements. It has 2 domains. ; management's view and user's view.

5.2. UMT (Unified Modeling Tools) and repository

UMT is a modeling tool supporting integration of outputs through entire life-cycle of implementation of information systems. User requirements are reflected by UMT effectively and make it easy to implement information systems by connecting modeling outputs to system deign and analysis of linkage among modeling. UMT presents tools as matrixes, graphs, diagrams, reports, algorithms, and figures.

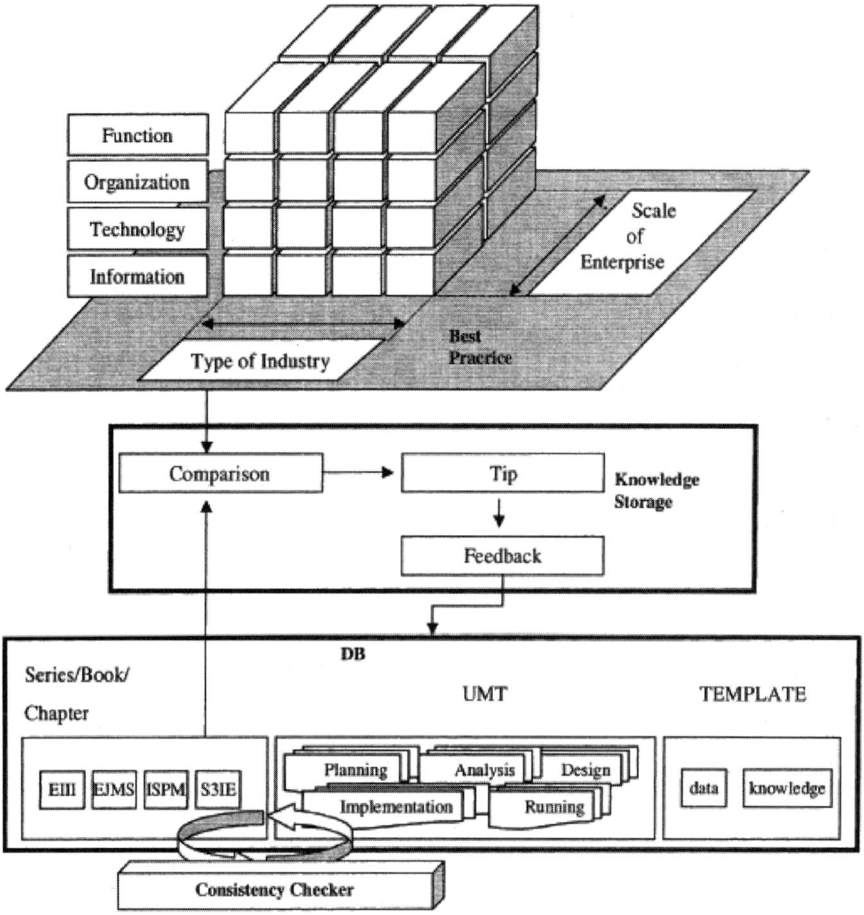

Figure 10. Architecture of Repository.

UMT supports a repository storing knowledge database. It contains industrial best practices, knowledge storage, database and consistency checker (King and Teo, 1994). Figure 10 illustrates the architecture of repository.

Best practices are collection of function, information, technology, organization models describing to-be enterprises. Other enterprises can refer these models to improve competitiveness. Consistency checker can eliminate redundant works and preserve integrity of data stored in the repository. Database store not only tools and techniques that UMT offers but also template of data. Knowledge storage is a repository that collects knowledge and data generated in the progress of project. Participants in the project are able to get important knowledge through the storage. That is, knowledge storage enables users to get many tips related to the problems they would face. Figure 10 shows architecture of repository.

Table 9 Major processes of S3IE

Stage	Sub-stages
Strategy	▪ Initiation ▪ Diagnose ▪ Strategy planning ▪ RFP preparation and software evaluation
Design	▪ Software installation ▪ Customization requirement analysis
Construction	▪ Customization and unit testing ▪ Integrated testing
Implementation	▪ Training ▪ Delivery

5.3. S3IE (Support Systems for Solution Introduction and Evaluation)

S3IE helps decision making of enterprise executives to plan package introduction strategy, to evaluate each package and select one. It is based on input data related each enterprise specific environment. This component supports whole processes that choose suitable products in enterprise environment through introduction preparation, enterprise environment diagnosis, introduction strategy planning, RFP, proposal document estimation and package estimation. Table 9 shows the processes of S3IE.

6. FURTHER WORKS

Though the integrated methodology for enterprise information systems is expected to help enterprise to carry the informatization projects, it still has several limitations to be researched hereafter. The additional studies which are not provided in this integrated methodology are able to be summarized as follows and should be researched.

- The efficient application of the special matters of enterprise by industry
- Improvement of application of each components
- Additional automated tools for the integrated methodology
- Practical use of the best practices and linkage with process knowledge library
- Linkage with business strategy
- Method for development of To-Be enterprise model.

REFERENCES

Bacon, C. J. (1992), The use of decision criteria in selecting information systems/technology investments. MIS Quarterly, September.

Baker, B. (1995), "The role of feedback in assessing information systems planning effectiveness," Journal of Strategic Information Systems, Vol. 4. No. 1, pp. 61–80.

Cassidy, A. (1998), A Practical Guide to Information Systems Strategic Planning, CRC Press.

Cerpa, N., and Verner, J. M. (1998), The effect of IS maturity on information systems strategic planning, Information & Management, No. 34, pp. 199–208.

DeLone, W. H., and McLean, E. R. (1992), "Information Systems Success: The Quest for the Dependent Variable," Information Systems Research, Vol. 3, No. 1, pp. 60–95.

Deming, W. E. (1986), Out of The Crisis, MIT Center for Advanced Engineering Stidy, MIT Press, Cambridge, MA.
Dickson, G. W., Leitheiser, R. L., and Wetherbe, J. C. (1984), Key information systems issues for the 1980's, MIS Quarterly, Sep, pp. 135–147.
Fazlolahi, B., and Tanniru, M. R. (1991), "Selecting requirement determination methodology-contingency approach revisited," Information & Management, No. 21, pp. 291–303.
Galletta, D. F., Sampler, J. L., and Teng, J. T. (1999), "Strategies for integrating creativity principles into the systems development process," Proceedings of the twenty-fifth Hawaii international conference on. 1999, pp. 268–275.
Goodhue, D. L. et al. (1992), "Strategic data planning: lessons from the field," MIS Quarterly, Vol. 16, No. 2, pp. 11–32.
Ha, J.-K. (2001), "A study on the supporting methodology for implementing and evaluating e-Business packages," Master thesis, Yonsei University, Korea.
Jeffrey, H. J. (1996), "Addressing the essential difficulties of software engineering, Journal of Systems Software, 32-2 (February), pp. 157–176.
Kim, D.-W. (2001), "A Study on Requirements Analysis for Information Strategy Planning", Master thesis, Yonsei University, Korea.
Kim, S. T. (2001), "A study on enterprise information system investment evaluation," Master thesis, Yonsei University, Korea.
Lederer, A. L., and Sethi, V. (1996), "Key prescriptions for strategic information systems planning," Journal of Management Information Systems, Vol. 13, No. 1, pp. 35–62.
Leem, C.-S. (1999), '99 Annual reports for evaluation of IS Performance, IT Research and consulting.
Leem, C.-S. (2000), '00 Annual reports for evaluation of IS Performance, IT Research and consulting.
Leem, C. S., and Kim, I. "An Integrated Evaluation System based on the Continuous Improvement Model of IS Performance," Industrial Management & Data Systems, will appear.
Leem, C. S., and Kim, S. (2002), "Introduction to an integrated methodology for development and implementation of enterprise information systems," The Journal of Systems and Software Vol. 60, pp. 249–261.
Mason, R. O. (1978), "Measuring Information Output: A Communication Systems Approach," Information & Management, Vol. 1, No. 5, 219–234.
McFarlan, F. W., McKenney, J. L., and Pyburn, P. (1983), The information archipelago-plotting a course, Harvard Business Review, Jan-Feb, pp. 145–156.
Myers, B. L., Kappelman, L. A., and Prybutok, V. R. (1997), A Comprehensive Model for Assessing the Quality and Productivity of the Information Systems Function: Toward a Theory for Information Systems Assessment, Information Resources Management Journal, Vol. 10, No. 1, pp. 6–25.
Nolan, R. L., and Wetherbe, J. B. (1980), Toward A Comprehensive Framework for MIS Research, MIS Quarterly, pp. 1–19.
Oh, B. (2001), "A Study on the Development of the Evaluation Framework for Information Strategic Planning," Master thesis, Yonsei University, Korea.
Robertson, S., and Robertson, J. (1999), "Mastering the requirements Process," ADDISON WESLEY.
Saunders, C. S., and Jones, W. (1992), Measuring performance of the information systems function, Journal of Management Information Systems, pp. 63–82.
Seddon, P. B., and Kiew, M.-Y. (1994), "A Partial Test and Development of the DeLone and McLean Model of IS Success," Proceedings of the International Conference on Information Systems, Vancouver, Canada (ICIS 94), 99–110.
Shewhart, W. A. (1931), Economic Control of Quality of Manufactured Product, D. Van Nostrand Company, Inc., New York.
Tan, D. S. (1999), Stages in Information Systems Management, Handbook of IS Management, CRC Press LLC, pp. 51–75.
Theo, J. W., and Berghout, E. W. (1997), Methodologies for information systems investment evaluation at the proposal stage: a comparative review. Information and Software Technology 39.
Venkatraman, N. (1997), Beyond outsourcing: Managing IT resources as a value center, Saloan Management Review, spring, pp. 51–64.
Vernadat, F. B. (1996), Enterprise Modeling and Integration: principles and applications, Champman & Hall, pp. 14–16, 317–334.
Zani, W. M. (1970), "Blueprint for MIS", Harvard Business Review, Vol. 48, No. 6, 1970, pp. 95–100.

INFORMATION SYSTEMS FRAMEWORKS AND THEIR APPLICATIONS IN MANUFACTURING AND SUPPLY CHAIN SYSTEMS

ADRIAN E. CORONADO MONDRAGON, ANDREW C. LYONS, AND DENNIS F. KEHOE

1. INTRODUCTION

In recent years manufacturing organisations have been facing increasing changes in their business environment. Those changes are being driven by customers demanding greater choice in products and services and competition from all corners of the globe. Moreover, manufacturing industry has been subject to a number of trends that include outsourcing, time compression, mass customisation and pricing pressures to mention just a few. Information and communication technologies can be used by manufacturing organisations to respond to changes in the business environment.

The need to respond quickly to changes in market conditions is forcing manufacturing organisations to become more dependent on information technology. Indeed, the pace of technology change offers manufacturing organisations the possibility of implementing new solutions to old problems. Definitions of information technology (IT) like the one provided by Boar [1] are still valid. The researcher described IT as the asset on which an enterprise constructs its business information systems. IT is the preparation, collection, transport, retrieval, storage, access, presentation and transformation of information in all its forms (voice, graphics, text, video, and image). IT has been recognised by Shaw et al. [2] as having a major influence on all manufacturing organisations, large or small, and the rapid evolution of IT brings new possibilities for work and collaboration. In manufacturing organisations IT enables information to flow between different business units. IT is considered means to facilitate codification, processing and diffusion of information supporting the development of new knowledge [3]. Such capabilities become increasingly important for manufacturing organisations facing increasingly competitive business environments.

The concept of information systems is broader than that of IT. According to Ezingeard [4], information systems encompass the whole range of procedures that are in place in an organisation. Information systems have been defined as the set of applications that gather individuals and information flow on IT based devices and infrastructure. Moreover, added functionality features to information systems enable the execution of new ways of work not experienced before (e.g. concurrent design operations).

The historical use of information systems in manufacturing industry is reviewed in the first sections of this chapter. Trends that are defining the direction of information systems in manufacturing are considered and current developments of information systems in manufacturing as well as future research opportunities are provided at the end of the chapter.

2. INFORMATION SYSTEMS USE IN THE MANUFACTURING INDUSTRY

The adoption of IT/information systems in manufacturing has been through an evolution process that started decades ago. The latest developments in information systems for manufacturing represent the utilisation of Internet-based electronic commerce (e-commerce) applications, active agents, widespread use of communication protocols, platform independent programming languages, virtual enterprise and integration not only at the enterprise level but with other organisations. However, information systems applications that were developed some decades ago are still widely used in the industry. Examples of information systems widely used include the use of MRP (Material Resource Planning), MRPII (Manufacturing Resource Planning), CAD (Computer Aided Design)/CAM (Computer Aided Manufacturing), CNC (Computer Numerical Control), SPC (Statistical Process Control), Data Management, extensive automation using PLCs (Programmable Logic Controllers), robots and AGV (Automated Guided Vehicles), CIM (Computer Integrated Manufacturing) and EDI (Electronic Data Interchange). The adoption of MRP systems, followed by MRPII, SFDC (Shopfloor Data Collection) and Data Management, represented revolutionary developments of information systems in the manufacturing sector, helping companies to improve their operations dramatically. Affordable hardware, ubiquitous use of PC's, and better performing applications triggered the massive use of information systems in manufacturing. The introduction of automation through the utilisation of PLCs, robots and AGVs, gave birth to the concept of CIM and extended enterprises begin to develop as customers and suppliers could be integrated through the use of EDI.

Manufacturing and production information systems can be classified in several ways. Table 1 shows a categorisation based on the impact information systems have on the strategic, tactical, knowledge and operational levels of an enterprise. According to Laudon and Laudon [5] strategic-level manufacturing systems deal with the firm's long-term manufacturing objectives. Long-term involve those objectives related to the installation of a new production line. Tactical objectives in manufacturing are involved in the management and control of production costs and resources. Knowledge

Table 1 Classification of manufacturing information systems in terms of enterprise levels

Strategic level systems	**Knowledge level systems**
Production technology	Computer aided design systems (CAD)
Facilities location applications	Computer aided manufacturing (CAM)
Competitor scanning and intelligence	Engineering workstations
Tactical systems	Computer Numerically Controlled (CNC) machine tools
Manufacturing Resource Planning	**Operational systems**
Computer Integrated Manufacturing	Purchase/receiving systems
Inventory Control Systems	Shipping systems
Cost Accounting Systems	Labour-costing systems
Capacity Planning	Materials systems
Labour Costing Systems	Equipment maintenance systems
Production Schedules	Quality control systems

(From Information Systems and the Internet, Fourth Edition 4th edition by LAUDON. © 1998. Reprinted with permission of Course Technology, a division of Thomson Learning: www.thomsonrights.com. Fax 800 730-2215.)

systems represent the creation and distribution of knowledge and expertise driving the production process. Operational information systems deal directly with all production tasks involving purchasing, shipping, materials and quality control.

3. INFORMATION SYSTEMS EVOLUTION IN MANUFACTURING

Shewchuk [6] described that the function of information systems in manufacturing is to support the planning, scheduling and control activities of an organisation. The use of computers in manufacturing is represented by different technology trends that have appeared in the last six decades, Next Generation Manufacturing Project 1997 [7]. The origins of the use of IT in manufacturing can be traced back to the 50's, but it was not until the beginning of the 70's when IT started to be widely adopted in manufacturing organisations, represented by applications such as CAM and Materials Transformation. The progress of the 70's saw applications and technologies such as Data Management, CAD/CAM, MRP, CNC and JIT (Just-In-Time) being developed and widely implemented in manufacturing enterprises. The 80's saw the development and implementation of technologies such as Intelligent Scheduling, Supplier Partnerships, CIM, Automation (use of PLCs in substitution of relay arrays), Robotics, EDI, CAE (Computer Aided Engineering) and MRPII. Gefen [8] highlighted that on occasions, MRPII systems are incorporated into larger ERP (enterprise resource planning) packages, enabling companies competing in the global marketplace to redefine, integrate and optimise their supply chains. The same researcher stated that MRPII systems are complex information systems that manage and coordinate a company's supply chain, inventory, bill of materials, production scheduling, capacity planning, job costing, and cash planning.

The 90's have witnessed the development of software based on Object Technology, and the widespread use of applications and technologies related to Operational Modelling, Enterprise Integration, Intelligent Sensors, Active Agents, Virtual Reality, APC (Advanced Process Control), e-commerce using the Internet and B2B (business to business). Communications across organisations using heterogeneous application systems integration has become a reality due to the use of protocols such as TCP (transport control protocol), HTTP (hypertext transfer protocol) and platform independent programming languages (e.g. Java). The first years of the 21st century have witnessed the consolidation of technologies such as XLM (extensible markup language).

The Next Generation Manufacturing project -NGM- [7] provided a description of information systems requirements to support the operation of manufacturing organisations facing an increase in competition and unpredictable business changes. The NGM framework proposed the creation of adaptive/responsive information systems to facilitate rapid response between enterprise partners and their suppliers and customers, enabling inter-enterprise integration. Enterprise integration has been defined as the discipline that connects and combines people, processes, systems and technologies to ensure that a manufacturing company can function as a well co-ordinated whole, by itself and with other organisations [9]. According to the NGM [7], in the future it will be the integration with other organisations that will enable manufacturing enterprises to survive. In a changing business environment, the information systems function of a company may deal with the problems of standardisation and integration of heterogeneous systems. Integration of information systems plays a significant role in the sense that legacy applications may be needed to keep an enterprise fully operational.

The evolution of IT in manufacturing has motivated researchers to develop a variety of means for classifying the use of IT in manufacturing. For example, Kathuria and Igbaria [10] provided a classification consisting of seven major functional areas: product design, demand management, capacity planning, inventory management, shopfloor systems, quality management and distribution. Randall from Compass Consulting [11] suggested that investments and use of IT/information systems in manufacturing organisations can be classified by the following:

- *Infrastructure* covers the Internet, Intranet, databases and operating systems. According to Broadbent et al. [12] infrastructure is the enabling base of shared IT capabilities which provide the foundation for other business systems.
- *Planning* covers MRP, ERP and APS. These are information systems applications for the assessment of materials and plant resources, business processes modelling and real time decision support. This element of the classification also includes applications used in design (e.g. CAD). According to Robinson and Wilson [13] ERP systems are one of the latest attempts to utilise the capacities of IT to extend management control of the process of capital accumulation. From a technical point of view, ERP systems comprise application domain, back-office and transaction-processing systems [14].
- *Execution* covers workflow and data warehousing among other functions. This element of the classification includes resources that facilitate minute by minute transactions and links other data streams within manufacturing operations, both internal (e.g. ERP systems) and external (e.g. customers, suppliers and service providers). Also, *execution* covers applications such as CAM and CNC used in design and manufacturing processes.

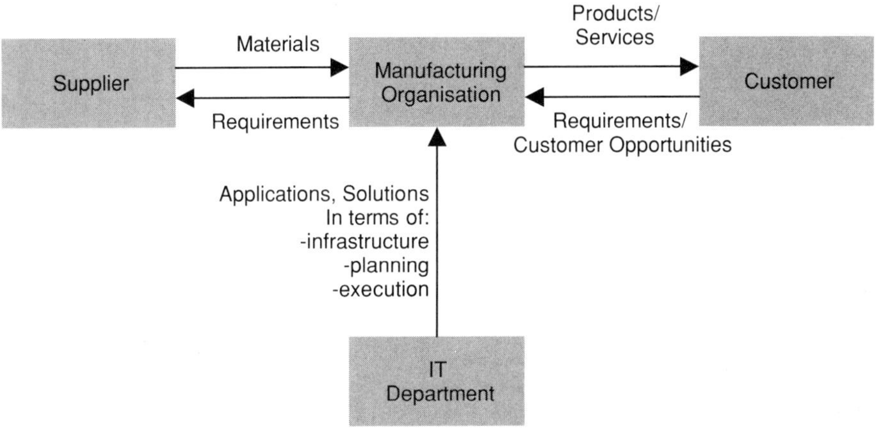

Figure 1. Information systems role in manufacturing.

Data warehousing technology has emerged as one of the most powerful tools in delivering information to end users. A data warehouse offers integrated, historical information that can be accessed by end users directly. The aim is to provide a consolidated view of information (both summary and detailed) to facilitate end user query for management and decision support [15].

Figure 1 depicts the traditional support the IT function provides in manufacturing enterprises. In this simplified model, the information systems department is responsible for providing the applications/solutions in terms of infrastructure, planning and execution. The organisation reacts to customer opportunities by providing the required services or products. Information systems applications/solutions used to support business processes link the IT function to the organisation. Certainly, the adoption of new manufacturing paradigms may require the IT function to impact not only the organisation alone but the interrelation between the organisation and its suppliers and customers.

Information systems in manufacturing are used to manage the bills of materials (parts needed to assemble a product), inventory, and procurement, integrating their management with production scheduling, capacity planning, and job costing (calculating the cost of each product according to inventory, machine and work time needed). All these activities are typically coupled with related systems, including accounts payable, vendor management, RFQ (request for quotation), order and delivery processing, and billing activities. Figure 2 shows a typical manufacturing information system, comprised of material requirements planning systems, bill of materials (production and reports) and material components data storage.

3.1. Infrastructure as an element of information systems in manufacturing

Infrastructure is an important component of information systems. Farbey et al. [16] in their benefits evaluation ladder identified the importance of infrastructure. They

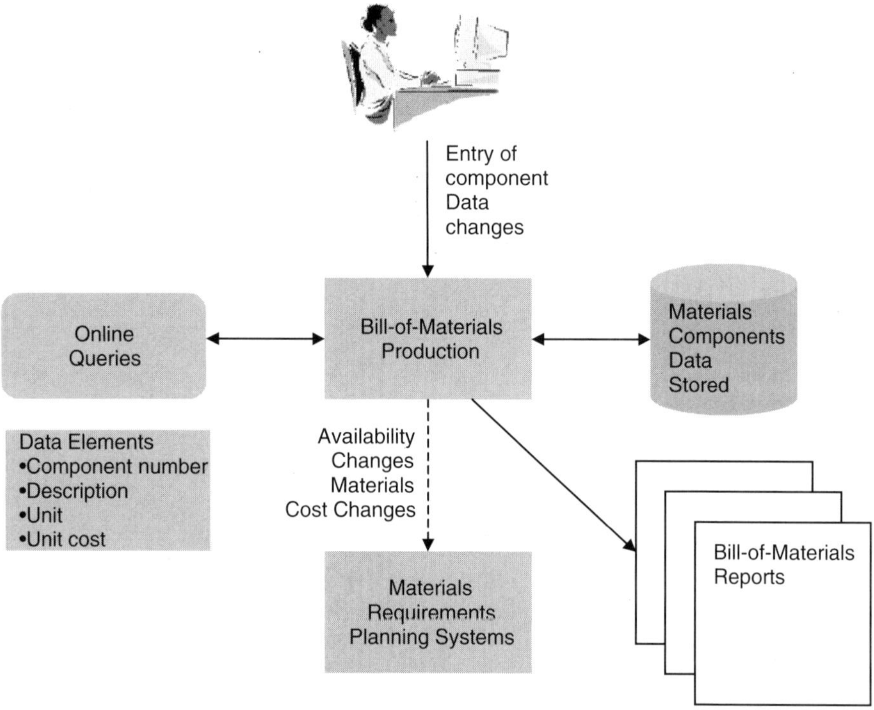

Figure 2. A typical information system used to support manufacturing enterprises. (From Information Systems and the Internet, Fourth Edition 4th edition by LAUDON. © 1998. Reprinted with permission of Course Technology, a division of Thomson Learning: www.thomsonrights.com. Fax 800 730-2215.)

explained that investments in infrastructure are intended to provide the foundation upon which subsequent value adding applications can be built. Infrastructure investments provide a general capability but may not be targeted at any specific application. Because investments of this type do not provide direct benefits to the business, they may therefore not figure prominently in the senior management's value systems. Investments justification needs to demonstrate the link between the infrastructure and subsequent projects whose value to the business can be demonstrated. Moreover, investments in IT infrastructure are seen as necessary in order for the company in question to respond rapidly to any moves by competitors.

According to Saaksjarvi [17], investments in infrastructure are long-term commitments accounting for a considerable share of the total IT budget. The researcher emphasised that infrastructure helps the company to integrate and accumulate earlier developments in transaction processing (e.g. Decision Support Systems and strategic information systems).

Broadbent et al. [12] defined IT/information systems infrastructure as the base foundation of budgeted-for IT capability (both human and technical), shared throughout the organisation in the form of reliable services. The focus of investment justification turns from specific applications to the capability of an infrastructure to support a range of future activities. However, IT infrastructure can be a constraint where systems are not compatible, or where inconsistent data models have been used in different parts of the business. The same researchers concluded that knowledge of the role of IT infrastructure capabilities remains largely "in the realms of conjecture and anecdote". Flexibility for information systems infrastructure is also an important issue. In fact, evaluation turns from specific applications to the capability of an infrastructure to support a range of future developments. According to Hanseth and Braa [18], benefits from IT infrastructure only accrue through business applications, infrastructure cannot be designed and managed in the same way as information systems, as it is created by several actors and can thus be changed only gradually. However, the contribution of IT can be directly measured through the support different applications provide for business processes.

4. ELECTRONIC COMMERCE AND MANUFACTURING INFORMATION SYSTEMS

Internet-based e-commerce applications are in part aimed at enabling inter-enterprise integration. Kettinger and Hackbarth [19] highlighted that e-commerce is about re-thinking business models by exploiting information asymmetries, leveraging customer and partner relationships and finding the right fit of co-operation and competition. Their work showed an evolutionary process faced by organisations in the areas of e-commerce strategy, business strategy, scope, payoffs, levers and the role of information. Table 2 shows the areas involved in this evolutionary process.

The levels of development shown in table 2 represent attributes required by manufacturing organisations to succeed in an environment in constant change. For example, in the *scope* area, cross-enterprise involvement collaboration is compatible with the

Table 2 Levels of development of e-commerce in organisations

Area	Level 1	Level 2	Level 3
e-commerce strategy	No EC strategy	EC strategy supports current business strategy	EC strategy supports breakout ("to be") business strategy
Business strategy	EC not linked to business strategy	EC strategy	EC is a driver of business strategy
Scope	Departmental/functional orientation	Cross-functional participation	Cross-enterprise involvement interconnected (customers, suppliers and consumers)
Payoffs	Unclear	Cost reduction, business support and enhancement of business processes	Revenue enhancement, increased customer satisfaction, drastic improvement in customer service.
Levers	Technological infrastructure and software applications	Business processes	People intellectual capital and relationship
Role of information	Secondary to technology	Supports process efficiency and effectiveness	Information asymmetries used to create business opportunities

attributes of enterprise integration and close supplier relationships emphasised in manufacturing paradigms such as agile manufacturing [20], or the attribute of customer satisfaction in the area of *payoffs* is compatible with the attribute of satisfaction of customer requirements in TQM or lean manufacturing. The attribute of leveraging the impact of people and information, Kidd [21], is addressed in level three of the Levers area. The foundations of e-commerce systems are the software components that deliver business-to-business (B2B) or business-to-consumer (B2C) services [22].

A close interaction between customers and suppliers is essential for manufacturing organisations in a business environment in constant change. In the view of Gunasekaran [23], the main motivation behind e-commerce is to improve the response time to customer's demand as quickly as possible by directly collecting the customer's requirements through an online communications system. The primary benefit of EDI to businesses is a considerable reduction in transaction costs by improving the speed and efficiency of filling orders.

E-commerce is a digital platform that pervades all functions and departments within a company. According to Gunasekaran [23], e-commerce can ensure higher quality, reduced costs, and increased responsiveness. The researcher declared that e-commerce applications are intended to provide the capabilities to manage the supply chain, that is the ability to deliver products faster, shortening the cycle from order to cash receipts. The addition of e-commerce in the development of information systems in manufacturing is compatible with concepts that emerged during the decade of the 90's like the extended enterprise [24], and the extended supply-chain [25]. In fact, e-commerce through the utilisation of the Internet may facilitate the seamless integration of suppliers and customers. According to Kasarda and Rondinelli [26] today, even small and medium-sized enterprises increasingly rely on international networks of suppliers, distributors and customers to improve their global competitiveness.

The use of e-commerce to integrate operations with customers and suppliers may ease responding to changing customer demand, facilitate adapting to a changing business climate and flexibility to redesign their processes towards suppliers and customers while enabling decentralized operations. Furthermore, the adoption of Internet-based e-commerce applications should be within easier reach of smaller manufacturers, compared to other more expensive applications. However, the ubiquitous access to information and acquisition of technology necessarily demands adequate management policies to deliver any sort of advantage.

5. VIRTUAL ORGANISATIONS AND MANUFACTURING INFORMATION SYSTEMS

Day by day operations in manufacturing organisations require the integration of information systems through scattered manufacturing plants. The utilisation of Internet technologies can bring together applications related to resource planning (MRP, ERP and cost accounting systems); manufacturing execution (factory level coordinating and tracking systems) and distributed control (floor devices and process control systems). This integration is the foremost step towards the consolidation of operations to form virtual organisations.

The wide utilisation of Internet based e-commerce supported by an IT/information systems infrastructure and applications for execution and planning, are key to the development of virtual organisations. Reid et al. [27] described that a virtual enterprise is conceived when a need is recognised in the marketplace and a business objective or set of objective(s) is/are established. To conceive a virtual enterprise it is important for organisations to understand customer expectations and what it will take to satisfy them. An enterprise is created when relationships are established to eventually bring together the requisite competencies. Different researchers [28] have provided guidelines to the formation of virtual organisations.

The virtual enterprise concept has been used to characterise the global supply chain of a single product in an environment of dynamic networks of companies engaged in many different complex relationships [29]. Manufacturing organisations need to implement information systems able to cope with several technical constraints such as concurrent engineering, inter-network applications, hardware heterogeneity, software for application communication and time constraints. Also, a sound methodology will be required to, if necessary, re-define business process, the states of synchronisation, the way collaboration is achieved and once a virtual enterprise has been formed under which organisation it will be managed.

6. PARADIGMS SHIFTS IN MANUFACTURING

Information technology/systems occupy a relevant place in the literature of a significant number of improvement paradigms for manufacturing such as agile manufacturing [31] and mass customisation [32,33]. Indeed, in almost all improvement initiatives for manufacturing organisations, information systems play a role. For example, JIT (Just-In-Time) emphasises minimising (if not eliminating) waste in the form of inventories in order to reduce costs. JIT empowers employees to check quality at the source and ensuring that products are consistently made to standards. Some information systems applications have been classified as JIT. However, some researchers argue that JIT is more of a philosophy than just another computerised planning system intended for repetitive environments with stable schedules, narrow product ranges and standard items [10]. In the early 90's Business Process Re-engineering (BPR) was the focus of attention in the manufacturing industry. BPR is essentially supported by IT. Then, lean thinking gained the attention of manufacturing managers. Lean means doing more with less resources; banishing waste, Womack and Jones [30].

Information systems have been identified as key enablers of concepts such as the extended and virtual enterprise [34] and hence, they are considered to be important components of agility. According to the originators of the concept of agility [31], agile manufacturing organisations operate in dynamic business environments. Success in a dynamic business environment requires information systems that enable the organisation to react quickly to emerging customer opportunities.

A dynamic business environment is typified by rapidly emerging customer opportunities. Researchers in the fields of industrial engineering and operations management have remarked upon the importance of a dynamic business environment in shaping all the activities of manufacturing organisations [31]. Manufacturing organisations need to grasp to those emerging customer opportunities to their advantage.

Another paradigm in manufacturing that has received attention is Build-to-Order (BTO). The concept of build-to-order does not imply mass customisation per se. Mass customisation is dependent on the adoption of BTO schemes that will enable the production of customised goods or products. Indeed, the capability to build goods without any sort of delay is a component of any mass customisation initiative aimed at meeting customer needs in the shortest time possible. BTO may provide manufacturers with the capability to grow in a business environment represented by tough competition and variation in customer requirements.

Given the importance of IT/information systems to support the concept of many manufacturing improvement paradigms, Huang and Nof [35] classified the impact of modern information technologies in three categories: *a*) speeding up activities, *b*) providing intelligent and autonomous decision-making processes; and *c*) enabling distributed operations with collaboration. According to them, utilisation of IT/information systems enables the creation of:

- New manufacturing/services.
- Strategic information and knowledge management.
- Enterprise integration and management.
- Virtual enterprise.
- Virtual manufacturing/services.
- Concurrent engineering.
- Rapid prototyping.

The same researchers found that IT improves enterprise activities in different areas, including:

Collaboration: Distributed designers can work together on a common design project through a computer supported collaborative work (CSCW) software system.
Decisions: Powerful computation allows many simulation trials to find a better solution in decision making.
Logistics: Information networks monitor logistics flows of productivity and packages.
Recovery: Utilisation of artificial intelligence techniques (e.g. knowledge based logic) to improve the quality of activities.
Sensing: Input devices (e.g. sensors, bar-code readers) can gather and communicate environmental information to computers or people.
Partners: A computer system in an organisation may automatically find co-operative partners (e.g. vendors, suppliers and subcontractors) to fulfil a special customer order.

6.1. IT and information systems for mass customisation

Da Silveira et al. [32] have provided examples of IT/information systems supporting mass customisation. Indeed, information systems have been defined as enabling technologies supporting mass customisation. The researchers provided examples that include Motorola using CIM-related technologies (such as Cartesian and gantry robots) to implement two MC factories.

Another example cited by Da Silveira et al. [32] is Perkins Diesel. The company based their MC system on a hybrid CAD/CAE (computer-aided engineering) system with flexible manufacturing assembly lines. Computer numeric control (CNC), flexible manufacturing systems (FMS), communication and network technologies such as computer-aided design (CAD), computer-aided manufacturing (CAM), computer integrated manufacturing (CIM), and electronic data interchange (EDI) are widely used in all business units of Perkins Diesel. The researchers emphasised that the main motivation behind the extensive use of communications and networks based on IT is to provide direct links between internal units (e.g. design, analysis, manufacturing and testing) and to improve the response time to customer requirements.

7. DEVELOPMENT OF INFORMATION SYSTEMS IN MANUFACTURING

The types of information systems used in manufacturing organisations can be classified in two major groups: In-house development of systems using Rapid Application Development (RAD) and purchase of systems commonly known as Commercial off-the-shelf applications (COTS).

RAD has aimed at fast development and high quality of products through:

- Requirements identification using workshops,
- Prototyping and early and continuous user testing of designs,
- Re-use of software components,
- Compliance to a fixed calendar of activities,
- Establishing informal communication channels between team members

Some software development firms offer products that provide some or all of the tools for RAD software development. These products may include requirements gathering tools, computer-aided software engineering tools, tools for prototyping, tools for communication among development members, language development environments such as those for the Java platform and XML and testing and debugging tools. On the other hand there is no guarantee that RAD developments would not face budget overrun, lack of communication between developers and behind schedule activities.

Certainly many organisations may avoid the development of their own information systems, turning themselves to commercial applications offered by different software vendors. COTS, commercial off-the-shelf applications describe ready-made products that can easily be purchased and implemented. Supporting this fact, Geffen [8] emphasised that given the complexity of MRPII systems and the cost of developing them, most MRPII systems are off-the-shelf software. Yet, although the code in these systems is seldom modified by the buyers, these systems do undergo extensive customisation before being successfully deployed. Whatever the type of application used by an organisation, RAD or COTS, information systems development consists of a cycle of seven stages that usually include process workflows, business modelling, requirements,

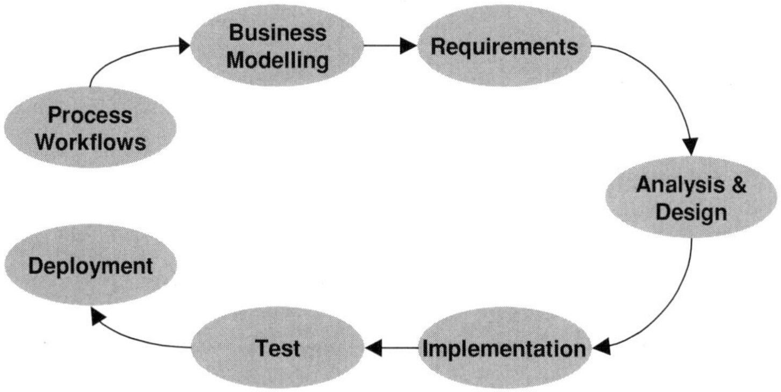

Figure 3. Information systems development cycle.

analysis and design, implementation, test and deployment [36]. Figure 3 depicts the information systems development cycle.

The information systems development cycle is augmented with the stages of maintenance and evolution. The last two stages represent serious challenges for many organisations. In the case of maintenance, the information system should have been developed in a way that guarantees that the related managerial and technical activities ensure meeting organisational and business objectives in a cost-effective manner. Evolution should guarantee that further changes to customer requirements can be accommodated. Moreover, according to Hevner et al. [37] in an e-commerce environment many companies try to juggle the need for projects to meet specific customer needs and the desire to create a fundamental product architecture that will produce a more stable future growth.

The adoption of new improvement paradigms in manufacturing will directly affect the complexity of developing information systems solutions. Indeed, software development organisations and in-house teams involved in the development of information systems for e-commerce have to face challenges prompted by a business environment in constant change and demanding customers with ill-defined requirements. The outcome of that situation involves priority conflicts between development teams and customer projects.

According to Hevner et al. [37] rigorous requirements for security, performance, reliability, portability and availability are essential in order to achieve high levels of customer satisfaction. The researchers stated that many e-commerce companies have moved to a software development environment where they simultaneously pursue product lines (the software components that are tailored to meet a market need in general) and projects (the software components designed to meet the needs of a specific customer).

The techniques developed for building and deploying information systems should pay emphasis to identifying the conditions in the marketplace and the requirements

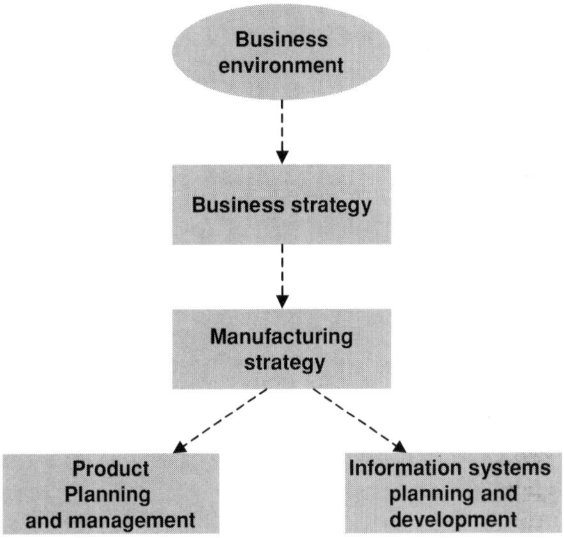

Figure 4. Information systems development for manufacturing.

of their customers which ultimately shape the functionality of the application. Based on the points highlighted by Hevner et al. [37], figure 4 shows that any information systems planning and development process is the direct consequence of clearly and previously defined manufacturing and business strategies.

Enterprises will not only face different conditions when developing information systems in-house or customising the acquisition of a particular commercial off-the-shelf application. Indeed, organisations will have to face the process of deciding the acquisition of information systems. Figure 5 depicts the acquisition process relevant for information systems that will guarantee meeting the needs of the manufacturing organisation.

Figure 5 depicts the involvement of enterprise business units such as engineering, personnel, information systems, marketing, finance and production (manufacturing and operations) in a decision process designed to first meet the immediate needs of manufacturing operations and then meet long-term organisational needs.

Manufacturing organisations require the use of tools that guarantee the translation of business needs and requirements into the development of e-commerce information systems. The Unified Modelling Language (UML) is seen as an effective way of managing requirements in information systems development. The adoption of requirements management is seen as a solution to the ongoing problems of systems development. The IEEE 833 standard defines a requirement for information systems as a capability that the system must deliver. According to Oberg et al. [38] a requirement is a capability of the system needed by the user to solve a problem or achieve an objective, a

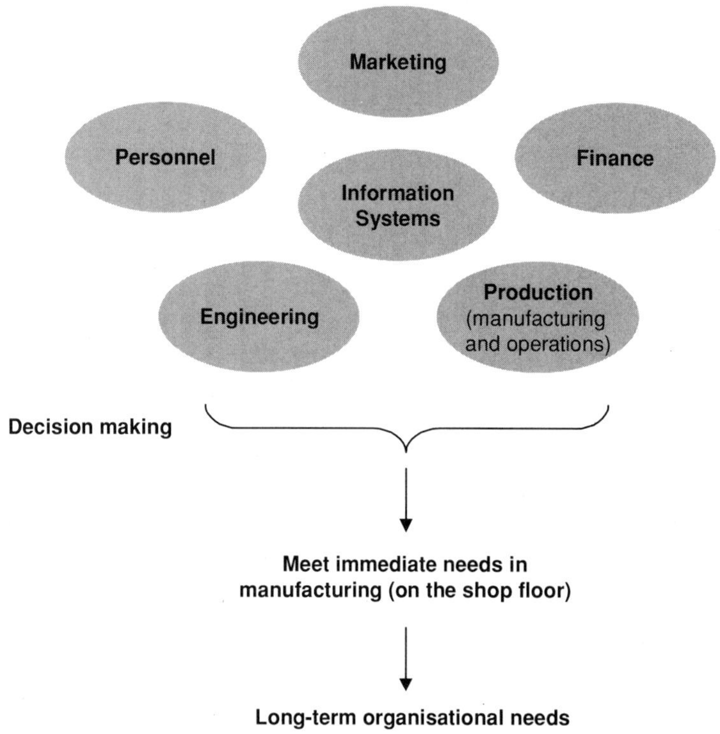

Figure 5. Information systems acquisition process.

capability that must be met or possessed by a system or system component to satisfy a contract, specification, standard, or other formally imposed documentation.

8. EXAMPLES AND HIGHLIGHTS OF INFORMATION SYSTEMS DEVELOPMENTS IN MANUFACTURING

There is consensus among academics about the enabling capabilities of information systems within manufacturing improvement initiatives. Researchers and practitioners like DeVor et al. [39] have stated that recent advances in information networking, processing and e-commerce are rapidly expanding the capability to achieve powerful interactive links among organisational and functional units of the manufacturing enterprise. The researchers discussed how the Internet and the evolution of global networking capabilities enable the creation of an architecture for an open data network. Improvement programmes for manufacturing will become a consumer of such information infrastructure functionality, and will focus on building information tools and resources. This approach focused mainly on the technical difficulties to join heterogeneous information systems. Future models and frameworks need to consider non-technical factors behind the performance of information systems in organisations wishing to participate in the virtual enterprise.

A significant number of works available in the literature have placed emphasis on technical factors regarding the development of information systems support of manufacturing operations. For example, Song and Nagi [40] described manufacturing improvement paradigms making use of modern IT to form virtual enterprises, swiftly responding to changing market demands. The researchers proposed the creation of an Agile Manufacturing Information System with the idea of providing partners with integrated and consistent information. Considerations for the system included partner information interoperability across companies, information consistency across partners in the virtual enterprise, partner policy independence and autonomy maintenance, and finally, open and dynamic system architecture. The researchers proposed in their model that each participating company becomes a node in a network linking companies to the virtual enterprise. Each company has its own systems (CAD, MRP, CAPP, DBMS) and works as an autonomous unit. Also data and workflow hierarchies that would enable organisations to share information and process queries and requests were contemplated in this model. The proposed framework does not take into consideration the current level of performance of the information systems used in participating companies. Also, attributes like IT skills of employees have not been considered in this model. Moreover, for the average SME the formation of virtual enterprises and collaboration with other organisations through information systems is less developed than other sectors like retailing and financial services.

On the same theme, Cheng et al. [41] developed an information systems architecture based on AI (artificial intelligence) and the Internet. This work was deployed to enable remote and quick access to design and manufacturing expertise. The researchers recognised that improvement initiatives in manufacturing are primarily business concepts but new technology is still one of its most important driving forces. Moreover, the researchers provided a scenario where the Internet is used to speed up information flow in a product development cycle and thus achieve reduced development time and costs. Bullinger et al. [42] developed an integration concept for heterogeneous legacy systems. Legacy systems are integrated into a company-wide IT architecture through the encapsulation of these systems into several business objects that can be re-used and transformed into an object-oriented architecture. The proposed architecture relies on the use of middleware standards for the integration of legacy systems.

Other researchers like Whiteside et al. [43] have investigated the use and development of middleware and distributed computing to develop robust information architectures that can be used in the integration of physically distributed design and manufacturing facilities within an enterprise. Researchers have recognised the importance of robust information architectures to support the success of adopting new manufacturing paradigms. Research has continued with the development of seamless enterprise data management solutions in support of manufacturing environments [44,45]. Nowadays XML is a mature tool used to integrate heterogeneous legacy systems. Figure 6 depicts the use of XML/Java applications used to insert/extract data in/from web servers.

Zhou et al. [46] developed an information management system for production planning in virtual enterprises. The researchers presented a distributed information

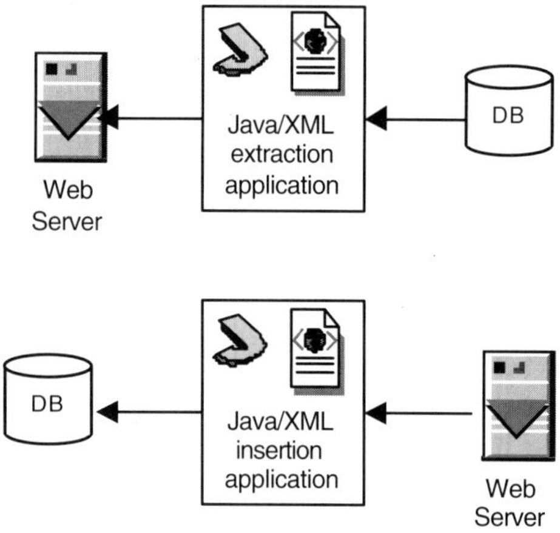

Figure 6. Use of XML/Java applications to insert/extract data.

management architecture for production planning and control in the manufacturing of semiconductors. The proposed architecture is based on the Internet and the use of an Object Request Broker.

Herrman et al. [47] presented the information required for three functions of agile manufacturing: prequalifying partners, evaluating a product design with respect to the capabilities of potential partners, and selecting the optimal set of partners for the manufacture of certain product. The implemented model is used as part of a decision support system for design, evaluation and partner selection.

The development and use of sophisticated IT/information systems applications like the examples previously shown confirms the importance of technology in the future of manufacturing not only at the managerial level but also at the shop floor level. Indeed, manufacturing operations in the shop floor will continue to be influenced by the adoption of e-strategies in automation systems, enabling transparent information management, real time control and condition monitoring across distributed industrial systems.

In the late 90's, agent technologies started to impact manufacturing information systems. According to Turowski [33] a software agent is defined as an autonomous problem-solving unit that may collaborate with other agents to achieve optimised results in a specific problem area. In a manufacturing environment characterised by the use of agent technologies, suppliers and manufacturers will require sharing information systems applications that will provide them with at least a proprietary interface for exporting and importing data in a non-standard format. Procurement of all parts from suitable suppliers and resulting demand reports may be transferred to agents. Moreover, the foundation of e-strategies in shop floor automation lies in the integration of networking and agent technologies developed on open architectures, facilitating the automation of large scale distributed industrial systems.

9. A BROADER SCOPE OF INFORMATION SYSTEMS IN MANUFACTURING

Information systems have been seen as an important tool to support the needs of manufacturing organisations facing the pressures of a turbulent business environment. Furthermore, it appears evident that the boundaries separating applications of being exclusively for manufacturing, logistics or purchasing operations have disappeared. Indeed, state of the art applications are modular in nature, and once expanded may cover whole departments and business units of manufacturing enterprises. Figure 7 depicts the integral approach of information systems covering not only configuration and procurement but production and distribution as well. In the diagram it is possible to appreciate that request and quotations are originated at the customer level. Further on, request and negotiation activities take place between the manufacturer and its first-tier suppliers, and then between first-tier suppliers and second-tier suppliers and so on. From the customer to lower tiers of suppliers, production and distribution, involves the placement of orders followed by the delivery of parts of components upstream in the supply chain.

Several information-related tools have emerged in recent years to help develop more robust information systems that will enable manufacturing organisations cope with reacting to customers' needs, reduced product life-cycles, reduced cycle times, cost cutting and rapid product development cycles among others.

Internet-based, e-commerce applications linking manufacturer, customers and suppliers made possible to overcome difficulties associated with the adoption of solutions such as EDI. Investing in EDI only pays off when almost all partners use it [33]. Indeed, high investment costs for the acquisition of EDI meant that SMEs were excluded from adopting it.

The use of Internet based tools in manufacturing has enabled the design of CIM interface systems reducing communication efforts from quadratic to linear complexity and by allowing the exchange of design data among manufacturing organisations based on the use of a previously defined language interface.

Active agents give the opportunity to automate a significant number of operations linking systems across the Internet. The functionality specified on the agents will certainly determine the impact and effectiveness of the application as a whole. Components of intelligent agents have been designed to address the needs of manufacturing organisations, including the definition of knowledge bases, problem solving directives and communication components.

9.1. Information systems role in improving manufacturing organisations performance

Present manufacturing improvement initiatives are highly dependent on the seamless integration of internal and external units provided by the use of efficient information systems. Indeed, internal units comprising design, engineering, manufacturing, all require seamless integration using information systems. Furthermore, the integration with external units, represents the link between customers and suppliers enabled by the use of information systems.

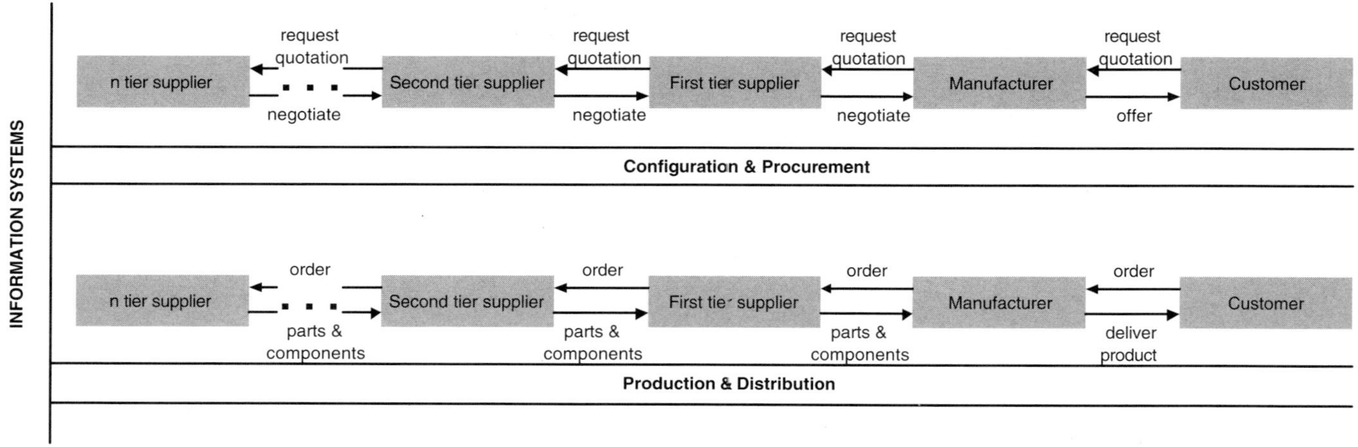

Figure 7. Manufacturing information systems integral approach.

According to Da Silveira et al. [32] information systems bring the opportunity of designing an effectively decentralised control architecture that will support the adoption of future manufacturing improvement initiatives such as mass customisation, BTO and agility among others. The control system will be composed of autonomous components with the purpose of reducing complexity, increasing flexibility and enhancing fault tolerance.

Also, further research needs to be accomplished in the area of enterprise modelling. Open systems architectures for computer integrated manufacturing and information systems integration like CIMOSA (CIM Open System Architecture) may be considered as background for future developments. Indeed, enterprise modelling encompasses modelling, analysis, design and implementation of integrated information systems. Certainly, any enterprise modelling methodology will need to consider information systems issues such as overall system architecture, product design, project management, software specifications, including data models and non-technical factors as well.

The potential benefits of any application supporting the needs of manufacturing organisations may depend significantly on the development of an information management infrastructure based on the integration of different standards or tools, including the Internet, STEP (Standard for the Exchange of Product Model Data) and full support of the object-oriented paradigm. Turowski [33] remarks highlighted that information systems applications used to support e-commerce can be seen as a competitive strategy requiring that different production types be employed simultaneously—especially single-item production with its normally high requirements for inter-company interactions.

10. INFORMATION SYSTEMS ENTERPRISE-WIDE SUPPORT: AN EXAMPLE

Information systems in manufacturing organisations cover not only manufacturing operations but also, finance, human resources and supply chain. Emerging tools and protocols are making possible enterprise integration but also integration with external enterprises as well. For a long period of time information systems were seen as islands where the information generated could not be retrieved by other applications. The intensification of competition, emerging market opportunities and changing customer requirements has motivated firms to start utilising information systems to influence processes comprising procurement, supply chain management, logistics and manufacturing operations.

Manufacturing is an information dependent activity. Indeed, it depends not only on the efficiency of manufacturing processes but on the quality of the information received, processed and transmitted. Erroneous data may lead to the generation of wrong production schedules, wrong BOM, wrong purchases and so on. Indeed, erroneous data is accountable for problems experienced in manufacturing such as surplus inventory and excessive lead-time. This has motivated researchers to study fluctuation and amplification of demand from the downstream to upstream of the supply chain, a phenomenon known as the bullwhip effect. Researchers have found that the source of such fluctuation and amplification of orders and inventory is mainly due to the lack of sharing of production information between enterprises in the chain [48]. Information systems are the facilitators of information flow.

Information handling becomes critical when manufacturing organisations start introducing initiatives such as flexible manufacturing, lean thinking and agile manufacturing. In fact, enterprises in manufacturing sectors such as the automotive industry have been trying to reduce costs by building tight links with their suppliers. The introduction of sequencing of operations involving first-tier and sometimes second-tier suppliers pushes to the limit the use and the reliability of the information required. To emphasise the importance of information systems in manufacturing and supply chains, it was considered convenient to present the case study of an information-intense industrial environment.

The company participating in the case study is a mid-volume manufacturer of mid-luxury vehicles. Indeed, the vehicle built is a very complex product. Thousands of combinations comprise the options available to the final customer. Currently, it takes 14 days for a vehicle to leave the plant from the time it was scheduled for production. Annual production of vehicles is aimed at 60,000 units.

10.1. Information dependency and intensity

The activities developed for this study involved using Value Stream Mapping to represent physical operations and input/output diagrams for information flow. Data sets were used to record information on the product, volumes, market and manufacturing operations. Data sets were seen as a repository for information collected during the fieldwork, and as a checklist against which required data could be collected.

The Value Stream Mapping methodology presented by Rother and Shook [49] was employed to identify the value stream of study. From the analysis, the seating system stream emerged as one value stream adequate for the objectives of this work. Particular characteristics of the seating systems of these vehicles include: (1) seats are independent modules, (2) with complex assembly processes, (3) with a complex sequence of use during vehicle assembly, (4) multi-tier in their own right and (5) very costly. Moreover, seating systems for these vehicles cover up to three tiers of suppliers. Figure 8, depicts the supply chain presented in this example.

The seating systems manufactured for these mid-luxury vehicles have the following options: two-basic styles (classic and sports), two different materials (cloth and leather), six different colours, plus power, safety and adjustment options.

Deliveries from the 2nd tier to the 1st tier supplier are in batches of 28. Deliveries from the 3rd tier to the 2nd tier supplier are in batches of 20. Only the 1st tier supplier manufacturing facility is based next to the vehicle assembly operations plant. The current offset lead time between the 3rd tier supplier and the primary demand at assembly vehicle operations is 3 days. During the study it emerged that non-value adding time is skewed towards the upstream processes, especially raw material storage and inventory analysis estimates showed 22 days worth of additional stock. Value adding time was 12.2 hours.

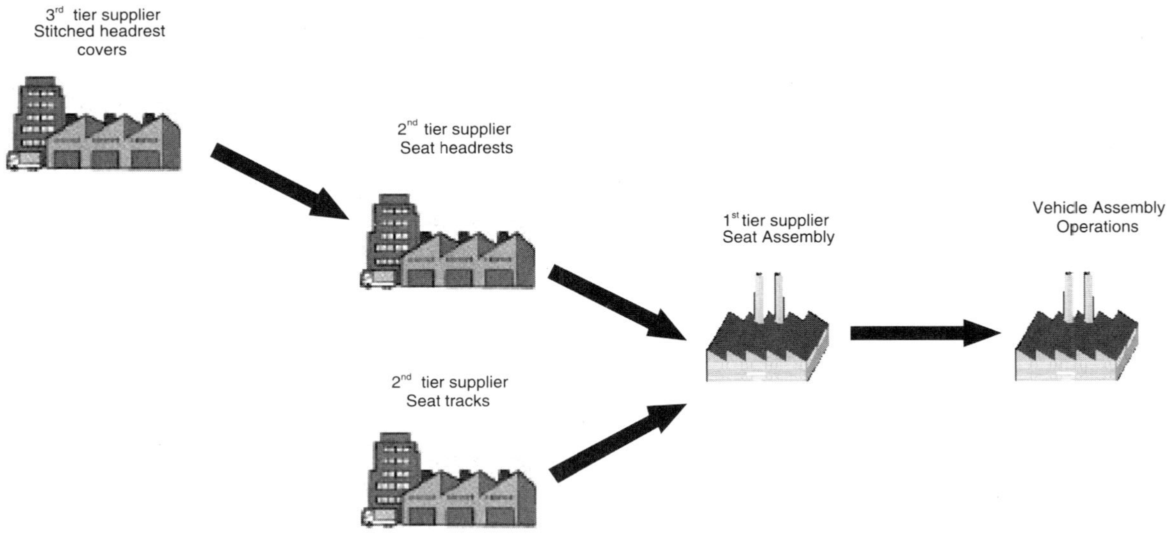

Figure 8. Manufacturing organisations supply chain.

10.2. Information flow and operation of the supply chain

The interface from vehicle assembly to seat assembly is demand driven. Assembly of a unique seat is triggered by the launch of its destination vehicle into the final assembly sequence, at which time the actual seat requirement is sent to the first tier supplier via a sophisticated broadcast system.

Previous to the broadcast of the actual seat requirements, aggregated daily seat requirements have been communicated to the supplier via an electronic file. Each day that file shows the next ten daily requirements, followed by a further forecast requirement in tentative weekly and monthly buckets.

The first tier seat supplier uses the information from the file to run its own internal material requirements planning system. The file is loaded each day, and once per week the MRP is run. The suppliers schedules are produced for each of the first tier component suppliers. In the past, schedules were sent to the suppliers via FAX, nowadays schedules are accessed by the suppliers via a web-based information system. These schedules normally contain daily requirements for the following week, as well as more tentative forecast requirements in weekly and monthly buckets. Figure 9 illustrates the flow of information observed in this example.

The diagram presented in figure 9 shows information systems involvement at an inter-enterprise level. In the manufacturing industry, the flow of information along the supply chain is as important as the flow of materials. To guarantee a reliable flow of information, manufacturing organisations have installed fibre optic links between them and their customers and their suppliers. In the case presented in figure 8, the first-tier supplier has a fibre optic link to vehicle assembly operations. The first tier supplier runs its own MRP system once a week and the output is sent to the second tier supplier. Information systems involvement covers the inter-enterprise level (as presented in figure 8) and shopfloor systems as well.

Inputs to the systems are provided by sensors placed at each of the workstations located along the assembly line and by buttons and signals triggered by the workers assigned to each workstation. Information systems control the flow of components along the assembly line based on the final assembly sequence provided by the vehicle manufacturer. Figure 10 depicts information systems controlling the operations involved in the assembly of seating systems.

The assembly line of the seats shown in figure 10 comprises ten different operations. These are sequenced operations and each of them is dependent on the final assembly file received from the manufacturer. The LCD displays situated along the assembly line tell the operators the number of the sequenced seat to be built. The seat components (e.g. headrests, tracks, frames, etc.) used in the assembly process have been put in sequence at the company's warehouse. The final assembly sequence file is transmitted via fibre optic link, giving the seat manufacturer a time period to deliver the assembled seats to the point of fit in the vehicle assembly line. In the diagram shown in figure 10 the displacement of the seats being assembled from one workstation to the other is directly controlled by the PLC. Moreover, the PLC is wired to buttons and signals triggered by the operators assembling the seats. Other activities undertaken to ensure the smooth

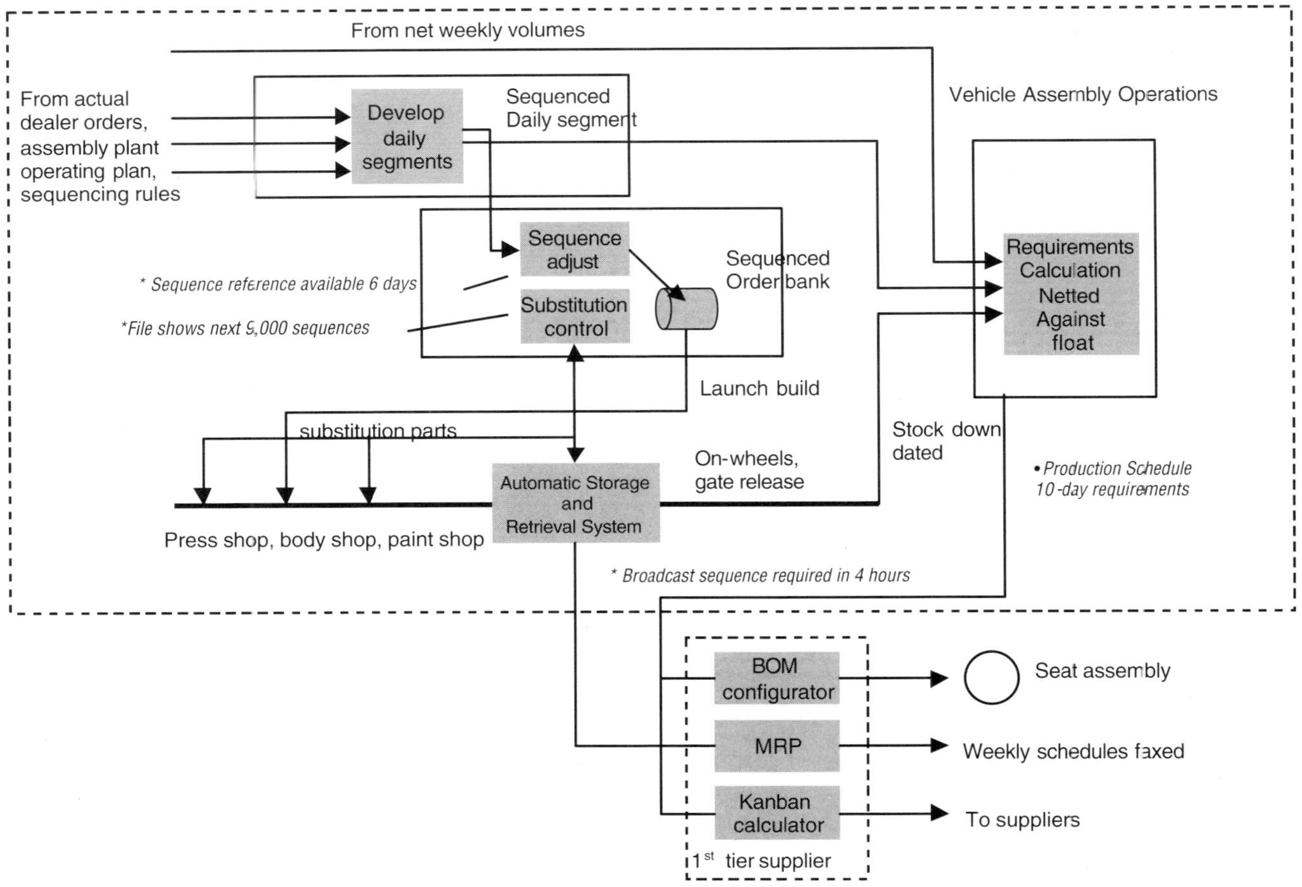

Figure 9. Flow of information in the manufacturing supply chain.

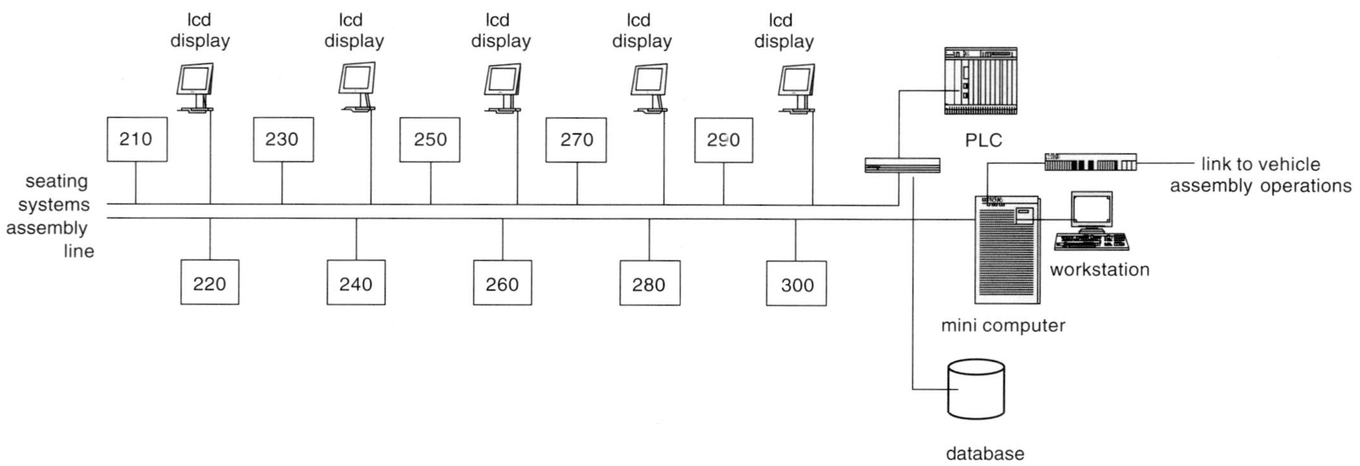

Figure 10. Information systems involvement.

Table 3 Seat assembly major operations controlled by information systems

Number of operation	Description	Time duration (sec)
ONE	Place in position set of pallet guides	70
****	Empty (adjust)	0.0
TWO	Cushion assembly	174.1
****	Empty (adjust)	0.0
THREE	Back seat assembly	132.3
****	Empty (adjust)	0.0
FOUR	Cut labels and check sequence	56.6
FINAL	Load seat	19.4

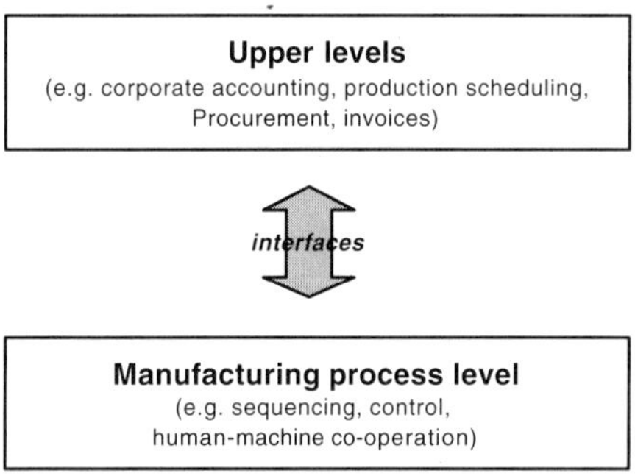

Figure 11. Information systems involvement at different levels in the enterprise.

running of the assembly line involves database recording of the codes of the seat sets manufactured. A minicomputer runs the system that processes (breaks down) the files received from vehicle assembly operations via fibre optic.

Table 3 shows major operations involved in the assembly of passenger vehicle seats. Each operation is done in coordination with the final vehicle assembly sequence.

The use of information systems to control the operations comprising an assembly line represents the use of information systems at the manufacturing process level. This basic level comprises the interaction of devices and machines controlled by information systems with the operators working in the assembly line. In the manufacturing sector, it becomes evident that the performance of information systems at the tool level will have a direct impact on the upper levels of the organisation. Upper levels for information systems comprise manufacturing planning and scheduling, corporate accounting and finance, procurement and human resources. Figure 11 depicts the involvement of information systems at the manufacturing process and the upper levels.

The flexibility of manufacturing operations enables the possibility of assembling seats with several options available. In fact, the adoption of flexible manufacturing is the first step towards the adoption of information systems that will support synchronised operations within the enterprise business units and with external enterprises.

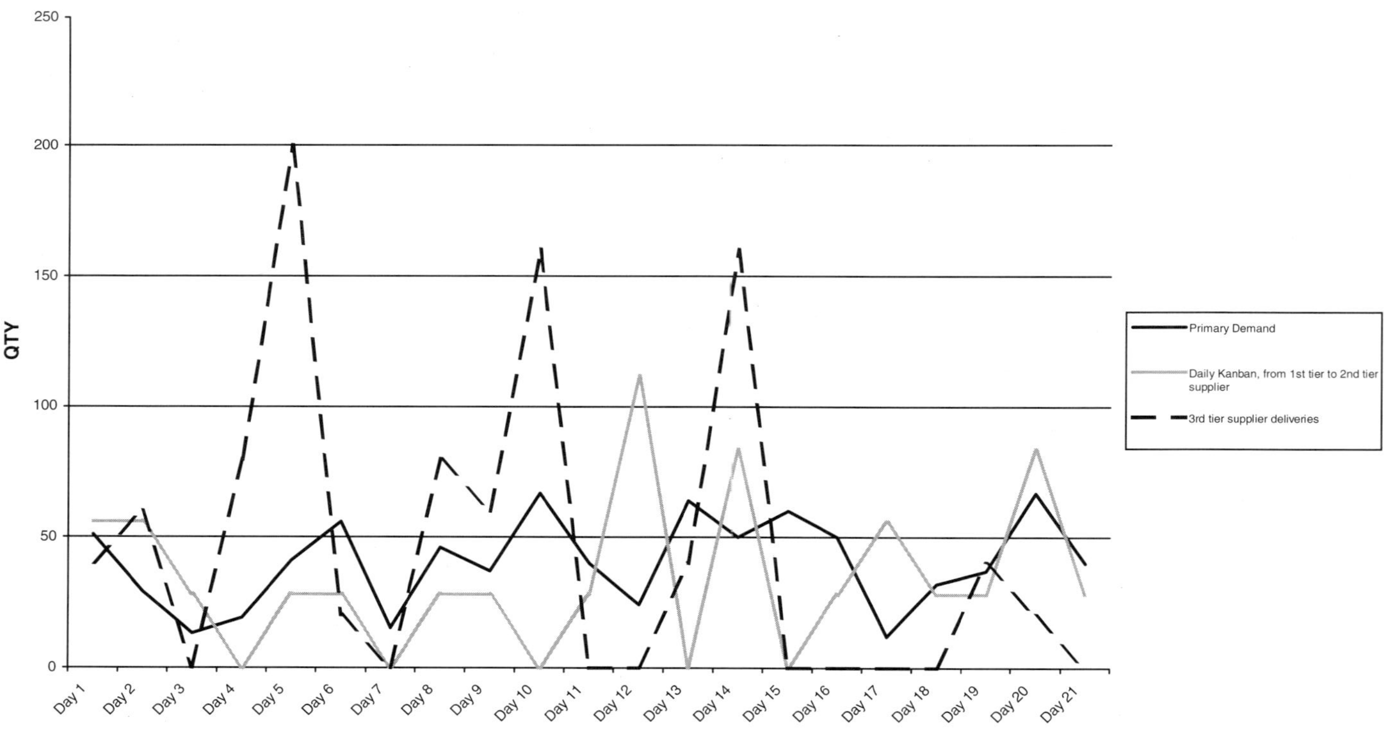

Figure 12. Comparing 3rd tier supplier deliveries against primary demand.

10.3. Analysis of information accuracy

The management of information used at the manufacturing process level (e.g. shopfloor systems linked to PLC's and other devices) did not represent a main concern for manufacturing enterprises. The main problem was with the data used to generate production plans, a problem closely linked to the accuracy of information. Indeed, the purpose of analysing the accuracy of information has been to isolate the effect of inaccurate demand information, and to determine the extra stock held in the pipeline to cover for this. This can be achieved by measuring the accuracy of demand information at various points in the supply chain. One particular trim option has been chosen to illustrate the problems generated by information inaccuracy.

The problems observed in the analysis of information accuracy are shown in figure 12. The graph shows significant peaks with deliveries of over 150 units twice and over 200 units once. On the other hand, building of vehicles with that particular trim option never reached 70 units any single day of that month. The above results are a direct consequence of the flow of information currently in place in the supply chain and suppliers' batching policies.

The problems observed prompted the development of a prototype information broadcasting architecture for the supply chain under study. Under this alternative all orders already launched into build are gathered in a single file and presented to the suppliers (i.e. suppliers access the file from a URL, Uniform Resource Locator, using a web browser). This scheme represents 3 days of production which is much more accurate than the original build plan being used in the supply chain. Rather than using a "go-see" method of production scheduling, the early release of this launch broadcast enables 2nd and some 3rd tier suppliers to redesign their operations so that manufacture and assembly can be driven by required rather than forecasted build.

Implications anticipated from the adoption of the proposed information broadcasting architecture to a build-to-order scheme include: (1) using electronic channels to broadcast information along different tiers of suppliers, facilitating customers the modification of products and (2) lower tier suppliers may have the opportunity of getting involved in handling product variety. The alternative information architecture specified for the supply chain under study is depicted in figure 13.

The architecture presented in figure 13 has the potential of making 100% transparent the flow of information and material along the supply chain. The configuration works in the following way, deliveries from the 3rd tier supplier become the stock of the 2nd tier supplier the following day. The stock at the 1st tier supplier is calculated as the difference between the stock in the 1st tier supplier the day before minus the stock available in the 2nd tier supplier the day before plus the current stock available in the 2nd tier supplier.

The results of this configuration are shown in figure 14. Furthermore, the current stock at the 1st tier supplier has the potential of being altered significantly if the output of the MRP system is followed. This implies that the stock at the 1st tier supplier is equal to the stock available the day before minus the number of components required by vehicle assembly operations plus the number of components received in batches of 28 by the 2nd tier supplier.

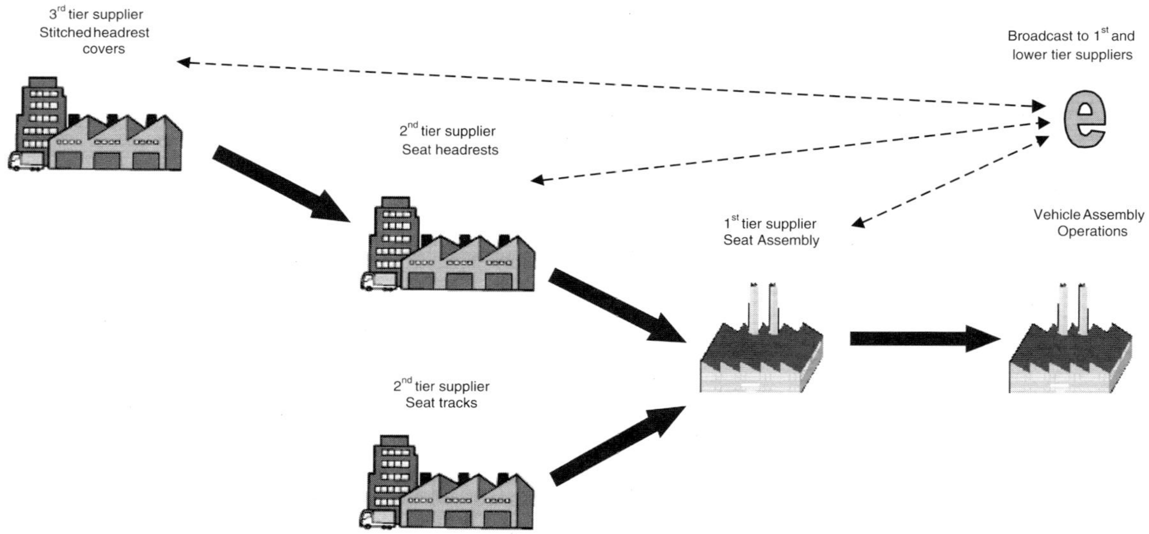

Figure 13. Information broadcast at all levels of the supply chain.

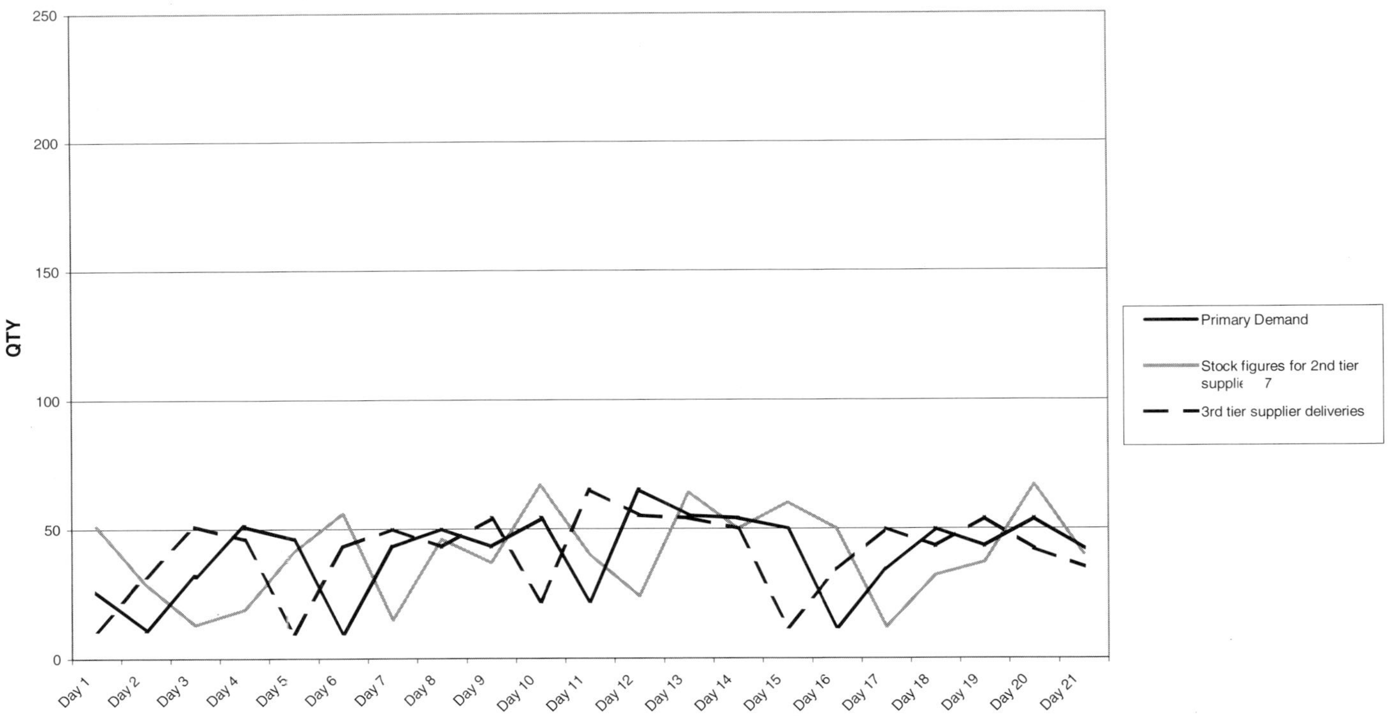

Figure 14. Primary demand against 3rd tier deliveries with wide access to data.

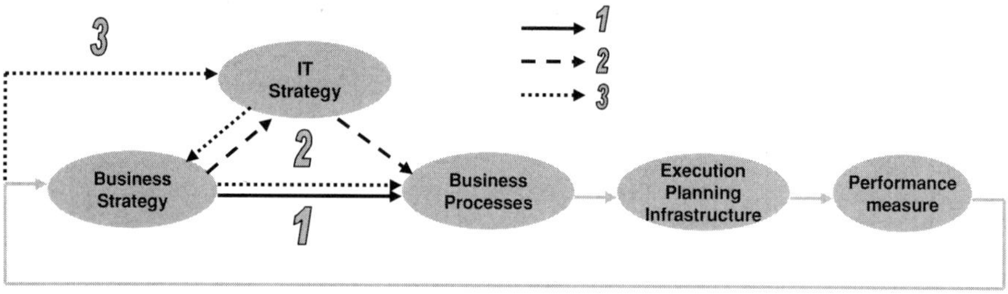

Figure 15. Stages used to guarantee IT positive contribution in manufacturing.

The results plotted in figure 14 show that the 3rd tier supplier deliveries could be significantly reduced in size. In fact, having a transparent access to information would enable suppliers to adjust their deliveries based on the figures of primary demand. Moreover, the stock of the 1st tier supplier could be significantly reduced because it depends on the deliveries of the 2nd tier supplier. The stock in the 2nd tier supplier is the same as in the 3rd tier supplier the day before.

11. ENSURING A POSITIVE CONTRIBUTION OF INFORMATION SYSTEMS TO THE ENTERPRISE

The case study presented in the previous section and numerous examples available in the literature have shown the use of information systems to improve the operations of manufacturing enterprises. A set of guidelines have been proposed to help managers understand the contribution of information systems to manufacturing enterprises.

The review of important initiatives in manufacturing such as lean thinking, agile manufacturing, mass customisation and build to order suggest that although information systems are important components that keep running the organisation, much of the impact is dependent on the design and implementation of sound business strategies and efficient manufacturing processes. An IT strategy in place is critical for having information systems aligned to business and manufacturing plans. The convergence of business, manufacturing and IT strategies in manufacturing organisations motivated the development of a framework for information systems use in manufacturing. The proposed framework is based on the dominant alignment perspectives planned by Henderson and Venkatraman [50] and consists of three main stages explained in the following paragraphs.

The first stage starts with developing efficient manufacturing processes based on a sound business strategy. The second stage consists of having a business strategy supported by an IT strategy. The last stage contemplates implementing an IT strategy to lead the company once it has been possible to achieve efficient manufacturing processes. Figure 15 depicts this framework. The following steps give details of the possibilities of improving manufacturing operations by using an IT strategy [53].

1. Development of enhanced manufacturing operations based on a sound business strategy

This stage consists of defining a sound business strategy that is the driver of all changes to manufacturing operations. Information systems at this stage are required to support critical operations, IT strategy is absent at this first stage and has no influence in the organisation. The purpose of the business strategy is to start developing the operations side of the company towards improving its manufacturing operations. For example, companies should develop the flexibility in the shopfloor (e.g. reduce of set-up costs, develop a flexible manufacturing base) where applicable.

2. Definition of an IT strategy to support the business strategy

The feedback received from the outcome of the implementation of the business strategy targeting the effectiveness of operations entails the definition of an IT strategy. Updates to the business strategy would involve the definition/utilisation of an IT strategy. An IT strategy is intended to support upgrades to the business strategy after changes have been introduced to business processes. For example, an organisation has finished or has made significant progress in developing flexibility in the shopfloor and it is ready to seek best IT competencies to further develop its business strategy.

3. Implement an IT strategy to lead the company once it has been possible to improve its manufacturing operations

Once it has been possible to achieve effectiveness in the operations side of the business and an IT strategy has been used to make upgrades to the business strategy, the next step is the exploitation of emerging IT capabilities to impact new products and services. This would enable IT to influence the business strategy of the company and develop new forms of relationships (e.g. extended inter-enterprise cooperation, formation of virtual enterprises). An organisation implementing an IT-led strategy seems to be a sound methodology to ensure the competitiveness of manufacturing operations and other business activities. Stage three is ready for implementation once the organisation has achieved substantial performance levels that can be considered benchmarks for the industry. An IT strategy used to influencing the business strategy of the company not only ensures the sustainability of improvements to manufacturing operations but also it increases the contribution and support of information systems to the firm. This stage has been envisaged to show that it is possible to have an IT strategy leading a company, enhancing the performance levels (benchmarks for industry) in manufacturing operations and other business processes in the organisation.

The case study presented in this chapter plus the numerous cases of information systems failure to deliver expected benefits in manufacturing [51] have motivated the use of a new tag-label to designate the role of information systems in manufacturing. This new tag calls information systems as "enhancing agents" of benchmark-like performance. E-commerce, virtual enterprises, electronic market places, and other IT-based tools should be re-named as second-order enablers or enhancement agents of benchmark-like performance. Indeed, companies with effective manufacturing operations may regard information systems behind other factors such as flexibility of

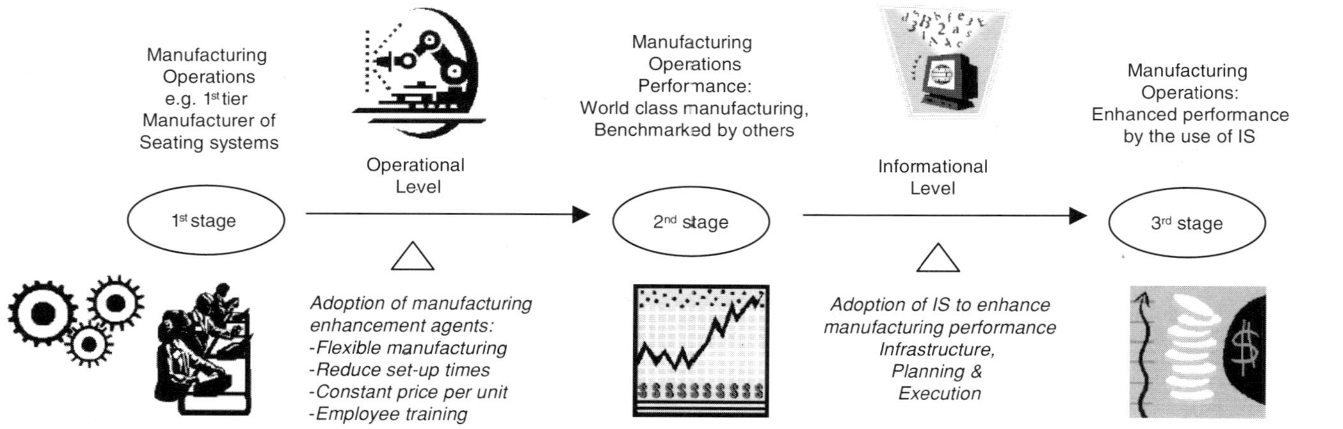

Figure 16. Phases of support of information systems.

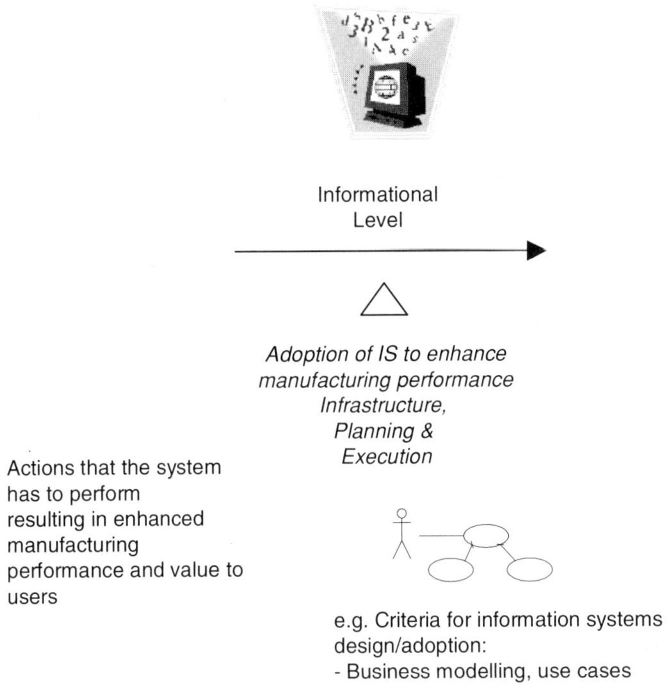

Figure 17. Specification tasks for information systems.

shopfloor operations. Figure 16 depicts the three stages involving the use of information systems to support manufacturing operations.

The adoption of information systems to enhance manufacturing performance may include infrastructure, planning and execution systems. However, the adoption process requires specifying the actions that the system will perform, such as enhancing the performance of operations. Tools providing support for those tasks include Use Cases. Figure 17 depicts the use of Use Cases to shape the design/adoption process of information systems.

Defining metrics to measure the contribution of information systems to manufacturing operations in frameworks like those depicted in figure 16 is of extreme importance. A set of metrics that may be helpful to measure the contribution of information systems is presented in figure 18. Actually, most manufacturing organisations are familiar with the list of measures provided in figure 18.

Benefits presented in figure 18 have been classified as strategic, tactical and operational in nature [52]. Several more metrics might be added to the above list. Information systems measurement is a research field on its own and not contemplated in the structure of this chapter.

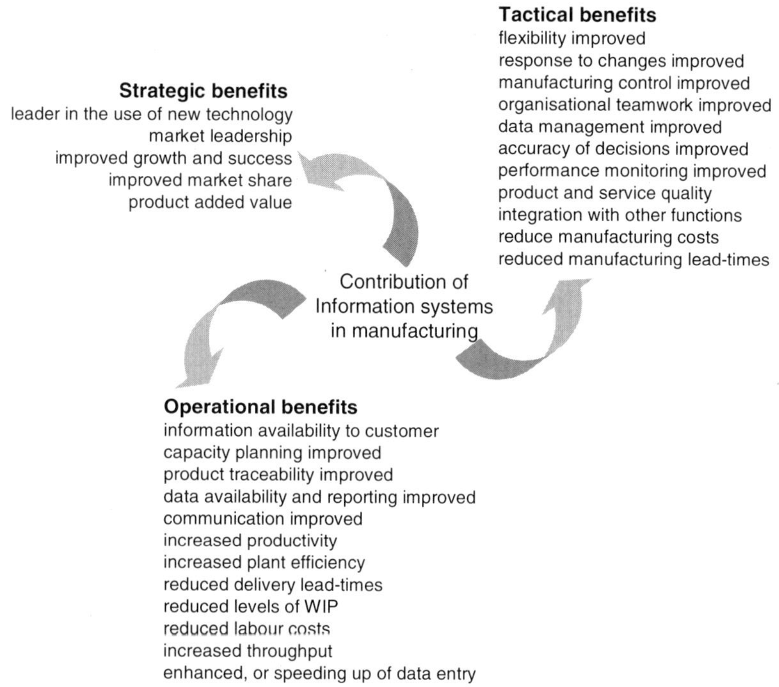

Figure 18. Metrics that reflect the contribution of information systems in manufacturing.

12. CONCLUSIONS

The relevance of information systems in manufacturing will continue to grow in the future with the development of new tools and technologies. Certainly, researchers like Turowski [33] have agreed that the deployment of efficient and effective information systems architectures is a key success factor for organisations implementing competitive strategies like BTO or mass customisation. Tools such as UML will continue to offer the possibility of translating business requirements that may be used to outline the architectures required to access remotely for example, manufacturing plants through Internet-like networks. Moreover, UML is a key tool for the translation of business requirements into information systems design.

A tough business environment also demands rigorous procedures to justify investments in IT/information systems. New types of applications and development tools will require the definition of new metrics to measure the performance of information systems investments. With the use of new development tools, implementation costs of information systems may be reduced since essential software components are reusable, platform independent and adaptable to meet particular customer needs.

Further on, manufacturing organisations will need closer and more reliable information links between its manufacturing operations, supply chain management, finance and human resources. Reliable information links will make it possible to reduce information variability not only at the enterprise level but also at the multi-enterprise level. In manufacturing industry the transparency of information across tiers of the supply chain has proven to be of extreme importance to eliminate excess. Indeed, unreliable information has been responsible for having high stock levels at all tiers in the supply chain. Unreliable information may lead to stockout incidents and backorders. In order to ensure a positive contribution of new IT tools/information systems applications, improvements to manufacturing operations (e.g. flexible manufacturing operations, reduced set-up costs, etc.) have to be continuously made. Indeed, any positive contribution of IT/information systems to manufacturing enterprises is dependent on the successful implementation of improvement initiatives in manufacturing operations.

REFERENCES

[1] Boar, Bernard H. 1994. Practical Steps for Aligning Information Technology with Business Strategies: How to Achieve a Competitive Advantage. Wiley, New York.

[2] Shaw M., Seidmann A. and Whinston A., 1997. Information Technology for Automated Manufacturing Enterprises: recent Development and Current Research Issues. The International Journal of Flexible Manufacturing Systems, 9, 115–120.

[3] Plekhanova, Valentina, 2001. Engineering the information technology requirements and framework. (945-947). Managing Information Technology in a Global Economy. 2001 Proceedings of the Information Resources Management Association International Conference, Toronto Ontario.

[4] Ezingeard J. N., 1996. Heuristic methods to aid value assessment in the management of manufacturing information and data systems. Ph.D. Thesis from the Department of Manufacturing and Engineering Systems. Brunel University, West London.

[5] Laudon K. C. and Laudon J. P., 1998. Information Systems and the Internet. A problem solving approach, 4th edition. The Dryden Press: Fort Worth, TX, USA.

[6] Shewchuk J., 1998. Measures of of design change potential for manufacturing information systems: an architecture-based approach. International Journal of Industrial Engineering, 5, 1, 38–48.

[7] Next Generation Manufacturing Project, 1997. Vol. II Imperatives for Next Generation Manufacturing. U.S. Department of Energy, Washington D.C. USA.

[8] Geffen. 2000. It is not enough to be responsive: the role of cooperative intentions in MRP_{II} adoption. DATABASE. The database for advances in information systems. Volume 31, No. 2, 65–79.

[9] Noori H. and Mavaddat F., 1998. Enterprise integration: issues and methods. International Journal of Production Research, 36, **8**, 2083–2097.

[10] Kathuria R. and Igbaria M., 1997. Aligning IT applications with manufacturing strategy: an integrated framework. International Journal of Operations and Production Management, 17, **6**, 611–629.

[11] Randall T., 1999. The value of IT in the Manufacturing Sector. Compass Consulting Analysis White Paper.

[12] Broadbent M., Weill P., and Neo B., 1999. Strategic context and patterns of IT infrastructure capability. Journal of Strategic Information Systems, 8, 157–187.

[13] Robinson B. and Wilson F, 2001. Planning for the market: enterprise resource planning systems and the contradictions of capital. DATABASE. The database for advances in information systems. Volume 32, No. 9, 21–33.

[14] Glass R. L. 2001. The software practitioner little red riding hood meets critical social theory. DATABASE. The database for advances in information systems. Volume 32, No. 4, 11–12

[15] Hackathorn R. 1995. Data warehousing energises your enterprise. Datamation, Vol. 41, No. 2, February 1, 38–45.

[16] Farbey B., Land F. and Targett D., 1999_{II}. A Taxonomy of Information Systems Applications: the Benefits' Evaluation Ladder. Working paper of the Department of Information Systems, London School of Economics and Political Science.

[17] Saaksjarvi M. 2000. The Roles of Corporate IT infrastructure and their impact on IS effectiveness. Proceedings of the 8th European Conference on Information Systems, 1, Vienna, Austria, 421–428.

[18] Hanseth O. and Braa K., 1998. Technology as Traitor: Emergent SAP infrastructure in a Global Organisation. Proceedings of the 19th International Conference on Information Systems, 188–196.

[19] Kettinger W. and Hackbarth G., 1999. Mastering Information Management, part seven: Electronic Commerce Special Supplierment. Financial Times, Monday March 15.
[20] Yusuf Y. Y., Sarhadi M. and Gunasekaran A., 1999. Agile manufacturing: the drivers, concepts and attributes. International Journal of Production Economics, 62, 33–43.
[21] Kidd P. T., 1994. Agile Manufacturing, Forging New frontiers. Addison Wesley, Wokingham UK.
[22] Mahadevan B., 2000. Business models for Internet based e-commerce: an anatomy. California Management Review, vol. 42, 55–69.
[23] Gunasekaran A., 1999. Agile Manufacturing: A framework for research and development. International Journal of Production Economics, 62, 87–105.
[24] Childe S., 1998. The extended enterprise-a concept of co-operation. Production Planning and Control, 9, **4**, 320–327.
[25] Marchand D., 1999. How to keep up with hypercompetition. Mastering information management, part four: The smarter supply chain. Financial Times, Monday February 22.
[26] Kasarda J. and Rondinelli D., 1999. Innovative Infrastructure for Agile Manufacturers. Sloan Management Review, Winter, 73–82.
[27] Reid R., Tapp J., Liles D., Rogers K. and Johnson M, 1996. An integrated Management Model for Virtual Enterprises: Vision, Strategy and Structure. IEEE International Engineering Management Conference, Vancouver B.C., 522–527.
[28] Venkatraman N. and Henderson J., 1998. Real Strategies for Virtual Organizing. Sloan Management Review, Fall, 33–48.
[29] Fouletier P., Park K. and Farrel J., 1997. An inter-organisational information systems design for virtual enterprises. Proceedings of the 1997 IEEE 6th International Conference on Emerging Technologies & Factory Automation EFTA'97, 139–142.
[30] Womack J. and Jones D., 1996. Lean Thinking, banish waste and create wealth in your corporation. Touchstone, London UK.
[31] Goldman S., Nagel R. and Preiss K., 1995. Agile Competitors and Virtual Organizations, Strategies for enriching the customer. Van Nostrand Reinhold, New York.
[32] Da Silveira G., Borenstein D. and Fogliatto F., 2001. Mass Customisation: Literature Review and Research Directions. International Journal of Production Economics, Vol. 72, 1-13. Permission granted from Elsevier.
[33] Turowski K., 2002. Agent-based e-commerce in case of mass customisation. International Journal of Production Economics. Vol. 75, pp. 69-81. Permission granted from Elsevier.
[34] Gunasekaran A., 1998. Agile Manufacturing: enablers and an implementation framework. International Journal of Production Research, 36, 1223–1247.
[35] Huang C. and Nof S., 1999. Enterprise agility: a view from the PRISM lab. International Journal of Agile Management Systems, 1, 51–61.
[36] Beynon-Davis P., Owens I. and Lloyd-Williams M., 2000. Melding Information Systems Evaluation with the Information Systems Development Life-Cycle. Proceedings of the 8th European Conference on Information Systems, Vienna Austria, 195–201.
[37] Hevner A. R., Collins R. W. and Garfield M. J. 2002. Product and Project Challenges in Electronic commerce software development. DATABASE. The database for advances in information systems. Volume 33, No. 4, 10-23, 2002.
[38] Oberg R., Probasco L. and Ericsson M., 1998. Applying requirements managementwith use cases. Technical Paper TP505, Rational Software Corporation, pp. 2–3.
[39] DeVor R., Graves R. and Mills J., 1997. Agile Manufacturing research: accomplishments and opportunities. IIE Transactions, 29, 813–823.
[40] Song L. and Nagi R., 1997. Design and implementation of a virtual information system for agile manufacturing. IIE Transactions, 29, 839–857.
[41] Cheng K., Harrison D. K. and Pan P. Y., 1997. Implementation of agile manufacturing—an AI and Internet based approach. Journal of Material Processing Technology, 76, 96–101.
[42] Bullinger H., Fahnrich K. and Linsenmaier T. 1998. A conceptual model for an architecture of distributed objects for the integration of heterogeneous data processing systems in manufacturing companies. International Journal of Production Research, 36, 11, 2997–3011.
[43] Whiteside R., Pancerella C., and Klevgard P., 1998. A CORBA-Based Manufacturing Environment. Proceedings of the 1997 IEEE Conference on Internet Technologies, 34–43.
[44] Wolfe P., Smith R. and Chi Y., 1998. WWW, Corba and Java: New information technologies for industrial engineering solutions. Proceedings of the 1998 IE Solutions Conference. Institute of Industrial Engineers, 1–6.

[45] Bocks P., 1995. Enterprise data management framework for agile manufacturing. Computer Engineering Division, American Society of Mechanical Engineers. New York, 7, 41–46.
[46] Zhou Q., Souben P. and Besant C., 1998. An information management systems for production planning in virtual enterprises. Computers and Industrial Engineering, 35, **1/2**, 153–156.
[47] Herrmann J., Minis I. and Ramachandran V., 1995. Information models for partner selection in agile manufacturing, Proceedings of the 1995 ASME International Mechanical Engineering Congress and Exposition, San Francisco CA, 7, 75–91.
[48] Lau J, Huang G. and Mak K., 2002, Web-based simulation portal for investigating the impacts of sharing production information on supply chain dynamics from the perspective of inventory allocation. Integrated Manufacturing Systems, 13, (5), 345–358.
[49] Rother M., and Shook J., 1999. Learning to See, version 1.2, (Lean Enterprise Institute Inc.)
[50] Henderson J. and Venkatraman N., 1999. Strategic Alignment: Leveraging information technology for transforming organisations. IBM Systems Journal, 38, 2/3, 472–484.
[51] Ewusi-Mensah K., 1997. Critical issues in abandoned information systems development projects. Communications of the ACM, 40, **9**, 75–80.
[52] Coronado A., Sarhadi M. and Millar C., 1999. An Evaluation Model of Information Systems for Agile Manufacturing. Proceedings of the Sixth European Conference on Information Technology Evaluation, 4-5 November 1999. St. Johns, Brunel University, West London, 203–213.
[53] Coronado Mondragon Adrian E., 2002. Determining information systems contribution to manufacturing agility for SME's in dynamic business environments. Ph.D. Thesis from the Department of Systems Engineering. Brunel University, West London.

MODELLING TECHNIQUES IN INTEGRATED OPERATIONS AND INFORMATION SYSTEMS IN MANUFACTURING SYSTEMS

Q. WANG, C. R. CHATWIN, AND R. C. D. YOUNG

1. INTRODUCTION

State-of-the-art production facilities require a wide variety of intelligent devices and automated processing equipment to be integrated and linked together through a manufacturing network in order to achieve the desired, cost effective, co-ordinated functionality. Devices within a manufacturing system may include: programmable logic controllers (PLCs), direct numerically controlled (DNC) machines, sensors, robots, vision systems, co-ordinate measurement machines (CMMs), personal computers (PCs), and mainframe computers, supplied by different vendors, using different operating systems, with different communication needs and interfaces. The successful integration of existing equipment using existing communication protocols and networks is crucial to achieve the functionality required for computer integrated manufacturing (i.e., CIM) systems. As a result, the performance of communication networks has become a key factor for successful implementation of integrated manufacturing systems, particularly, for time-critical applications. Hence, the analysis, design and performance evaluation of manufacturing systems can no longer ignore the performance of the communication environment.

Until recently, however, system designers lacked feasible and practical combined modelling and simulation methods or tools, which would permit them, at the early design stage, to assess such things as how the maximum message delay impacts the shortest machine processing time. That is because most research on the performance of a manufacturing system using modelling and simulation has focused on the 'operational system's aspect'. The term 'simulation' used in a narrow sense always indicates the performance of manufacturing operations. The 'information processing system's aspect' has had very limited or often separate investigation without considering the overall performance by taking both aspects into account within the manufacturing plant. One of the major reasons why there are so few studies related to this area is the high level of complexity. Recent reviews of manufacturing system modelling methods have concluded that, despite the significant number of integrated modelling methods that have been reportedly developed, such as: GIM (GRAI integrated methodology), SIM (Strathclyde integration methodology) and ICAM DEFinition (IDEF) simulation methods, there is no single conceptual modelling method which can completely model a manufacturing system or describe most of its sub-systems based on the currently developed simulation tools. Although it is argued that it is not practical or possible to model all aspects of manufacturing systems during their life-cycle engineering and ongoing development, the modelling simulation protagonists continue to enhance models to incorporate an increasing number of features such as model conceptuality, functionality, dynamic aspects and so on. On the other hand, it is generally accepted that traditional planning methods and mathematical or analytical modelling techniques are not appropriate if detailed analysis is required for complex manufacturing systems [2, 3, 4, 5, 6, 7, 8, 9, 10, 11, 12].

The performance of the communication system is related not merely to the electronic characteristics of the transmission media, but also to the protocol requirements. For example, many manufacturing companies across the EU have implemented and continue to use the IEEE 802.3 CSMA/CD (carrier sense multiple access/collision detection-ethernet) protocol within their manufacturing environment to improve the performance characteristics of random access LANs (local area networks) at extremely low cost. One of the main drawbacks with using this protocol is that it uses a contention random method to gain access to the network, i.e., the media access time is non-deterministic. Consequently, this leads to uncertainty when a station, which needs to transmit, has to wait an undetermined amount of time before it is able to send a message to its destination. Under certain circumstances, this time, which is referred to as maximum message delay, may be crucial in production, as a long time-delay between two communicating devices may result in lost production or even damage to the system especially when handling peak traffic network load. Previous studies from Higginbottom [13] have shown that there are almost no delays in a station's access time to the CSMA/CD protocol network at low or medium network traffic load, but performance is dramatically reduced when the load is heavy. It is important to determine, at the early design stage and under all conditions, that the maximum message delay through a LAN is less than the shortest workstation (machine) processing time. This enables the manufacturing system to operate without breakdown in production. However, it is often difficult to determine the maximum message delay as it is subject to factors, which are controlled by the characteristics of the complex flexible manufacturing system (i.e., FMS) and its stochastic system behaviour. For instance, Higginbottom's [13] recent work based on a mathematical analysis of LAN performance only works out the mean delay as a function of network throughput or network utilisation. However, system designers lack a feasible and practical combined modelling and simulation method or tool, which allows them, at the early design stage, to assess such factors as to how the maximum message delay impacts on the shortest machine processing time. Frequently, the LAN designer just simply increases the capacity of the network until it delivers a reasonable performance for the manufacturing system. The approach herein offers a quick and visible overview (or preview) of the system performance by considering both the above factors. This can also help the designers obtain some useful information in advance on alternative solutions to meet both operational system and communication system requirements by providing them with an estimate of network efficiency for the assumed conditions. This will also reduce unnecessary investment in systems that have excessive capacity in order to achieve a common commercial objective: to build a network with very good performance for a minimum cost.

There are a few publications in the literature that analyse and compare the performance of three IEEE 802 standard networks for manufacturing systems. A classical comparative study is often made based on open system interconnection (OSI) transport and datalink layers' performance in order to determine the relative merits of CSMA/CD, token bus, and token ring networks. For manufacturing environments, the major problem of the ring network is its physical topology, which is always a poor fit to the layout of most processes and assembly lines. Some delay in gaining access to the ring is encountered at low network load because the station has to wait for the token. The disadvantages of the CSMA/CD network include: a limited cable length (2.5 km with repeaters), which may restrict the layout of the manufacturing plant. The network efficiency drops as the network load increases. At high network load, message collisions are a major problem and the network performance deteriorates rapidly. Obviously, such a situation cannot be allowed to take place for real-time applications in manufacturing. In contrast, the bus network is the most popular topology for a factory's local area network because its layout can be made to closely match the layout of machines in the factory. The token bus protocol network has excellent throughput and efficiency at high loads, which is supposed to satisfy requirements for process control applications. But the major concern is that the token bus is a complex protocol, which can raise the cost of the communication equipment. These advantages and disadvantages are always debated when implementing communication systems for manufacturing industries. The debate is greatly curtailed if the protagonists take an integrated modelling and simulation approach, and simultaneously investigate the performance of the communication and manufacturing systems.

1.1. Review of integrated modelling simulation methods or tools for manufacturing systems analysis, design and performance evaluation

Because of fierce competition, industry is now being forced into implementing expensive factory automation and is, therefore, carefully re-examining its operating policies and procedures. For the past decade, several computer-based modelling and simulation methods or tools for modelling, analysing and designing different aspects of manufacturing systems have been developed. The following reviews some of the major developments in the modelling simulation methods and the integrated modelling simulation tools that are used for manufacturing systems [14, 15, 16, 17, 18, 19, 20, 21].

- The GRAI (graph with results and actions interrelated) method was developed based on the early development of a variety of graphical modelling methods, which are explored in a branch of mathematics relating to graph theory. The GRAI is based upon a conceptual reference model, which uses graphical tools and a structured approach. The reference model is decomposed into three sub-systems, namely: physical, information and decision systems. The GRAI graphical tools consist of GRAI grids and GRAI nets. The GRAI grid is represented by a table of rows and columns, and is constructed using a top-down analysis approach. The columns of the grid represent the types of function and the rows contain the decision time scales. The relationships between decision centres are represented on the grid by a simple arrow (an information link) and a double arrow (a decision link). The GRAI net describes the structure of the various activities in each of the decision centres identified in the GRAI grid and is constructed using a bottom-up analysis approach. The activities are the fundamental elements in the grid. Each activity has an initial and a final state, and requires the support of information and produces results. An activity result can be the connecting resources or input to another activity. Another well-known graphical application is Petri nets, which can be used to model more complex systems.
- The ICAM (integrated computer-aided manufacturing) DEFinition (IDEF) consists of a hierarchy of diagrams, text and glossary. IDEF includes three different modelling methods: IDEF0, IDEF1, and IDEF2 for producing a functional model, an information model, and a dynamic model respectively. The IDEF0 functional modelling method is designed to model the decisions, actions and activities of the system. It allows the user to 'tell the story' of what is happening in the system. The diagram represents the main component of the IDEF0 model. It presents the system functions as boxes, and data or object interfaces as arrows. The attachment point between arrows and boxes indicates the interface type (input, control, output or mechanism). The generation of many levels of detail through the model diagram structure is one of the most important features of IDEF0 as a modelling technique. The IDEF0 model starts by representing the whole system as a single box (the highest level), which is labelled A0. The A0 box can be broken down into more detailed diagrams until the system is described in the necessary detail. The top level of the model presents the most general system objective and is followed by a series of hierarchical diagrams to provide more detail about the system being modelled. Some simulation tools have been developed based on IDEF models, such as Design/CPN, Mapping IDEF3 and ARENA.

- SADT (structure analysis and design technique) uses a number of graphical tools including diagrams, actigrams, datagrams, node-lists and data dictionaries. Actigrams describe the relationships between the activity elements and datagrams describe the relationships between the data elements in the diagram structure. A node list is a record of the node contents (title and number) of the actigram or datagram used to provide the structure of the subject system. A SADT model depends upon top-down decomposition, starting with a single function, which is broken down into child-actigrams and datagrams in order to achieve the necessary level of details.
- SSADM (structured system analysis and design method) provides interfaces between the method procedure and techniques. It breaks the system down into modules containing activity steps. Each step has several tasks as inputs and outputs. SSADM contains a number of techniques including data flow diagrams (DFD), logical data structure (LDS), entity life histories (ELH) and relational data analysis (RDA) to support its modelling methodology. The role of the DFD in the SSADM is to provide a functional model of the data flows throughout the system being modelled. The LDS is used to identify system entities from the source of information flow and specify the relationship between these entities in order to build a diagram, which represents the logical data structure. The ELH is used to validate the DFD and investigate system data dynamics. The RDA supports the data structures, which are stored in data tables.

Due to the limitations of these methods and techniques, a number of other integrated modelling simulation methods and modelling simulation tools based on the above techniques have been developed by different groups:

- GIM (i.e., GRAI integrated methodology) was developed to support an overall systems analysis and design. Therefore, the GIM method integrates four different modelling domains: functional, information, decisional and physical, and presents them in a GIM modelling framework. Furthermore, GIM combines three modelling methods: GRAI (to model decisional systems), MERISE (to model information systems) and IDEF0 (to model physical systems). GIM is supported by a computerised graphical editor called IMAGIM, which offers access to the graphical editors of method formalisms. The package utilises the GRAI grid and net, IDEF0 and entity/relationship editors. In addition to providing unclear support of dynamic aspects of manufacturing systems, the linking of the GIM formalisms is not well supported by IMAGIM.
- SIM (i.e., Strathclyde integration methodology) comprises two modelling methods of DFDs and GRAI grids to model information systems in the manufacturing environment. The application of IDEF0 was introduced into the method to complement the use of DFDs. SIM is an effective method for modelling manufacturing information systems but it does not consider dynamic aspects of physical sub-systems in the manufacturing environment.
- The GI-SIM (i.e., GRAI/IDEF-Simulation) integrated modelling method has reportedly been developed to meet the needs of analysis and design by capturing the

characteristics of a manufacturing system 'completely'. Precisely, the GI-SIM tool provides three interfaces which can link (integrate) three existing modelling simulation tools (GRAI grid, IDEF0 and SIMAN), which have been used for evaluation of manufacturing systems. SIMAN (now called ARENA) is a powerful simulation package, which is mainly used to model and simulate various manufacturing environments. The interfaces, which appear as an enter-information window and have been developed using a visual programming language, can also translate data between different simulations tools. However, this integrated modelling method does not provide a function or facility, which can be used to model the information (communication) systems aspect.

The above integrated modelling simulation methods or tools are designed to be used to either model operational functional dynamic behaviour or to model the information system for manufacturing. Most authors agree that there is no single mature technique, which can completely model both aspects of a manufacturing system. Nevertheless, manufacturing system's analysts, designers and their clients have an increasingly important requirement for a 'full' system evaluation, which can involve modelling the basic manufacturing operations incorporating the effect of the information (communication) systems particularly for investigation of highly integrated time-critical manufacturing systems. These factors eventually lead to the development and implementation of an integrated approach that will be presented in this chapter.

1.2. Research objectives

In resolving these problems, we have developed an integrated modelling simulation methodology to a mature stage; this technique permits users to determine the relevant impact on logical interactions and interrelationships between operations and information (processing) systems within a manufacturing environment. This has been achieved by formulating an integrated model, in which both operational system's function and information system's function can be modelled, simulated and examined together based on existing simulation tools, along with other statistical techniques. In addition to this major task, this established integrated simulation model has the capability to help designers gain a comprehensive preview of the system's performance and behaviour and provide the performance prediction that allows designers to build a system that gives an optimal solution before implementing a real system. This tool particularly provides a distinct improvement in optimising a system's performance within a time-critical manufacturing environment. In principle, this technique is valuable for analysing a wide range of manufacturing systems (CIM, FMS, dynamic process control systems, etc.).

Since manufacturing systems involve many aspects, including financial and marketing systems (especially within CIM systems), it is essential to narrow the scope of the analysis and focus on the systems that will benefit the most from an efficient communication network. In this project, a fairly complex flexible manufacturing system for printed circuit board assembly (i.e., PCBA) is selected as a case study, and the integrated simulation model of its operational system and communication system has been built using two major modelling simulation packages, namely: ARENA 3.0 and COMNET III. An interface has been established to allow analysts to analyse and convert relevant statistical data between them. A series of 'countless' pilot simulations have been successfully executed. Since the generated simulation results are of considerable volume, only those that are valuable for use in the specific research and to meet users' requirements are customised and chosen. In this case, the simulation results, which represent the interactions and interrelationships between the operational and the information processing systems, are reported, analysed, plotted and discussed herein.

This chapter presents a detailed description of this integrated modelling simulation methodology with its established integrated simulation model, supported by an overview of previous research work and the fundamental knowledge of the updated modelling simulation approaches and the most popular optimisation techniques for evaluation of manufacturing systems. Furthermore, this method has been implemented, tested and demonstrated based on an application of the printed circuit board assembly (i.e., PCBA) system, the feasibility and benefits of using this tool and an analysis of various simulation outputs are also presented and discussed.

Our research has shown that this approach can provide a useful basis for developing existing modelling frameworks and a practical means of exploring existing integrated modelling simulation methodologies. The research work has been described in a series of international publications [22, 23, 24] which report the research achievements.

2. THE PCBA SYSTEM

Automated assembly lines are used for the assembly of products in most repetitive assembly sectors. In general, an automated assembly line consists of a number of machines or workstations that are linked together by a conveyor or some other material handling systems. The transfer of work-parts occurs automatically and the workstations carry out their specialised functions automatically. The present-day automated assembly system increasingly uses software-controlled equipment and performance tends to be more and more determined by organisational and logistical constraints rather than by technical constraints.

Automatic assembly of printed circuit boards (i.e., PCB) constitutes a core manufacturing process in the electronics industry. The PCBA system is a very highly integrated, automated, flexible and time-critical manufacturing system, which is normally configured as several independent flexible working cells or assembly areas that are mainly equipped with SMT machines using advanced robotics technology and a sophisticated vision system. These assembly cells are basically linked together by a conveyor system and are integrated by a communication network to co-ordinate individual assembly systems. Some manufacturing integration companies such as Universal™ provide the networking software that can be used to integrate a number of equipment units for electronic production systems. The integration software tools also allow the user to transfer data between a host computer and any of the devices used in the various

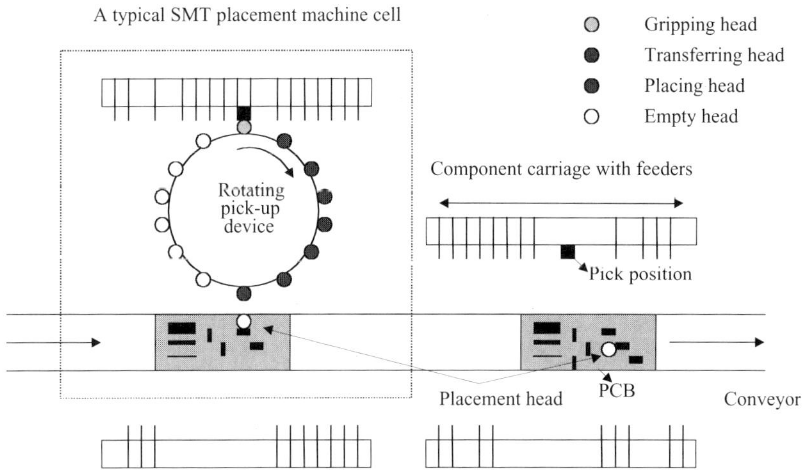

Figure 1. A typical placement cell for PCB assembly.

assembly processes, which are controlled by computerised controllers (such as PLCs) that direct all of the functions and operations throughout the PCBA system. The operation programs can be downloaded and uploaded from the host to the assembly units.

The PCBA system represents a typical case, in which large amounts of electronic components are placed automatically on the boards by using so-called surface mount technology (SMT). An SMT machine is equipped with one placement head and two component carriages. One or more parallel assembly lines are usually available to place the components on the boards. These lines consist of several placement machines that are linked together by a conveyor system. Each machine in the line places a subset of the required components on the board, and the last machine completes the assembly.

Figure 1 illustrates a typical line layout of PCBA cells. The PCBA line consists of two placement machines. Each machine is equipped with one placement head and two component carriages, one at each side of the machine. These carriages can move horizontally. Feeders that contain the components are stored at the stock positions of the carriages. The small vertical lines at the component carriages denote these feeders. The placement head can move in both horizontal and vertical directions. To place a component the head moves to the fixed pick position (indicated by the little black square), where the feeder that contains the required component type has already been moved. The head picks up the component and places it at the appropriate position on the board. During the assembly of the PCB at a machine the board cannot move.

In the last decade PCBA companies have been faced with very high service level requirements, in terms of throughput times and delivery reliability. The size of PCB assembly batches, the demand for different PCB types as well as the types of components at the assembly lines varies with time; as a result, the layout of the PCBA system is re-configured frequently and therefore must be determined. A closer look at the PCB assembly process reveals that the planning and scheduling of PCB assembly is usually very complicated.

For example, an unbalanced distribution of the assembly workload of a particular PCB type between the SMT machines in a line can cause loss of machine assembly capacity. If the workload that is assigned to an SMT machine is high compared to the workload of the other machines in the line, then the latter machines have to wait until this machine has completed its part of the assembly. When the number of orders increases it becomes very difficult to achieve a good balance for each order; this results in idle times for the SMT machines. Therefore, there is a line balancing problem, this requires investigation via animated simulation to minimise the load imbalance between the machines; simulation results provide insight into such factors as the assembly capacity utilisation at each SMT machine or workstation. This is a very important factor at the machine planning level for the PCBA system. If the workload is equal for each machine in a line for a particular order, then the line is said to be perfectly balanced. The workload consists of picking and placing components and gluing to the boards. Sequencing is another complicated issue during PCB assembly due to the requirement for different types of PCB components for different board designs. To solve this problem, the PCBs are tracked from their entry into the system and throughout the processes by making use of bar code labelling and scanning.

Due to the lack of management structure in planning the assembly lines in the PCB industry, line balancing decisions were often left to the operators [25, 26, 27]. Figure 2 shows a hierarchical planning and scheduling approach by Fokkert's [26] research that dealt with the complexity of PCB assembly lines. This relatively complete approach consists of three planning levels: department level planning, line level planning and machine level planning. However, it does not give any details as to how to implement this approach for scheduling and planning, particularly with a focus on the two latter levels of a complex PCBA system. Furthermore, the fatal weakness of this development is that the developed models and the method are all based on a deterministic approach. However, the PCBA system is a typical stochastic system. Moreover, it also ignores the effects from the PCBA communication system, which plays a key role in such a highly automated time-critical integrated system.

Therefore, the emphasis on developing a comprehensive but practical integrated approach for analysis, scheduling and design of complex systems such as the PCBA system, is essential in order to achieve cost-effective operations for a wide range of product types.

3. SIMULATION TOOLS USED

In this project, two simulation tools (ARENA 3.0 and COMNET III) have been utilised to capture the main modelling characteristics (functional and information dynamic aspects) of the complex flexible PCBA system. This has been achieved by developing an integrated simulation model through an interface that allows analysis

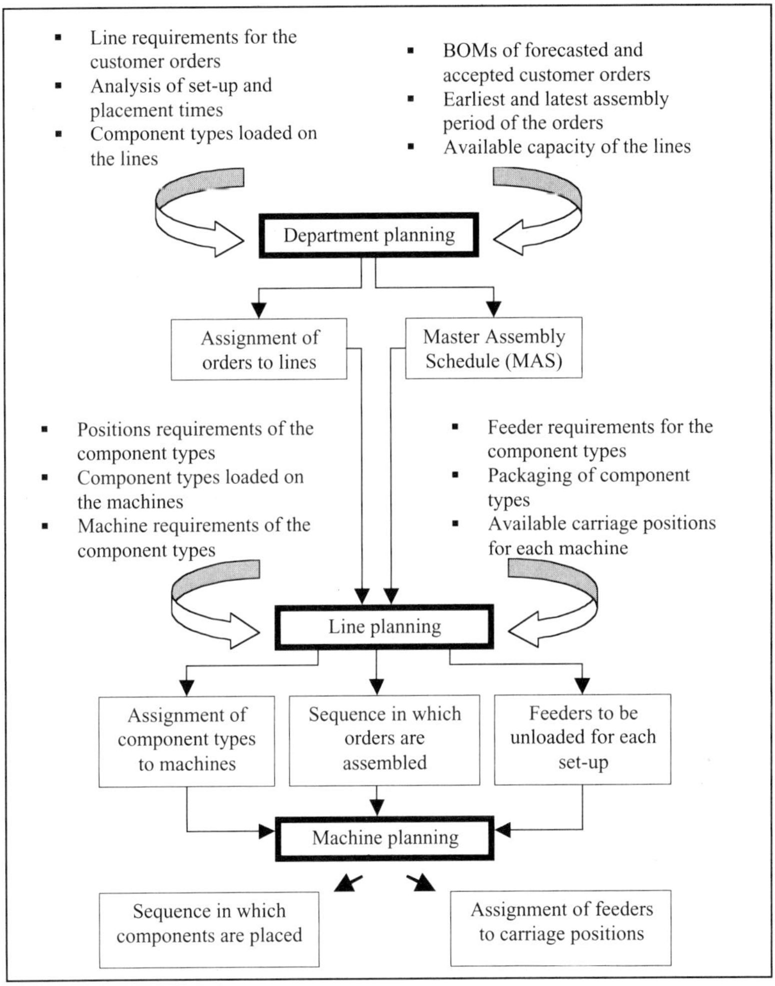

Figure 2. A hierarchical approach for planning and scheduling of a PCBA system.

and conversion of relevant simulation output data from the ARENA model to the COMNET model. This integrated model can help the system designers modify and justify the system model parameters in order to detect the system bottlenecks and to improve its design so as to obtain optimum system performance.

3.1. Operational system model development based on ARENA 3.0

The ARENA software (Systems Modelling Corporation), which is developed using the SIMAN simulation language, divides the simulation process into three steps:

- System model development.
- Experimental frame development.
- Simulation data analysis.

SIMAN is one of the most popular modern simulation languages specially designed for modelling large and complex (discrete, continuous, and/or combined) manufacturing systems. SIMAN is designed around a logical modelling framework in which the simulation problem is segmented into a 'model' component and an 'experiment' component. The model describes the physical elements of the system (machines, workers, storage points, transporters, information, parts flow etc.) and their logical interrelationships. The experiment specifies the experimental conditions under which the model is to run, including elements such as initial conditions, resource availability, type of statistics gathered, and length of run. The experimental frame also includes the analyst's specifications (specified external to the model description) for such things as the schedules for resource availability, the routing of entities, etc.

The ARENA modelling framework draws a fundamental distinction between system model and experimental frame. The system model describes the physical elements and their logical interrelationships by placing and interconnecting a thread of logic simulation modules with specific rules to form a model of a system from its engineering description. The experimental frame defines the experimental conditions, including analyst's specification, under which the model is run to generate specific output data. The experimental conditions are specified external to the model description; therefore, a given model can link up with different experimental frames resulting in many sets of output data without changing the model description.

Once a system model and experimental frame have been defined, they can be linked and executed by ARENA (i.e., through a link processor) to generate output data files. The output data can be displayed as statistical bar charts, functional plots and data tables, which may be customised to accommodate the analyst's needs [28, 29, 30].

3.1.1. Operational system model development

Figure 3 illustrates an example of part of the logic program to build a model of the printed circuit board assembly (PCBA) system based on ARENA. Figure 3 shows an ARENA model that is constructed by placing and connecting modules, which have already been developed individually as integrated 'blocks or modules' using the SIMAN simulation language to represent distinct process modelling functions in the model window. The appropriate input data can be entered through the modules' dialogues. A model is constructed by selecting standard modules from the available set. The blocks are arranged and linked in a linear logical sequence, based on their functional operation and interaction, to depict the process through which the entities move in the system.

A system model generally consists of a number of individual logic modules and data modules. The logic modules are connected in a logical sequence to define the process through which entities flow (customers, work-pieces, patients, communication packets, etc.). During the simulation run, entities may arrive at and depart from logic

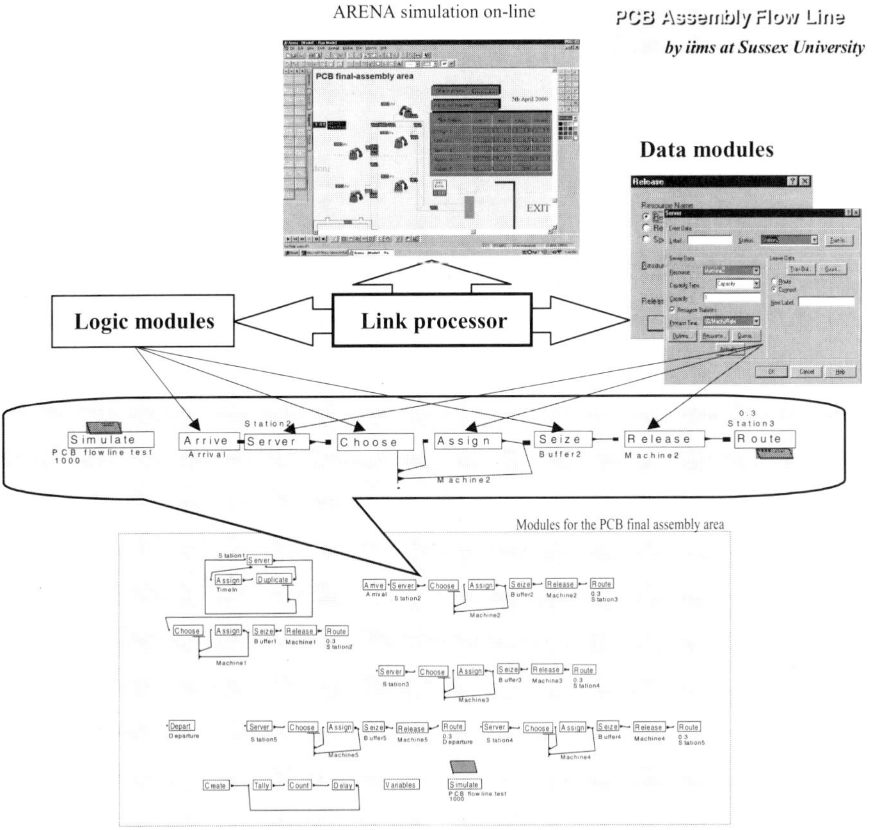

Figure 3. ARENA system model development methodology.

modules that remain dormant until they are activated by the arrival of an entity. In contrast, data modules are used to define data associated with the model. Unlike logic modules, data modules are not connected to other modules. Entities do not arrive at or depart from a data module. Data modules are passive in nature and are used only to define data associated with the system parameters.

There are three categories of ARENA modules for manufacturing systems' models: work-centre modules, component modules and data modules. They consist of simulation models to represent the real system [30].

- **Workcentre** modules describe the logical portion of the manufacturing system. Each of the workcentre modules incorporates all of the logic necessary for processing a part in a specific area, hence: enter the workcentre, exit material handling process, determine the next workcentre, get material handling, and move to the next workcentre. The workcentre modules are Receiving, Workcentre, Buffer, Assembly, and

Shipping. The callout box in figure 3 represents a typical group of workcentre modules to describe assembly operations of PCBs.

Arriving entities (PCBs) are generated or transferred from the 'ARRIVE module' to another station or module (SERVER to be processed). The ARRIVE module essentially contains the Create, Station, and Leave modules combined into one module. An entity is created, immediately enters a station, and is transferred to another station or module. In the 'SERVER module', an entity (PCB) enters a station, seizes a server resource (components to be assembled onto the PCB), experiences a processing delay (such as EXPO (1) or 1 minute), and is transferred to another station or module. The SERVER module defines a station corresponding to a physical or logical location where processing occurs. The 'CHOOSE module' provides entity branching based on the 'If conditional rule' in conjunction with the deterministic 'Else and Always rules'. When an entity arrives at the CHOOSE module, it examines each of the defined branch options and sends the original arriving entity (the primary entity) to the destination of the first branch whose condition is satisfied. If no branches are taken, the arriving entity is disposed of. When an entity arrives at an 'ASSIGN module', the assignment value or state is evaluated and is assigned to the variable or resource specified. If an attribute or picture is specified, the arriving entity's attribute or picture is assigned the new value. The 'SEIZE module' allocates units of one or more resources to an entity. The SEIZE module may be used to seize units of a particular resource, a member of a resource set, or a resource as defined by an alternative method. The 'RELEASE module' is used to release units of a resource that an entity previously had seized. For each resource to be released, the name and quantity to be released are specified. The 'ROUTE module' transfers an entity to a specified station, or the next station (station 4) in the station visitation sequence defined for the entity. A delay time to transfer to the next station may be defined.

- **Component modules** are single elements of workcentre modules. These modules are typically used when the logic within a workcentre module is not sufficient to represent all or portions of the system concerned. Shown in the right and left icons of figure 4, there are 29 component modules available to be chosen. They can be categorised by two types of purposes:
  1. For processing operations.
  2. For material handling and transfer operations.
- **Data modules** allow the definition of specific detailed information about objects that are referenced into workcentre modules and component modules to represent the logical flow of a manufacturing system. The detailed information may include the Process Plans at Machines, Operators, and Parts modules. There are 17 data modules available. Figure 4 illustrates some of them. The following is a list of the data modules and a brief description of their functionality.
  1. Parts_part name, process plan, attribute assignments.
  2. ProdePlan_Creation of parts into system.
  3. Dispatch_Creation of requisitions and transfer requests into system.
  4. Machines_Machine name, capacity, breakdowns, statistics.
  5. Areas_Area name, capacity, statistics.

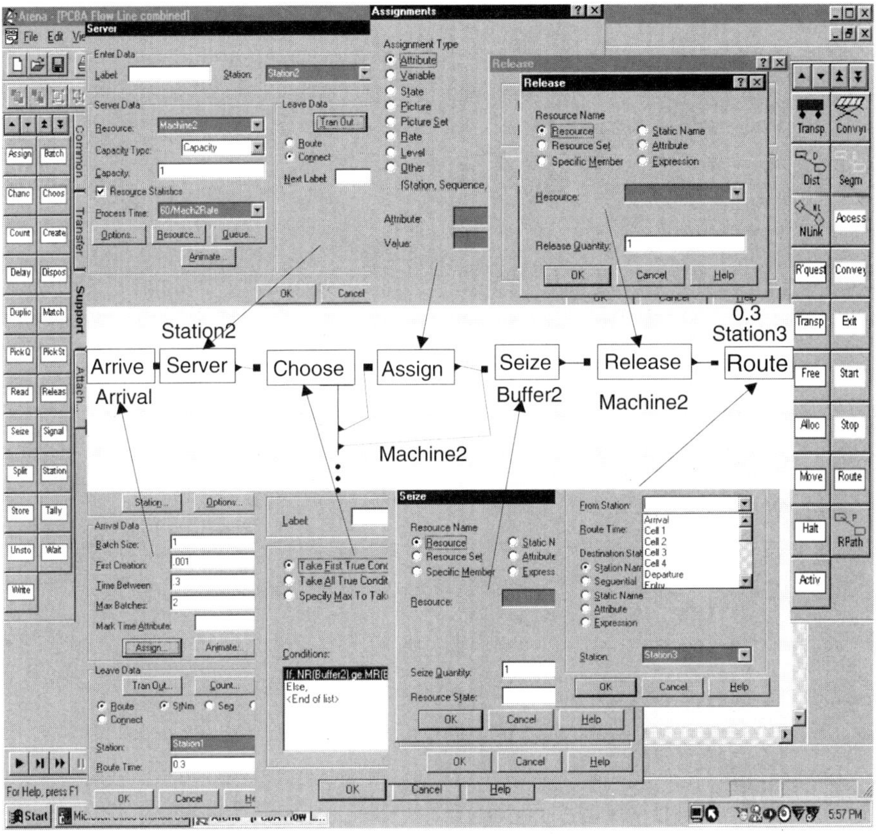

Figure 4. Data modules and component modules for ARENA modelling.

6. Operators_Operator name, capacity or schedule name, statistics.
7. MoveOper_Moveable operation names, schedule information, locations, velocities.
8. OperSched_Operator schedule name, information.
9. Opersets_Set name, operations in set, selection rule.
10. Transporter_Transporter name, velocity, characteristics.
11. Conveyor_Conveyor name, velocity, type, and characteristics.
12. Analysis_Simulation run time, number of replications, detailed statistics.
13. Variables_System variable names, initial values.
14. Paths_Unconstrained, moveable operator, transporter and conveyor, animated paths for movement of parts.
15. Networks_Paths for guided transporters.
16. ProcPlans_Sequence of workcentre steps a part takes with associated processing information.
17. ProcData_Groups of processing information (statistics) for use with process plans.

In summary, the development of an appropriate conceptual, logical simulation model by programming is one of the major tasks in simulation model construction. Although there are many simulation languages commercially available and there are hundreds of other locally developed languages being used by companies and universities, the trend for simulation software development has been an emphasis on an integrated simulation environment to provide ease of use. However, the definition of the model boundary is usually a trade-off between accuracy and cost, a valid model should include only those aspects of the system relevant to the study objectives.

Model verification is a process of determining the computer code of a model to ensure that the simulation program is a correct implementation of the model. This process does not ensure that the model appropriately represents the real system; it only ensures that the model is free of errors. Validation is concerned with the correspondence between the model and reality, i.e., model validation is a process of determining that a model is a sufficiently adequate approximation of the real system that the simulation conclusions drawn from the model are correct and applicable to the real-world system.

Although most simulation tools can automatically detect certain types of errors introduced by a programmer and may be able to display intentional errors in a model's logic, it cannot automatically correct or debug the errors. It is also unable to find errors of the model to represent the system, as in this situation the program is often correct. A manual verification process is used to avoid common errors, such as: data errors, initialisation errors, errors in the units of measurement, flow control, blockages and deadlocks, arithmetic errors, overwriting variables and attributes, data recording errors, and language conceptual errors. It is found to be very useful to detect and expose such errors by running animation as a verification aid; such direct observation of errors in model execution, speeds the debugging process.

3.1.2. Experimental frame development for ARENA models

It is important to have appropriate data to describe or represent the real system activities in order to drive its simulation model. In most simulation studies, the determination of what data to use is a very difficult and time-consuming process especially for the case of the design of a stochastic simulation model. Regardless of the method used to collect the data, the decision of how much to collect is a trade-off between cost and accuracy. Perera [20] has summarised and ranked a number of factors that affect accuracy of analysis and identification of the collected data, namely:

1. Poor data availability.
2. High-level model details.
3. Difficulty in identifying available data sources.
4. Complexity of the system under investigation.
5. Lack of clear objectives.
6. Limited facilities in simulation software or packages to organise and manipulate input data.
7. Wrong problem definitions.

In general, we can try to obtain data about the systems from a number of sources [28, 31, 32]:

- Historical records
- Observation data
- Similar systems
- Operator estimates
- Vendor's claim
- Designer estimation
- Theoretical considerations

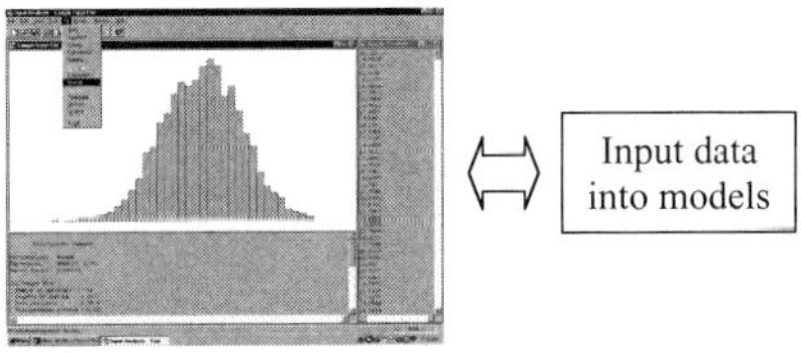

Input Analyser

Stochastic systems contain one or more sources of randomness. Common sources of randomness for manufacturing systems are:

- Inter-arrival times of entities, such as parts, jobs, raw materials to the system.
- Processing or assembly times for an entity required at various machines.
- Operation times for various processing machines.
- Repair/or breakdown times for a certain machine.

Therefore, the sources of input data for a manufacturing simulation model may include inter-arrival times, demand rates, loading and unloading times, processing times, failure times for different machines, repair times, etc. Most of which are probabilistic.

Three methods are used to process data from stochastic systems for random simulation models. We can sample directly from the empirical distribution, or, if the collected data fits a theoretical distribution, we can sample from the theoretical distribution, or we can choose a probability distribution based on theoretical considerations, prior knowledge, or past research.

If empirical data are to be used, they are input in the form of a cumulative probability distribution. Observed values are input in the form of an empirical cumulative distribution by arranging them in ascending order, grouping identical values, computing their relative frequencies, and then computing their cumulative probability distribution.

The collected data can also be used to fit a theoretical distribution, which can then be selected as an input data generator for the simulated model. First, the collected data are summarised and analysed manually or by using existing software packages: several excellent computer software packages are available to perform these functions. These packages can simplify the task of selecting and evaluating a distribution. Figure 5 presents an example of statistical procedures using an ARENA 'Input Analyser' facility to analyse and process the external modelling (empirical) data in terms of a histogram to fit and to form a standard distribution for model uses. The right window shows the input data and the left window displays the entire shape of the histogram that conforms to a normal distribution. The bottom window displays a summary report of the recommended distribution. Input Analyser can be used to determine the quality of fit of probability distribution functions to the input data for the system's model. The collected data files that can be loaded in and are processed by the Input Analyser

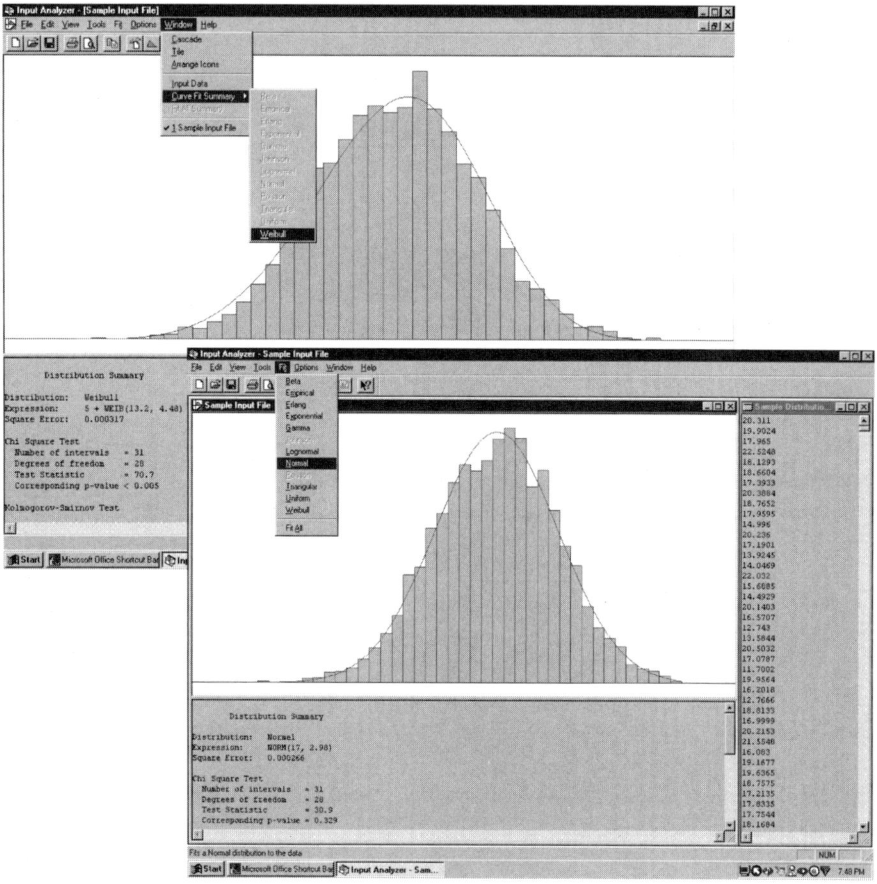

Figure 5. Fitting empirical data as a sample distribution using 'Input Analyser'.

typically represent the time intervals associated with a random process in terms of a histogram in the Input Analyser Window. Once a specific distribution to fit the histogram is selected, it is always essential to assess the quality of its fit (i.e., to fit the best distribution to the data). This can be achieved by using formal statistical tests or by employing a simple graphical method in which an overlay of the theoretical distribution is displayed on a histogram of the data and a visual assessment is made to determine the quality of the fit [20, 30, 33].

ARENA contains a set of built-in functions and provides an interface (through various dialogue windows) to allow users specifying 'operands' for random variables to obtain samples from the commonly used probability distributions. Each of the distributions has one or more parameter values (mean, standard deviation, etc.) associated with it, which depends on the distribution of the random variables. Figure 6 illustrates

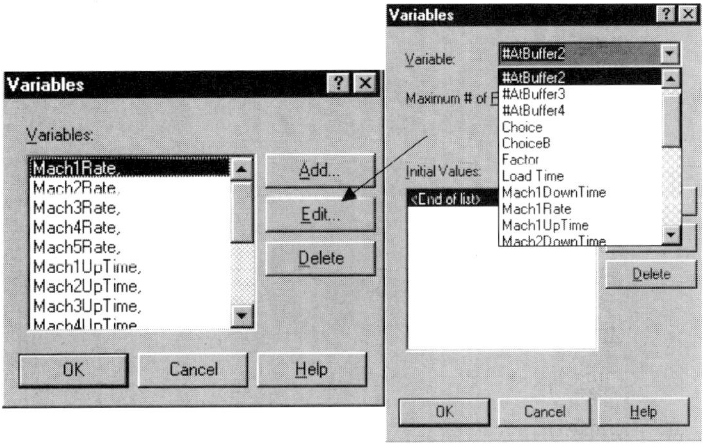

Figure 6. Random variables used for the PCBA system modelling.

the 'VARIABLES module' to be used to specify user-defined global variables and their initial values.

The main idea of statistical inference is to take a random sample from a population (i.e., the entire group from which we may collect data) and then use the information from the sample to make inferences about particular population characteristics such as the mean (measure of central tendency), the standard deviation (measure of spread) or the proportion of units in the population that have a certain characteristic. A sample is generally selected for study because the population is too large to study in its entirety. The sample should be representative of the general population. This is best achieved by random sampling.

Because a sample examines only part of a population, the sample mean will not exactly equal the corresponding mean of the entire population. Thus, an important consideration for those planning and interpreting sampled results is the degree to which the sample produces an accurate estimate of reality. In practice, a confidence interval is used to express the uncertainty in a quantity being estimated. Inferences are based on a random sample of finite size from a population or process of interest. Therefore, one gets different data (and thus different confidence intervals) each time [21, 28, 32, 33, 34].

The sampling distribution is the probability distribution or probability density function of the statistic. It describes probabilities associated with a statistic when a random sample is drawn from a population. If the parameter in a system varies continuously then it is possible that it conforms to one of the standard statistical probability distributions, such as: Uniform, Normal, Exponential, or Poisson. Thus, this behaviour can be sampled from a distribution.

For instance, operation times at a workstation can be sampled from a distribution. First, the type of distribution must be determined, and its parameters must be calculated. To do that, the actual operation times are studied and plotted as a frequency distribution. If the shape of the distribution suggests that it does conform to one of the standard distributions, then the 'goodness of fit' of the observed data can be assessed and the parameters for that distribution can be computed. If the frequency distribution of the actual times do not conform to a standard distribution, then the observed data can be expressed as a histogram and samples drawn from that. It could also be sampled from the histogram giving the probability of an operation being performed at each workstation [31, 33, 35, 36].

The definitions of each of the distributions used for ARENA models in this project will be summarised together with those used for COMNET models in section 3.2.1.2.

3.1.2.1. INPUT DATA ACQUISITION AND ANALYSIS FOR STOCHASTIC SYSTEM MODELS. The essence of this procedure is abstraction and simplification; the real difficulty in modelling is to determine which elements should be considered and included in the model [36, 37]. For establishing a flexible manufacturing system (FMS) model, these inputs could be abstracted by considering:

1. The basic configuration of the FMS, and its production scheduling, which defines the entities and activities involved in the model and the logic sequences that occur for each activity.
2. Number of workstations or machines that should be included in the simulation model.
3. How many types of processed parts need to move through the FMS, do they have similar processing requirements or not?
4. Buffer capacities for each machine.
5. Transport: conveyor or AGV and their track.
6. Profile of operations allocated to each workstation or machine.

Once these elements, together with logical functional relationships and their relevant descriptive information (descriptive variables) are determined, the simulation model can be built as a logical flow block (or pseudo-code) to describe and represent the real system to be investigated [30, 34, 35, 38, 39].

The authors believe that the input data collection and analysis play a key role in successful implementation of simulation model construction and simulation execution. Typically, more than one third of project time is spent on identification, collection, validation and analysis of input data. Although very little research work has paid attention to the development of systematic approaches to input data gathering, a number of researchers have raised issues surrounding data collection [20]. Basically, the quality of available data is a key factor in determining the level of detail and accuracy of the model.

Stochastic models typically depend upon various uncertain parameters that must be estimated from existing data sets if available; otherwise, if the data does not exist they can be sampled directly from theoretical probabilistic distributions. With manufacturing systems, there is no standard method for collecting the required information [36]. Data resources can possibly be collected from a literature survey, interviews with domain experts, industrial data reviews and state of the art assessments.

System design documentation includes data such as: drawings, specifications, production records and so on, it is important that such data reflects the current configuration of the system. Although these resources are usually reasonably accurate, they may be inaccurate or insufficient, as historical records often do not represent the performance of the current system. Even though there is frequently copious data from reliable sources, simulation experts always argue over how we should use the data. If we sample directly from the empirical data, we may faithfully replicate the past but no values other than those experienced in the past can occur. If we fit the data to a theoretical distribution and then sample from it, the simulation may give values either bigger or smaller than the historical data, so the accuracy of representing the system is in doubt. This debate still continues, and an appropriate solution is still unclear.

If empirical data is to be used, it is input in the form of a cumulative probability distribution, which can be plotted by appropriate tools such as the so called 'Input Analyser' which arranges data in ascending order, grouping identical values, and computing their relative frequencies. To organise raw data, first the collected data can be summarised and grouped into classes or categories so that we can determine the number of individuals belonging to each class. The observed number is called the class frequency. We can then form frequency distributions by determining the largest and smallest numbers in the raw data, thereby defining the range, and breaking the range into a convenient number of equal class intervals. Next, we can determine the number of observations falling in each class interval to find out the class frequencies, and then the frequency distribution can be graphically plotted as a histogram, which represents a relative frequency distribution. Several excellent software packages, including ARENA, can perform these functions. These packages can simplify manual tasks in selecting and evaluating a distribution for model input data [20, 28, 32, 40].

The most difficult case in simulation studies is when the data for modelling systems does not exist either because the system does not exist or because it is not possible to obtain the data. Nevertheless, there are a number of possibilities to get data input for system's models: estimation or theoretical distributions.

Vendors, designers and modellers can make the estimations. This greatly depends on factors from different people who have different experiences and use different measurement systems. The research has shown that people are very poor at estimating events even though they are very familiar with the systems. Therefore, the input data based on estimations may be highly unreliable; also in many cases it is hard to estimate. Instead, more popularly, we can choose a probability distribution based on theoretical considerations, i.e., using well-known statistical knowledge, so that we only need to determine how close this distribution is to reality by specifying the appropriate parameter values associated with the specific system [28, 30, 35].

One of the important skills of a simulation expert is to know how to summarise the data, to simplify the modelling process and to minimise the sensitivity of the results to errors in data estimates. Thanks to past studies of industrial engineering statistics, we already know many statistical distribution functions that can be used particularly to 'represent' (or generate) various types of activity in industrial processes. For instance, it is already known among simulation experts that for a random process, inter-arrival times of customers (assembled parts) normally follows the exponential distribution, represented as EXPO. (ParamSet), which is thus often used to model random arrival times of events (and breakdown processes), but it is generally inappropriate for modelling process delay times. Also, the exponential distribution is typically not a good choice for representing service times, as most service processes do not exhibit the high variability that is associated with the exponential distribution. The normal distribution is used for the processing times when the mean is at least three standard deviations above zero. The uniform distribution is used when all values over a finite range are considered to be equally likely, which is generally used to represent 'worst case' results.

Each distribution has one or more parameter values (mean, standard deviation, etc.) associated with it. However, the parameter values associated with relevant distributions are also based on statistical estimations that often depend on the phenomena being represented. For example, the mean value of inter-arrival times can be estimated, if the times vary independently and randomly, and the estimated value is not large, then the time between arrivals can be modelled as an exponential distribution. This estimation can be considered reasonable [28, 33, 40].

3.1.3. Simulation data analysis

The simulation results include all the statistical summary reports in terms of text-based tables or graphics, which show the system's performance measures pre-defined in the experiment file. In general, a standard simulation result reports in text, presenting statistical data in the format of the sample mean, coefficient of variation, and minimum and maximum observed values to represent such factors as all kinds of times, queue length, machine utilisation, etc., within the investigated system.

Simulation results can be used for designing new systems, and/or modifying and improving the operation of existing systems. One of the ultimate goals in the project is to compare and select the simulation-generated data to make inferences in order to improve the real-system performance. For instance, we want to use the model to draw conclusions about the expected maximum time that a job spends at each processing station so that we can find the system bottleneck in order to modify the system model to obtain a balanced system performance and to maximise the effectiveness and efficiency of the system.

ARENA provides a facility called 'Output Analyser'. Similar to the 'Input Analyser', output files generated by simulation models can be transferred, plotted, displayed and analysed in the 'Output Analyser Window'. This can be useful for comparing the results of a simulation run with actual system data (by loading an external data file into the Output Analyser) for the purpose of validating a simulation model. ARENA also provides a facility to allow users to export output data files in one of two standard ASCII (American standard code for information interchange) file formats by using the 'Generate DIF' file and 'Export' options through the menu items. The Generate DIF (a standard file format) file option converts the data in the specified data file to the DIF file format. Since a variety of software packages use this DIF format, this allows supplementary analysis or display of simulation results. The Export option reads unformatted data from an output data file and creates an ASCII-formatted file. This option is used when the results of a simulation need to be transferred to different types of computer operating systems or read into other software packages. On the other hand, external data files can be imported into a data group window with the 'Load ASCII' file and 'Import' options. The Load ASCII file option reads a free-unformatted data ASCII data file (without an output data file header) and creates unformatted data for use in the Output Analyser. This interface is used to exchange information between the two simulation tools [30], ARENA 3.0 and COMNET III, the latter being used to simulate the information system's performance. In addition, during the simulation the ARENA animation function can be displayed on the ARENA window, thus progress of the simulation can be observed and inspected by users.

3.2. Communication system model development based on COMNET III

The COMNET III package [41] was developed based on its former version Network II.5, LNET, and Simscript 2.5, which is written in a high-level, object-oriented simulation programming language MODSIM II. COMNET III is a graphic-oriented simulation tool that can be used to analyse and predict the performance of existing networks ranging from simple LANs to complex enterprise-wide systems, and to allow designers to evaluate alternative network designs by collecting simulation performance statistics. COMNET III supports a building-block approach where the blocks are 'objects' consisting of a model representing the real-world network. This network modelling approach allows a wide variety of network topologies and routing algorithms to be accommodated. This includes LAN, WAN, MAN and inter-networking systems; circuit, message and packet switching networks; connection-oriented and connectionless traffic; adaptive and user-defined algorithms. The network's operation and protocol parameters are set through as a series of IEEE tab dialogue boxes, which perform all functions of model design, model execution and presentation of results. COMNET III divides its simulation process into three phases [14, 40, 42, 43, 44, 45]:

- Network description and model construction.
- Network simulation.
- Simulation results and analysis.

3.2.1. Network description and modelling constructions

This process can be split into two phases:

- Building a network architecture model.
- Building a network load profile for the resulting model network.

COMNET III's graphical user interface allow users to create and modify the network's topologies with various nodes and links and to enter its operation and protocol parameters data through a series of IEEE tab dialogue boxes which perform all functions

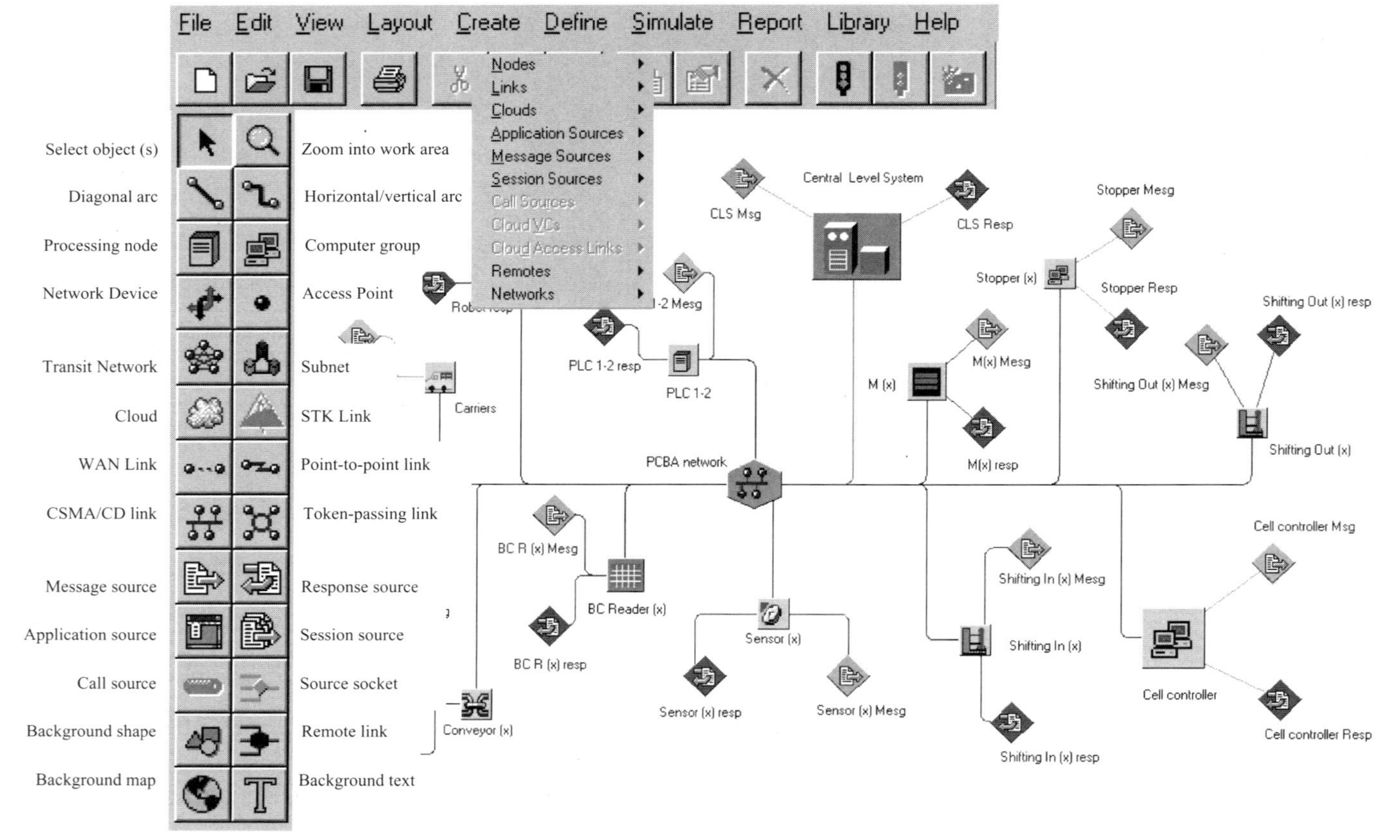

Figure 7. COMNET III user-interface for network modelling.

of model design, model execution and presentation of simulation results. As shown in figure 7, the COMNET III tool palette facility is used to create: Nodes (communicating devices), Links (a link to which nodes may be connected and protocols or rules for scheduling applications and routing traffic), Traffic Sources (workload across the network) and other tools for editing. The COMNET main menu bar and its pull-down menus, which follows the standard format of Microsoft Windows and Microsoft NT, give users easy and quick access to use other functions of the COMNET window interface [41].

3.2.1.1. MODELLING OF NETWORK TOPOLOGIES. The first step of building a COMNET III simulation model is to construct a topology for the physical network to be investigated. That is because an automated manufacturing system is a large complex on-line system, which further consists of several distributed systems. Each distributed system involves any kind of intelligent devices (robots, PC, PLCs etc.,) of a computer network (including sub-networks). If a communication network is to support manufacturing applications, the network topology must be designed and determined so that the overall system is maintained on-line.

As shown in figure 7, the physical layout of a network model (which consists of a network topology shown in figure 8 in manufacturing) for the PCBA communication system can be built based on three basic components: Nodes, Links, and Arcs. Nodes to represent hardware (computers or switches), Links that carry traffic between nodes, and Arcs to show a node's port connection to the link. In addition to these basic facilities, there are three objects with internal topologies: Subnet, Transit Net and WAN cloud. The WAN cloud is used for modelling WAN services, while the others are used for modelling independent routing domains and hierarchical topology.

- **Nodes**

Nodes in COMNET III models can be switches, hubs, network devices, end systems, pads and general network components. COMNET III provides four basic types of nodes including Network Device Node; Processing Node; Computer Group Node; which generate or receive messages, and Router and Switch Nodes, which are only used for routing traffic.

Processing Nodes model computer hosts as well as communication processing devices. Each Processing Node has an internal processor that executes software and process packets. The Processing Node that is represented in the model support the following applications: an input buffer for each link transmitting packets to it; a processor to execute commands and process packets; an output buffer for each link to which it can route packets; local disk storage capacity for modelling local read/write commands; a pending application list of currently scheduled applications; a received message list for saving received messages until they are used; a list of files that may reside in local disk storage.

- **Links**

As shown in figure 9, Links are used to model a variety of different transmission media, ranging from LANs to wide-area point-to-point links.

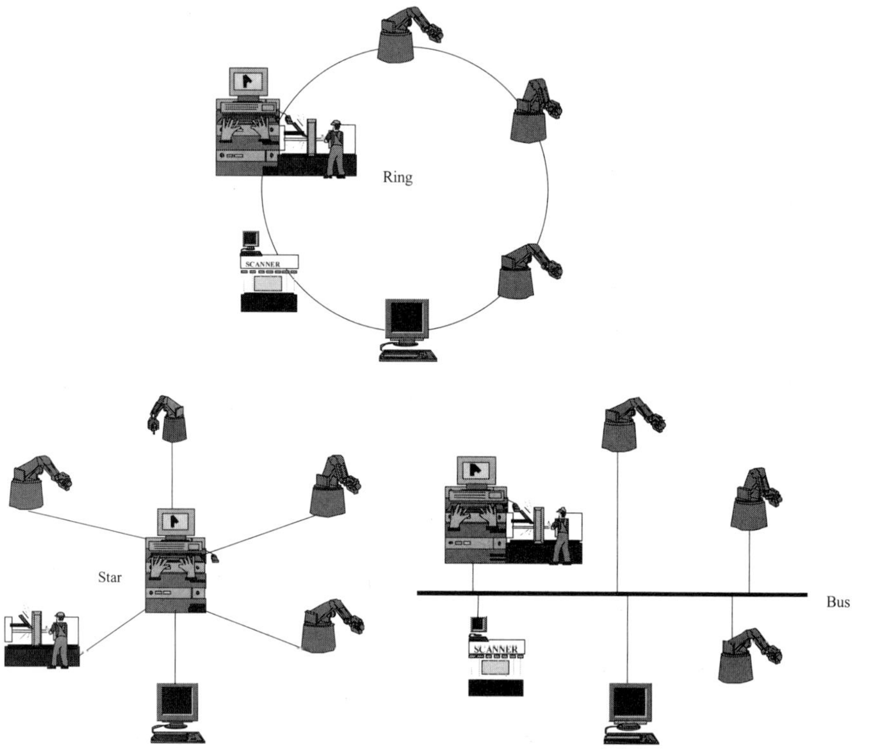

Figure 8. Three-network topologies for manufacturing (supported by ARENA 3.0).

COMNET III provides various types of links corresponding to the types of medium access protocols for users to select, including Aloha, CSMA, CSMA/CA, CSMA/CD, DAMA, Dial-up, FDM/FDMA, FDDI, Link Group, Modem Pool, Priority FDDI, Polling, Point-to-Point, Satellite (STK), TDM/TDMA, Token Passing, Virtual, and WAN. The CSMA/CD library provides parameter sets based on the IEEE 802.3 standard. The token-passing library provides parameter sets based on the IEEE 802.4 and 802.5 standards.

▪ Sub-networks, transit networks and WAN clouds

The Sub-networks (Subnets) in the COMNET III model are used primarily for modelling interconnected subnets of independent routing algorithms. A complex network may be built hierarchically using subnets hiding detail from an upper view.

Transit Nets can be considered as an intermediate network modelling the flow of packets through the transit nets and can behave both as a subnet and a link.

WAN services are abstractly modelled in terms of Access Links and Virtual Circuits using the WAN Cloud object [41].

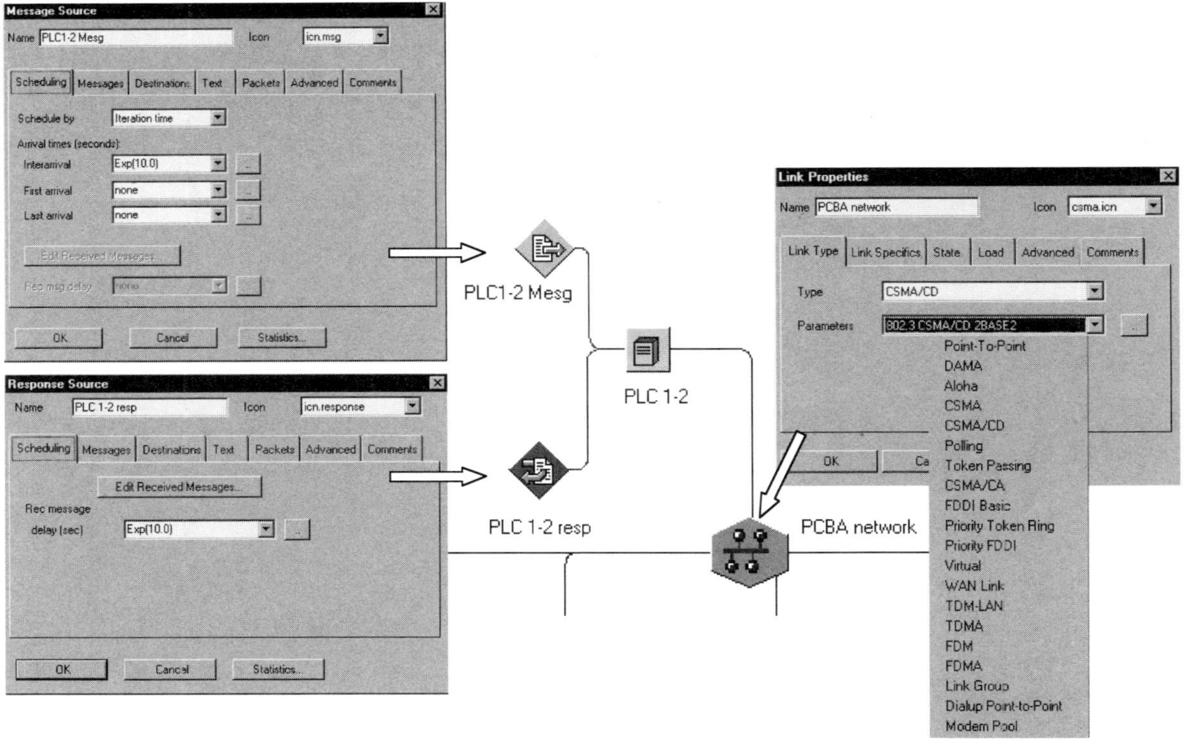

Figure 9. Building a network load profile for different types of networks.

3.2.1.2. NETWORK TRAFFIC AND WORKLOAD. Figure 9 also illustrates traffic sources in COMNET III that include 'Message Source', 'Session Source' (not shown in the figure) and 'Response Source'. The Message Source is the combination of an application source with a 'Transport Message Command' and is used for modelling specific user or protocol-control messages. The Response Source is the combination of an 'Application Source' with an 'Answer Message Command' and is used for modelling replies or acknowledgements to messages. The Session Source is the combination of an Application Source with a 'Set-up Command' and is used for modelling sessions of multiple message, bursts of messages, or messages that are routed in virtual circuits.

In addition to the sources mentioned above, Call source is the source to use for modelling circuit-switched calls. They specify calls by means of inter-arrival times, duration and the bandwidth requirements. COMNET III allows external sources to be introduced into the COMNET model through an external traffic file by using the 'External' traffic menu. The external traffic file is a formatted text-based file containing a record for each traffic event: each record contains information about the time of the event, the source and destination and other information that occurs in a real network. The traffic file may come directly from various network analysts or it may be created from some other tools. COMNET III can interpret events in the files as being messages, sessions, or calls. The COMNET Baseliner utility is used to read in external traffic files and format them into an intermediate file for COMNET III use. This utility allows multiple traffic sources to be merged into a single intermediate file. This useful function has been applied to link ARENA simulation results to COMNET. The COMNET input data interface will be illustrated further in the next section.

The parameters of sources for network traffic and workload are added through the (call, message, response, session, packet flow or packet rate matrix) 'Source Dialogue Boxes' to drive the simulation. Network traffic refers to the messages sent between nodes in the network topology. The workload is the internal activities of the node's processors or busses. Application sources execute commands that introduce either traffic into the network or workload inside the node. Message, Response, Session and Call sources simply generate traffic between nodes. Since nodes may have processing requirements for traffic moving between them, the workload commands can delay traffic by utilising the processor when the traffic needs to use it. Connectionless traffic and the response as the receiving part of the connection are modelled using Message Source, while connection-oriented traffic can be mainly modelled using Section Sources.

Traffic sources can be scheduled in three manners: iteration time, received message text and trigger. The iteration time method allows sources to be scheduled according to an interval from the previous arrival, while the received message text method provides scheduling sources dependent on messages received at the node.

Applications consist of several different commands specified within the nodes. They provide a flexible means to model both traffic generation and workload at a particular node. Some of these commands are Read, Write, Transport Message, Set-up Session, Answer Message, Process, and Filter [41].

In most cases, activities or events in a communication system as well as a manufacturing system in production are stochastic. Furthermore, its samples for random variables within the system can be obtained from the commonly used probability distributions, such as exponential and uniform distributions, etc. ARENA 3.0 and COMNET III provide a set of built-in analytic distribution functions, which can be used to generate input data for models to drive simulation engines. Figure 10 illustrates such a case; these distributions have been used for ARENA and COMNET models to represent the PCBA system, they are summarised below. More information related to engineering statistics can be found in references: [28, 30, 33, 40, 41, 46].

- **Exponential distribution—Exponential (Mean)**

This distribution is widely used to model arrival times of events that follow a Poisson pattern. Each sample chosen from the exponential functions specifies the time that will elapse before the next arrival. This is called the inter-arrival time. Samples have a high probability of being less than the mean. This implies that the distribution has a long tail and will occasionally provide a sample significantly higher than the mean. This behaviour is very useful in modelling random arrival and breakdown processes, but it is generally inappropriate for modelling process delay times.

- **Uniform distribution—Uniform (Min, Max)**

All values between minimum and maximum are equally probable, excluding values of the minimum and maximum. This distribution is used when all values over a finite range are considered to be equally likely and is sometimes used when no information other than the range is available. Because of its large variance, this distribution can be used to model 'worst case' results such as message response time for fixed (or maximum) message sizes.

- **Normal distribution—Normal (Mean, StdDev)**

The normal distribution is often used empirically for many processes that are known to have a symmetric distribution and for which the mean and standard deviation can be estimated. The distribution should only be used for processing times when the mean is at least three standard deviations above zero. In COMNET III, the normal distribution is truncated so that it does not produce negative numbers. If the mean chosen is more than about three times the standard deviation there will be little effect, since there will only be a very small portion of the normal distribution to the left of the origin. A message could be described as having a mean size of 20000 bytes and a standard deviation of 5000 bytes.

- **Triangular distribution—Triangular (Min, Mode, Max)**

The triangular distribution is commonly used in situations in which the exact form of the distribution is unknown, but estimates for the minimum and maximum, and most likely values are available.

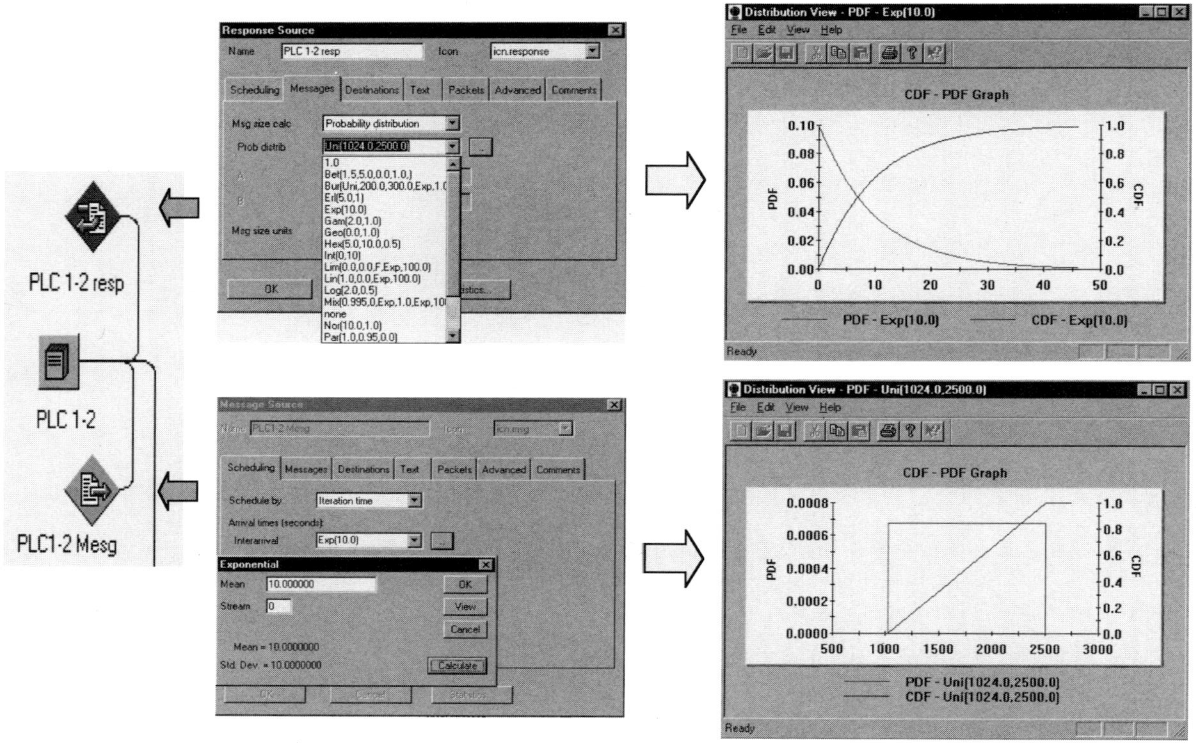

Figure 10. Building a traffic load profile using standard probability distributions.

3.2.2. Network simulation

After a model has been built, COMNET III can test the model automatically using Verify command for correctness and completeness and using Run Parameters Dialogue define a simulation experiment including the replication time for the duration of the simulation for: statistics collection, the warm-up period when statistics are not collected, the number of replications for the number of reports, and two check-boxes for re-setting the system to empty and idle at the end of each replication and for running a warm-up for each replication. COMNET III can perform animation during the simulation by setting animation parameters, though this will significantly reduce the speed of simulation.

3.3. Simulation result analysis

COMNET III provides two forms of reports, namely real-time and non real-time reports. The former provides a graphical on-line representation of selected performance parameters of links and nodes during the simulation. Figure 11 shows such an example. The latter provides all the various statistical results selected based on various objects or items (nodes, links, traffic sources, etc.), which can be viewed at the end of the simulation run for further studies. The textual reports at the end of each replication of the model can be selectively turned on by choosing the 'reporters dialogue' box. However, the major reports include: message delay reports, response and session resources, and channel utilisation reports for links [41].

4. INTEGRATED MODEL APPROACH

Figure 12 illustrates the principle of the integrated model and the connection between ARENA 3.0 and COMNET III. The model is established based on these two simulation tools; the output of one provides important input data to the other. Since ARENA and COMNET are two separate software packages, an interface has been developed that links the two packages together. This allows the statistical results (SDF files) generated by ARENA to be passed to the COMNET model.

4.1. Establishment of an integrated model

As mentioned in section 1, this research attempts to investigate the performance of time-critical flexible manufacturing systems, in which all the communicating facilities or equipment are beneficially integrated through an efficient communication network. In order to allow an overall investigation, those factors, which may potentially affect the system's behaviour and may cause a fluctuation around the system's bottleneck, must be modelled. Such a fluctuation depends on complex factors, which may have a significant impact on the dynamics of the system; these should be identified and included in the model.

For the PCBA system, the performance evaluation should be completed based on those factors (or performance measures), which will influence the entire system. These factors stem not only from aspects of the PCBA operational system but also from aspects of the PCBA communication system. Therefore, these factors and their

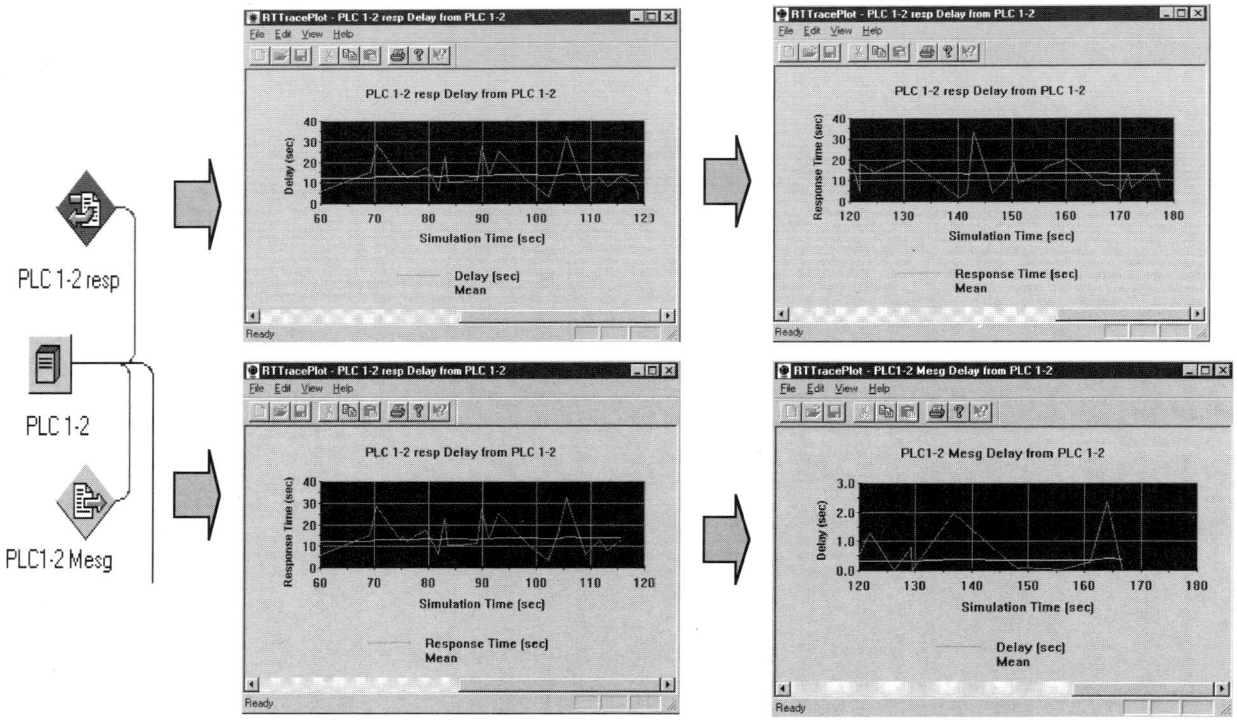

Figure 11. Network simulation on line.

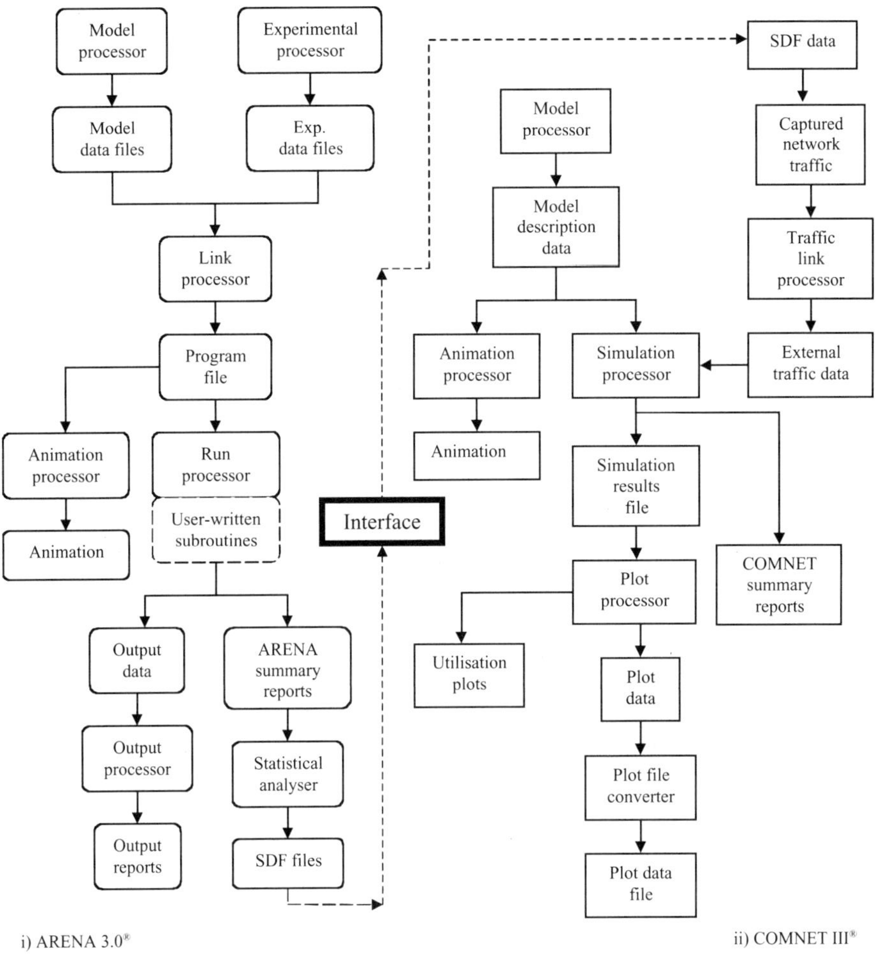

Figure 12. Flow chart for the integrated model based on ARENA 3.0 and COMNET III.

variables should be identified. However, in this particular investigation, we do not include those resources (such as the design department for production scheduling, etc.) that are also linked and are integrated into the system but operate in a relatively slow manner and thus do not significantly affect the performance of on-line production. Other assumptions for the established integrated PCBA model are summarised below:

- The production operates continuously and constantly without breakdown due to physical failures of machines and devices on the assembly lines.
- The number of available machines or devices and their capacities at the assembly lines to perform both the assembly and changeover activities are fixed and known.

- Each workstation consists of one assembly robot (i.e., SMT machine) with input and output buffers. There are no buffers between workstations. Each product is assembled at least once in the assembly schedule, which was determined previously.
- For communication networks, assume that all communicating devices (or machines) are able to communicate with each other properly, and each device has a suitable interface that allows connection to the communication networks without physical failures.
- This study does not evaluate issues concerning production costs, such as costs arising from assembly, labour, changeover, and miscellaneous things.

Based on the above assumptions for building an integrated model some key requirements and steps are summarised as follows.

1. Define all the relevant equipment (or workstations) in the real-system to be modelled, including number of machines and devices or workstations, number of part types and number of operations for each part, capacity of each machine, buffers and their capacities at each machine, and machining sequence.
2. Analyse the operational functions of the system in order to form all appropriate input data (i.e., so-called experimental files) for ARENA models, such as physical and logical sequencing and timing parameters to represent the operational function for individual items of equipment. The timing parameters include loading/unloading times for each machine (and/or each loading/unloading station), material handling times for each assembly robot, machining times for each operation, arrival times for each type of part, and other parameters such as batch size, conveyors' (and/or AGVs') speed and travelling distances. These data resources heavily depend on different systems to be investigated.
3. Determine how to schedule the information processing function related to information events. The timing of information events is derived from the statistical analysis of the operational simulation output (statistical results) provided by ARENA simulation models.
4. Analyse and extract the output of statistical data from ARENA simulations and interpret it into statistical distribution functions (SDFs) as input variables with the particular parameter values, which are required for COMNET models. The SDF files for COMNET models are mainly related to the type of distribution for representing the information flow activities between two communication devices via the communication network. Moreover, the most important consideration in choosing the specific probability distribution with one or more parameter values for the specific random communication behaviour is the degree of closeness to which it resembles the real information events. Obviously, the output statistical data from ARENA simulation models that represent the random operational aspects (or processes) will certainly affect the probability distribution chosen for COMNET modelling. Moreover, the selection of the distribution's parameter values is one of the most critical procedures, because if it is not accurate, simulation work using COMNET will not represent the real-system's behaviour.

5. Ensure that the logical sequence and interaction of all components and the inter-relationship between the operational function and the information processing function in the system are precisely defined, thus, a complete simulation model can be implemented.

Once the generic model has been verified and validated, it can be run to represent the actual (physical and logical) operations of the real-world system without re building the system model for the different system's investigation scenarios, and it is also easy to add or remove components to investigate the effect of system alterations. The aim is to utilise the simulation-generated data to observe the impact on both systems' function and to assess the entire system's performance by making inferences with the system model. From this, an optimal system specification can be drawn up.

4.1.1. Operational system

The process of assembling electronic components provides a typical flexible manufacturing system, which involves complex items (part types) being produced in limited quantities. For example, there may be short-term variations in size, quantity and frequency of the lots to the system. This stochastic variation is termed 'flexibility' [25]. This type of assembly system is also a time-critical application.

• ARENA model of the PCBA system

A flexible manufacturing system from the printed circuit board assembly sector represents a stochastic manufacturing scenario extremely well.

Figure 13 shows a layout of the PCBA system, its graphically animated simulation model was constructed using ARENA 3.0. The system is composed of pallets, load/unload machines, pick and place machines, shifting–in devices, shifting-out devices, fixing devices, sensors, bar-code readers, stoppers, assembly robots (or so-called SMT placement machines), cell controllers, carriers and flexible conveyor systems, which are routed and controlled by PLC's throughout the system.

To summarise the operational sequence: unprocessed components (printed circuit boards) are held in pallets for transport into the 'Enter System' and then loaded onto the loop conveyor by the loading machine at station M1. The assembled PCB's are unloaded at station M2 with a high priority given to exiting the PCBA system. Unfinished components enter another cycle until all assembly operations are complete. The sequence of operations at stations is arbitrary. The entire operation is controlled by one of the cell controllers, which interact with others at the relevant workplace locations to accomplish the individual activities. The detailed system description and its parameters are explained below:

1. The arriving unprocessed palletised PCB enters the buffer area, where a sensor senses the arrival of each palletised PCB. The sensor sends a message to notify the cell controller waiting for the decision for access to a gravity slide, which feeds the loop conveyor containing the palletised PCB's queuing for assembly. If not available, the

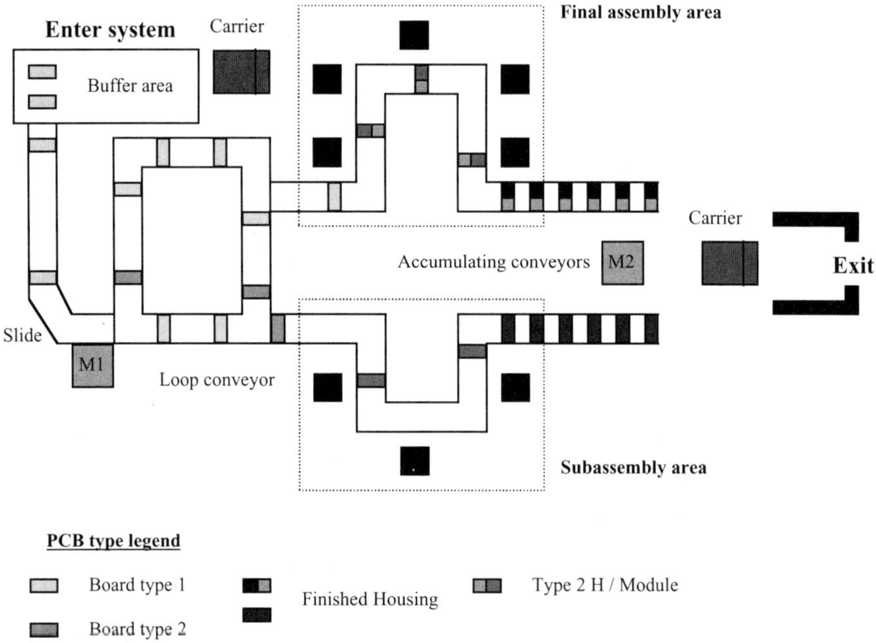

Figure 13. The layout of the PCBA system.

sensor activates a stopper to halt the palletised PCB and stop it moving into the slide. Only two palletised PCB's are allowed on the slide at any one time to avoid damage to the circuit boards. The time it takes to traverse the slide follows a normal distribution with a mean of 3 minutes and a standard deviation of 1 minute.

2. Once a palletised PCB reaches the end of the slide, it must wait for a space on the non-accumulating loop conveyor that is controlled by a PLC. The loop conveyor, which has a length of 18 meters, has space for 30 circuit boards waiting for assembly. When an open space becomes available at the end of the slide, the cell controller will inform the PLC to stop the loop conveyor, and the arriving palletised PCB is loaded onto the loop conveyor at station M1. This loading process requires an operation time that follows a triangular distribution with a minimum of 0.2, mode of 0.3, and maximum of 0.5 minutes, when the loading operation is completed, the loop conveyor is re-activated by the PLC.

3. The palletised PCBs then travel on the loop conveyor at a speed of 9 meters per minute until they reach their required assembly lines: final assembly area for type 1 parts and the sub-assembly area for type 2 parts. Bar-code readers scan bar-code labels to identify the status of each arriving PCB. PCB types are notified to the cell controller to update their status. The queue in front of each assembly operation has room for two circuit boards. If the queue is full, the palletised PCB continues around the loop conveyor until it can enter the queue. If space is available in the queue, the

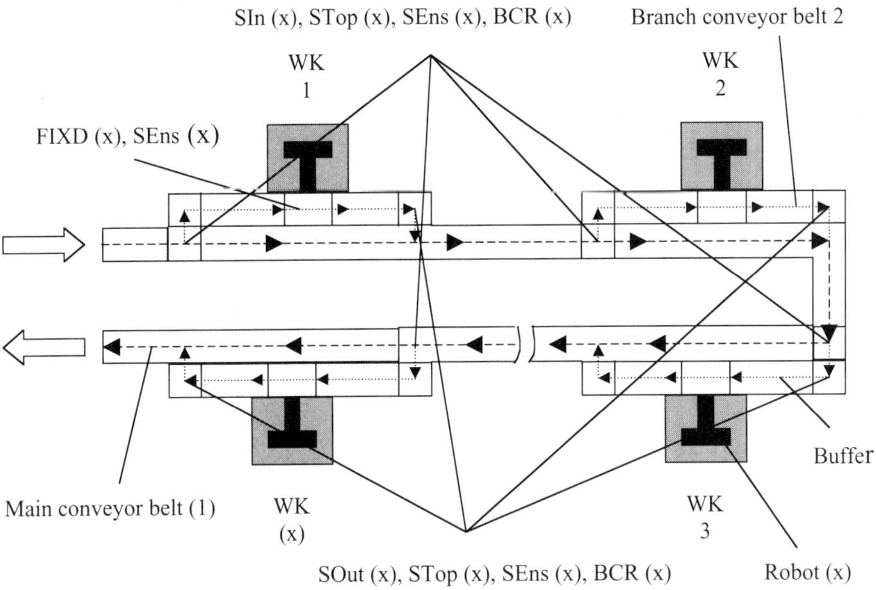

Figure 14. Schematic layout of the PCBA final assembly area.

palletised PCB is automatically diverted off the loop conveyor into the appropriate assembly system. The diversion of palletised PCBs from the loop conveyor does not cause the conveyor to stop.

4. The entire processing times at the sub-assembly area and final assembly area conform to a normal distribution with a mean of 6 minutes and 7 minutes, and a standard deviation of 1 minute and 1.5 minutes, respectively. Once the assembly operation has finished, it exits the assembly operation and enters an accumulating roller conveyor; each one is 3 meters long, and parts travel at a speed of 8 meters per minute. However, if the accumulating roller conveyor is full, the assembled parts are not permitted to leave the assembly operation, thereby blocking its operation. The bar-code readers will scan finished parts at the end of the roller conveyors and send a message to the cell controller to update their status and request transportation by one of two available carriers. The carrier (AGV) moves to the end of the roller conveyor; picks up the processed parts, and leaves towards its destination, which is selected according to the shortest-distance rule [28].

For an individual workstation WK (x) at the final assembly area shown in figure 14, when each palletised PCB is coming in on belt 1, if the PCB is to be processed at station WK (x) where the buffer in front of WK (x) is not full, it will shift to belt 2x via the shift-in device SIn (x) to start the assembly operations by robots or queue in the buffer area. During the assembly, the pallet is held stationary by the fixing device.

Other pallets behind it have to wait behind the shift-in device until the shifting process is completed. The pallet moves on belt 2x to SOut(x) where the palletised PCB will be shifted back to the system conveyor, belt 1, with priority over those coming from the left on Belt1.

After definition and validation of the system model, each simulation was run by simulating 8 hours of assembly activity with a 30-minute warm-up time. This took approximately 25–30 minutes on a 266 Mz PC. The results from initial simulations were used to optimise the system model to give a continuous flow of PCBs. In addition, all time variable statistical information, such as tallied frequencies of the time interval between the arrivals of two palletised PCBs at each workplace, was analysed as a reference resource to determine their statistical distribution functions related to communication events. This was used as input data to the COMNET model and represents the traffic resource required to handle the PCBA communication traffic.

4.1.2. Information processing system

Within the PCBA system, the communication network (LAN) must be able to provide a mechanism for communication and synchronisation among several workstations (robots, etc.) working together to accomplish assembly operations without system's failure due to network problems (such as overload etc.).

• COMNET model of PCBA system

Figure 15 shows the established COMNET model for the PCBA communication system that was designed for the PCBA system. There are 93 communicating devices that are connected to a single local area network (i.e., LAN).

All these devices have a suitable interface that allows connection to the local area network without physical problems. The network communications link into: load/unload machines at stations M1 and M2, shifting-out devices, shifting-in devices, fixing devices, conveyor systems, sensors, bar-code readers, stoppers, cell-controllers, assembly robots, PLCs and a central control-level system (PC). Their functions have been described in section 4.1.1.

COMNET simulation models for large networks often divide the traffic into two types: foreground traffic and background traffic. Foreground traffic represents detailed models of applications and their protocols, and background traffic represents the existing utilisation that competes with the foreground traffic. Such models require a mechanism for modelling background or baseline loading of the network. Often, this load is known only from a measurement of utilisation on the link without any information as to the nature of that traffic. Modelling background traffic with message sources is often impractical because the size of the network requires too many message sources to be configured, and the message sources themselves require entry of many detailed attributes. It is very common that most of the above details on background traffic are unknown or that the only information known about the traffic is the utilisation that is present on the individual links in the network. Therefore, the COMNET

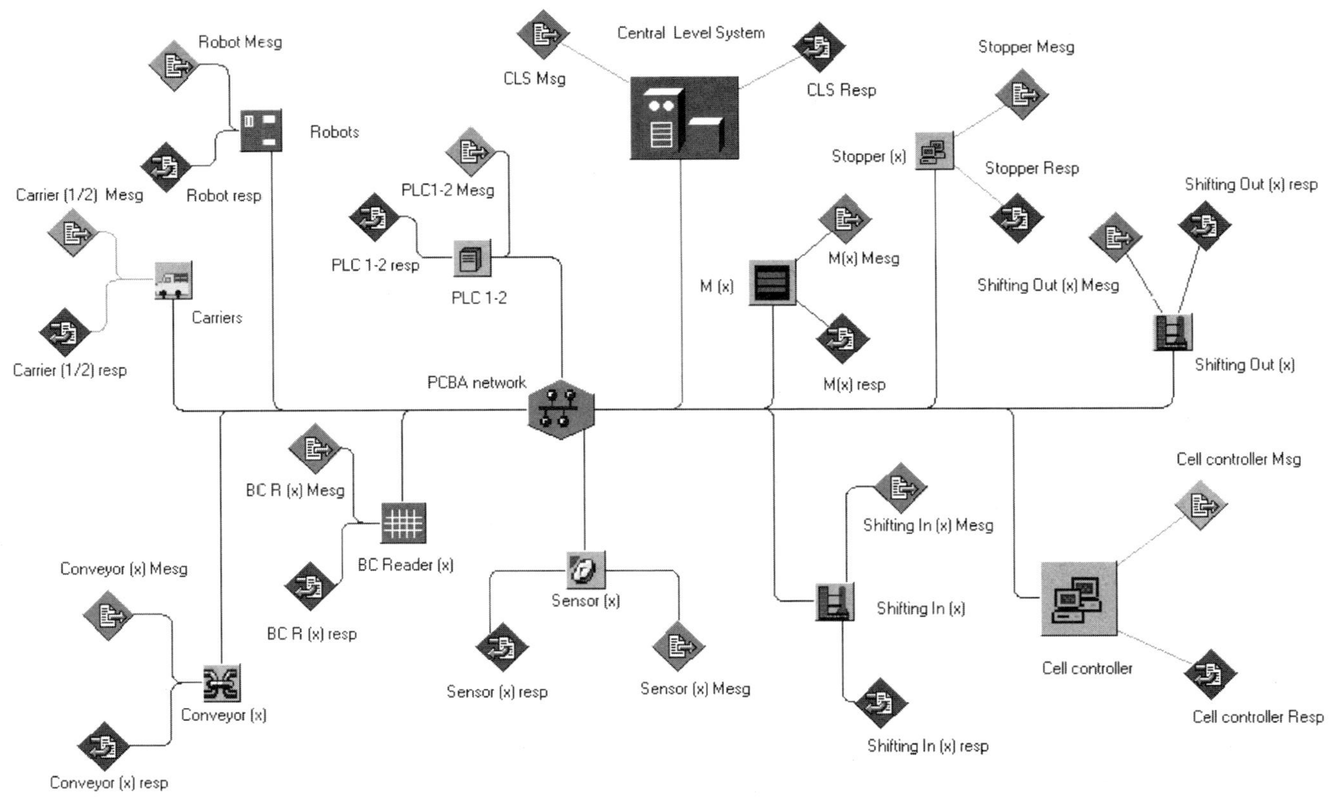

Figure 15. Model of the PCBA communication system built by COMNET III.

model requires statistical distribution functions (i.e., SDFs) as input variables, which characterise the actual information flow activities of the network.

To implement a simulation, traffic events among the system's devices should be scheduled individually by formulating a series of information flow charts, shown in figure 16, to identify information activities. These traffic events are further summarised statistically using the matrix analysis method to indicate traffic events in terms of SDF files. The SDF files must then be formatted as so-called external traffic files, which are a formatted text-based files containing a record for each traffic event. Each record contains information about the timing variables of the event, the source and destination, and other relevant information [2, 36, 41].

COMNET III provides a tool called 'Baseliner' that has been used to read in external traffic files and to format them into an intermediate file for use of COMNET models. This utility allows multiple traffic sources to be merged into a single intermediate event file that contains input data in the form of SDF files. Since the activity in the operational function is a random process, the activity in the information processing function is also a random process. Establishing a meaningful statistical distribution function corresponding to each group of information activities between two devices is a critical issue for the simulation. Determining which ARENA simulation statistics are valuable for formulating the COMNET simulation input is a difficult time consuming task.

There are three methods to select appropriate probability distributions. The first is to use actual data values, the second is to derive an empirical distribution, and the third is to use the best theoretical distribution. In the absence of data the best way is to choose the most suitable theoretical distribution. Nevertheless, some of the required data does not exist, other data does exist but with limited resolution, plus there will always be controversy over which method of statistical analysis is suitable for processing existing data. For example: should we use empirical data as input in the form of a cumulative distribution or should we use historical data to fit a theoretical distribution and then sample from it. In this project, both approaches are used, since the accuracy of selection of input data plays a very important role in representing the real system in a precise manner. To ensure that the simulation is realistic, a so-called 'Input Analyser', which is provided as a standard component of the ARENA environment, has been applied in order to determine and examine the quality of fit of probability distribution functions to input data for the COMNET model.

However, all information flow activities between two communication devices have the following features:

1. Transmitter sends the message to a specified destination, i.e. receiver.
2. Receiver receives the message from the transmitter.
3. Receiver sends response message to transmitter to confirm receipt.
4. Transmitter receives the confirmation message.

It is assumed that all communication devices except the cell controllers have sufficient memory to temporarily store data or processing programs to accomplish their specific

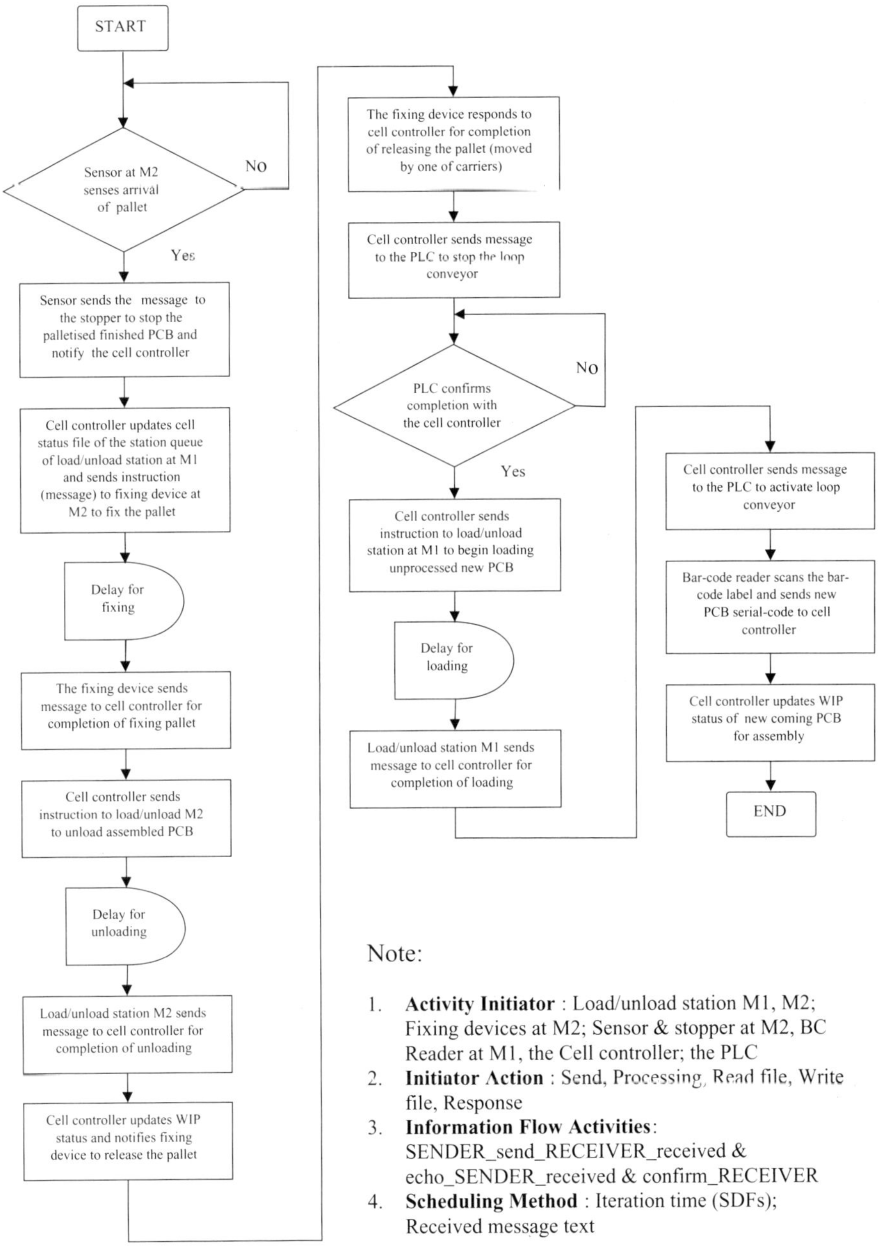

Figure 16. Information flow and activities on load/unload operations.

tasks. The cell controller has a 140 Mbytes built-in hard disk to store all necessary data from other devices or processing program files from the system level computer. The system control level computer only communicates with one of two cell controllers to send processing program data or receive an hourly WIP status report collected by this cell controller that also has a duty to distribute files into individual workstations. Another cell controller will communicate with any of the devices to give instructions or receive fault reports, etc., to control system's operations. The SDF for this device is exponential.

5. SIMULATION RESULTS, ANALYSIS AND DISCUSSION

Extensive simulation results can be produced from the established integrated generic model after simulations are completed. Selection of which simulation results will prove valuable and useful for analysis depends on the specific investigation required or on the clients' needs. The purpose of analysing and using the simulation results for this project is to assess the function of the operational and information systems to ensure that there are no fundamental weaknesses in the PCBA system. This includes:

1. A full investigation of the capacity and equipment utilisation within the operational system and the information processing (communication) system that consists of the entire PCBA system in order to identify any bottleneck that is involved in production processes, such as product flow, parts routing, resources' assignment, assembly line-balancing and the network efficiency.
2. Besides this, the key contribution of this research is to have developed an integrated method that allows system designers and analysts to determine the relevant impact on logical interactions and interrelationships between the operations and information processing systems based on an analysis of various simulation results. This unique feature will be particularly stressed and demonstrated throughout this chapter.
3. Furthermore, a comparison of the performance of alternative systems using different communication protocols for the PCBA communication system was also investigated to maximise the system performance and to obtain an optimal solution.

Since it is impossible and unnecessary to display and analyse all the generated ARENA/COMNET simulation output data in this forum, not just because the data volume is vast but also because the displayed data is always heavily dependent on the end users' requirements for their specific investigation. Figure 17 presents an example of a text-based summarised simulation output (report) generated by the ARENA model of the PCBA system. Table 1 summarises the network performance measures and the related parameters that are investigated for end users in this study. For the operational aspect of a manufacturing system, the performance measures corresponding to related parameters are mainly presented in table 2.

File Edit Search Help

FREQUENCIES

Identifier	Category	--Occurrences-- Number	AvgTime	Standard Percent	Restricted Percent
STATE(Machine1)	Starved	1	.30100	0.03	0.03
	Busy	553	.61031	33.75	33.75
	Failed	5	29.821	14.91	14.91
	Blocked	553	.92784	51.31	51.31
STATE(Machine2)	Starved	8	13.263	10.61	10.61
	Busy	355	1.0371	36.82	36.82
	Failed	16	21.789	34.86	34.86
	Blocked	347	.51031	17.71	17.71
STATE(Machine3)	Starved	18	23.630	42.54	42.54
	Busy	25	16.200	40.50	40.50
	Failed	2	13.515	2.70	2.70
	Blocked	7	20.373	14.26	14.26
STATE(Machine4)	Starved	489	.86773	42.43	42.43
	Busy	493	.74682	36.82	36.82
	Failed	4	8.5726	3.43	3.43
	Blocked	5	34.641	17.32	17.32
STATE(Machine5)	Starved	504	.87726	44.21	44.21
	Busy	504	.66964	33.75	33.75
	Failed	8	27.545	22.04	22.04

Simulation run time: 7.55 minutes.
Simulation run complete.

Figure 17. An ARENA summary report after simulation.

Table 1 Performance measures and related parameters for end user's interests (1)

Performance variables	Parameters
Application functionality	Number of Stations
User friendliness	Message/packet/address sizes
Response time	Station delay
Throughput	Network topology
Queue length/delay	Redundancy
Network utilisation/bus utilisation	Load characteristics/data rate etc.
Physical topology	Buffer size
Transparency/protocol compliance	Protocol interface/channel access scheme
Reliability/loss probability	Hardware delays
Capital cost	Hardware/software, channel access etc.

Table 2 Performance measures and related parameters for end user's interests (2)

Modelling elements	Modelling data (Added/removed)	Measurement (Any bottleneck)	Typical ARENA template (corresponding to)	Schedule (Priority rule)
Parts	Number of part types Arrival/leave time Batch size Max. batches	Output/queue	CREATE ARRIVE/ DEPART	CHOOSE/ ROUTE
	Processing times	Work-in-process	DELAY	
Machines	Number of machine types	Utilisation	SERVER/	SEIZE/
	Number of operations for each part Machine sequence		RESOURCE	RELEASE
	Choice of machining process		CHOOSE	
	Machine time for each part Input/output buffer etc.	Delay/capacity		
Load/unload station	Number of machines Capacity of each machine Loading/unloading time of each machine Input/output buffer capacity etc.	Utilisation	SERVER	SEIZE/ RELEASE
AGV	Number of AGV Speed/travelling distance between two stations	Delay	TRANSPORT	
Robot	Number of robots Processing time	Utilisation	SERVER/SEIZE	/RELEASE
Conveyor	Number of conveyors Speed/travelling distance	Capacity	CONVEYOR	
Workers	Quantity	Utilisation	RESOURCE/	SEIZE/ RELEASE
Buffers	Types Capacity of each buffer	Delay/capacity	DELAY	

The following provides an analysis and discussion of the performance of the PCBA system based on its simulation results, with an emphasis on its communication system's effects and in particular on how to use the integrated method to quantify the logical interactions and interrelationship between the operations and information processing systems of the entire system in order to obtain an optimal design solution.

5.1. Operational system's aspects

Shown in figure 13, the system is divided into two assembly (final and sub-) areas and two load/unload stations. The final assembly area contains 5 workstations (assembly cells) and the sub-assembly area contains 3 workstations. As illustrated in section 4.1.1, the simulation model of the PCBA operational system has been built up using the ARENA tool based on techniques introduced in section 3. A series of pilot simulations

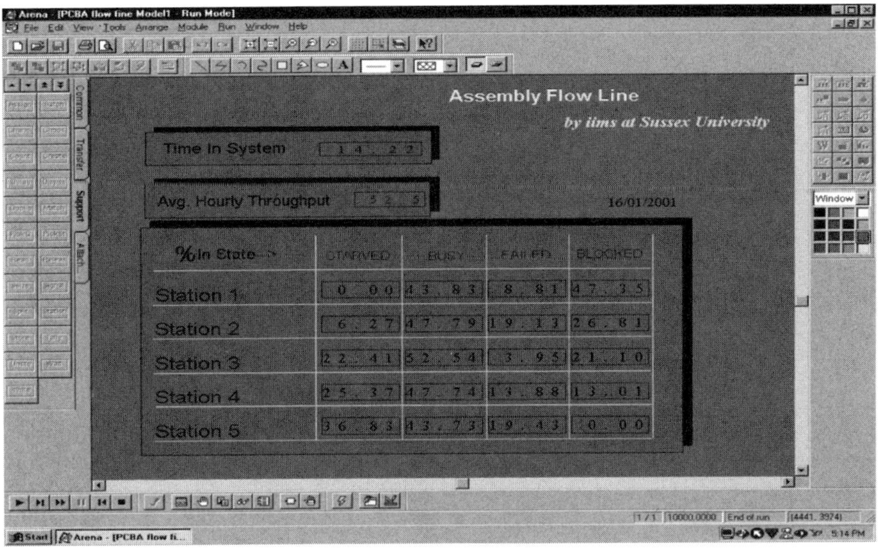

Figure 18. An overview of ARENA on-line simulation results.

have been utilised to capture and optimise the dynamic behaviour and the characteristics of the PCBA assembly process. An analysis and interpretation of statistical simulation results serves as the primary basis for much of the client's decision-making. However, the main tasks in evaluating the operational system for this particular study involve:

5.1.1. Line-balancing and collecting critical data

Line balancing is a major requirement of the ARENA investigation for the PCBA system throughout the simulation. The line-balancing activity attempts to arrange the individual processing and assembly tasks at the workstation so that the total-time that is required at each workstation is approximately the same. In most practical situations it is very difficult to achieve a perfect balance, so the slowest station generally determines the overall production rate of the line.

Figure 18 shows a performance snapshot of the optimised final assembly area during the course of the simulation. It shows the states of each workstation, their percentages of utilisation are 43.83, 47.79, 52.54, 47.74 and 43.73 respectively. These figures are quite close to each other indicating that the throughput at each workstation is in balance; moreover, the entire optimised final assembly area also satisfies the production requirements.

During the simulation, it is also observed that the system entered a steady state almost immediately after the simulation started, even though the time between arrivals is described by an exponential distribution. This can be explained by the fact that the loop conveyor serves as a buffer area that is good enough to absorb the variability that is caused by the exponential arrivals into the system. However, as seen in figure 18,

Table 3 Minimum processing times in seconds for PCB of type 1 and type 2

Station	Assembly area	Type 1	Type 2
WK1	Final	14	15
WK2	Final	25	28
WK3	Final	10	16
WK4	Final	23	13
WK5	Final	15	24
WK6	Sub-	12	23
WK7	Sub-	18	19
WK8	Sub-	21	16
M1	Loading/unloading	4	4
M2	Loading/unloading	4	4

workstation 1 has a higher percentage of 'blocking', this is thus identified as a bottleneck that would constrain the system performance.

Typically, manufacturing utilisation ranges between 40 and 60 percent, and automated manufacturing systems can have an average device utilisation between 85 and 95 percent [1].

Table 3 shows a summarised report of minimum processing times for completion of each process (in seconds) tallied for each type of PCB on each workstation. It is a valuable reference when it is compared with maximum message delay obtained from the COMNET simulation results, which will be shown and discussed in section 5.2.

5.1.2. Using animated simulation to investigate system performances

Some definitions:

- *Starving* of a machine or workstation—IDLE_RESource
  If a machine or workstation cannot continue to operate because it has no parts to work on, the state of a machine or workstation is defined to be starved or idle.
- *Blocking* of a machine or workstation—Blockage_ID
  This occurs when a machine or workstation has completed its processing cycle and cannot transmit its part to the downstream machine or buffer. The state of the proceeding or upstream machine or workstation is said to be blocked. In some circumstances, this is a dangerous situation during production.
- *Failed* machine or workstation—FAILED_RESource
  A resource is in the failed state when a failure is currently acting on the resource.
- *Busy* machine or workstation—BUSY_RESource
  A resource is in the busy state when it has one or more busy units.

Computer simulation, especially with animated graphics, can be very useful for assessing the performance of these complex production systems and for identifying their design flaws and operating problems. Simulation animation brings a simulation model to life by generating a moving picture of the model operation, therefore, production problems are easily visualised, it also helps systems designers determine the capacity of the flow line's storage buffer, etc.

For example, the ARENA animation system allows analysts to visually find any bottleneck at each machine on the computer screen and then allows them to make some modifications by re-setting system parameters in models until obtaining the best performance results. Figure 19 shows a set of PCBA animated pictures (snapshots) at different stages of operations of the final assembly area during the same period of simulation. For instance, it can be clearly observed on the ARENA screen that a workstation can only release the work if the next input buffer has a free space available. If not, the work must be held, this phenomenon is known as 'blocking'. One of the factors that cause this problem is the inadequacy of the input buffer at the station. Simulation animation can provide a visual overview of this kind of bottleneck, which occurs at each station. This helps system designers to modify the system's design, and hence its model, to gain improved performance.

Other primary benefits of simulation animation include:

1. Verifying and validating the model:
   A successful process of model verification of simulation programmes does not ensure that the model appropriately represents the real system; this only ensures that the model is free of errors.
   Animation is the most effective way to tackle most problems (i.e., errors in logic) of model verification. This decreases the likelihood of undetected errors. As discussed earlier, model validation is the process that determines that a model is a sufficiently adequate approximation of the real system. Animation allows us to communicate model operation to our clients who know the real system but have little knowledge about modelling.
2. Providing visual insights into dynamic interactions within the model:
   Such as material flows and work-in-process levels that are not easily obtained by examining statistical simulation outputs and presenting instant on-line simulation results in terms of figures or histograms.
3. Furthermore, the simulation animation can communicate modelling analysis and results to manufacturing managers and convinces them that the results are valid.

However, we normally cannot draw conclusions regarding system performance just from watching an animation of the system; therefore, using text-based simulation results is essential for evaluation of manufacturing systems [1, 5, 14, 16, 25, 28, 29, 30, 32, 35, 39, 47, 48, 50, 51, 52, 53].

5.2. Information system's aspects

Since the PCBA system is an integrated system, any problem with any device will affect the operation of the entire system. For example, a LAN designed with a high message delay time will certainly fail to deliver timely messages to networked devices and will certainly fail to inform the cell controller to stop the entire system when some fault has occurred. In all such production scenarios, it is crucial to ensure that the maximum message delay must be less than the shortest workstation (machine) processing time as shown in table 3. This guarantees each piece of equipment access to the network

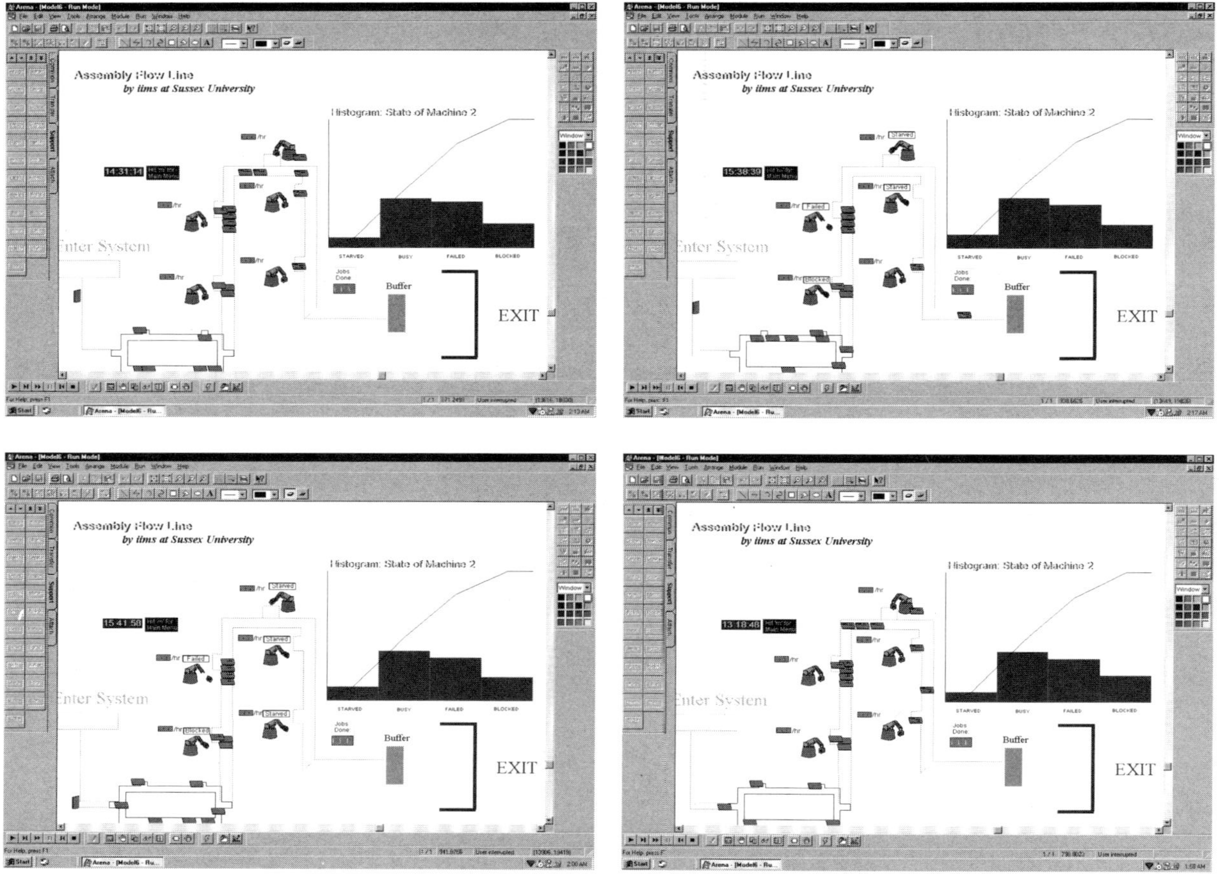

Figure 19. Animated simulation to detect bottlenecks of the PCBA system.

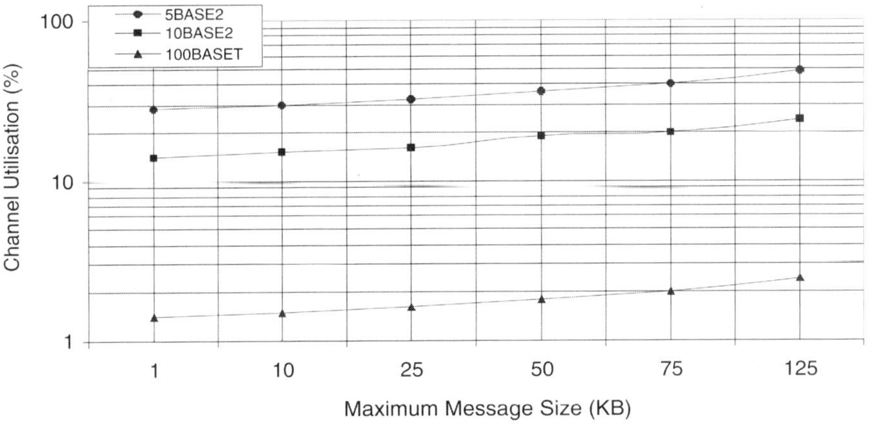

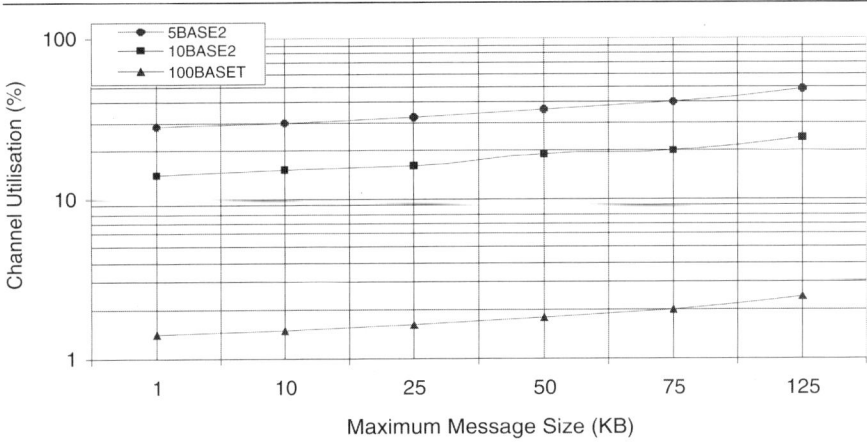

Figure 20. Channel utilisation vs maximum message sizes for three different transmission rates.

within its production cycle time without breakdown. Applying the integrated model, which examines both functions, has the capacity to provide answers at the early design stage to ensure that the maximum message delay does not cause production problems.

In this study, simulations have been executed repeatedly using the IEEE 802.3 CSMA/CD protocol, IEEE 802.4 and IEEE 802.5 token passing protocols by setting different parameters to compare the performance of the communication system. Various generated simulation outcomes including network capacity, message throughput, loss probability, message delay, and channel (or LAN) utilisation can be used to investigate the network performance, depending on the user's requirements. For this project, an investigation of critical factors which affect communication systems' performance and have an impact on the operational and information processing systems have been detected, extracted and displayed in graphical forms and are analysed and discussed below.

5.2.1. Channel utilisation (%)

The Channel (also called LAN or network) utilisation is one of the most significant factors affecting network performance. In this investigation, the channel utilisation is the total usage time divided by the simulation run length that expresses the period of production.

Figure 20 shows that the channel utilisation is affected by two factors that must be taken into account. One is the LAN transmission rate, which is provided by the communication protocol (CSMA/CD) with LAN transmission rates at 5 mbps, 10 mbps and 100 mbps. The other is the maximum message size sent between communicating devices. In this case study, the maximum message sizes were set in a range from 1 Kbytes to 125 Kbytes. This corresponds to a channel utilisation increase from 1.43% to 2.42% when using IEEE 802.3 CSMA/CD 100BASET, and from 14.19% to 23.92% when using IEEE 802.3 CSMA/CD 10BASE2 and from 28.39% to 48.34% when using

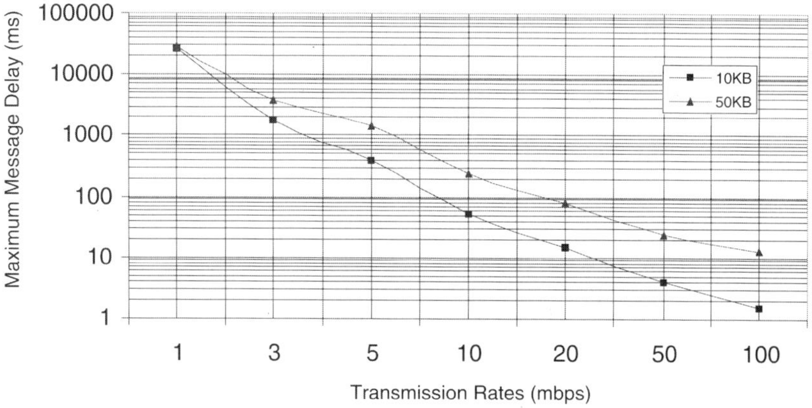

Figure 21. Maximum message delay vs transmission rate for two different maximum message sizes.

IEEE 802.3 CSMA/CD 5BASE2. According to practical experience and published reports, the communication-load (the amount of network traffic) on a LAN should typically be 5-10% of the maximum loading. Therefore, a LAN utilisation of more than 33% may be unacceptable for the control system of a manufacturing plant.

Often, there is a misunderstanding by system designers who think that the selection of high-speed processors to minimise data processing time must significantly reduce LAN traffic congestion. The research shows that there is no direct link between these factors. For a high load communication system, high-speed devices lead to a very busy LAN especially at peak times or at the moment when the whole system starts up. This reduces any advantage gained by using high-speed devices and can adversely affect the performance of the whole system.

In reality, network designers simply increase the capacity of the network until it delivers a reasonable performance for the manufacturing system. Nevertheless, it is always a commercial objective to build a network with a very good performance for a minimum cost. The approach presented herein can provide network designers with a useful system overview at the design stage. It can also help the designers obtain information on alternative solutions to meet capacity requirements and provide them with an estimate of network efficiency for the assumed conditions. This will reduce unnecessary investment in systems that have excessive capacity.

5.2.2. Maximum message delay (ms)

It can be seen from figure 21 that the maximum message delay increases rapidly as the LAN transmission rates decrease for both maximum message sizes (10 Kbytes and 50 Kbytes). It is observed that the maximum message delay is also affected by the maximum message sizes that are transmitted between the devices via the LAN.

It is interesting to see that, for both maximum message sizes, the maximum message delay is relatively small when the range of transmission rates is set to more than 10 mbps

Table 4 Collision-based protocols investigated for implementation of the PCBA network

Protocol standard: IEEE 802.3 CSMA/CD			LAN (%)		
			Maximum Message Sizes		
Protocol Standard	Data Rates (mpbs)	Access Method	10KB	50KB	125KB
1BASE5 STAR	1	collision	92.96†	93.71†	93.79††
3BASE2	3	collision	50.24	61.16	80.20
5BASE2	5	collision	30.03	36.31	48.28
10BASE2	10	collision	15.13	18.33	24.04
20BASE2	20	collision	7.57	9.11	12.04
50BASE2	50	collision	3.00	3.66	4.86
100BASET	100	collision	1.50	1.82	2.42
Gigabit	1000	collision	0.16	0.19	0.25

†Results in first 1200 seconds simulation time
††Results in first 600 seconds simulation time

and relatively large when the range of transmission rates is set to less than 3 mbps. It is also observed that when the transmission rate is set at 1 mbps, the LAN has a very high channel utilisation of 92.96% and 93.71% (see table 4) for both message sizes in the first 1200 seconds of simulation times, the simulation collapsed after 1200 seconds. This indicates that a LAN with transmission rates less than 1 mpbs is incapable of handling the required communication load for the PCBA communication system.

Furthermore, using the integrated simulation model of the PCBA system enables the designer to make a comparison between the maximum message delay obtained from COMNET simulation results and the minimum tallied machine processing time. Figure 21 shows that the maximum message delay is 1850 ms for a maximum message size of 10 KB, and 3776 ms (corresponding to the LAN at 3 mbps) for a maximum message size of 50 KB. By inspection of the minimum machine processing times shown in table 3, it can been seen that a LAN with a transmission rate that is more than 3 mbps for both maximum message sizes guarantees that the maximum message delay should be less than the shortest workstation processing time. This ensures all facilities access to the network in time, during the PCB assembly process.

The simulation results show that for both maximum message sizes, a LAN with a transmission rate at 5 mbps has a maximum message delay of 396 ms and 1499 ms, and has a maximum message delay of 51 ms and 233 ms when the transmission rate is 10 mbps, these are very small delays. Therefore, a LAN with a transmission rate ranging from 3 mbps to 10 mbps would certainly guarantee operation of the manufacturing communication system without failure.

5.2.3. Comparative dynamic performance of LANs for the PCBA system

In this study, simulations have been executed repeatedly using IEEE 802.3 CSMA/CD protocol, IEEE 802.4 and IEEE 802.5 token passing protocols by setting different parameters to compare the performance of the communication system based on the user's requirements. Various simulation outcomes include message throughput, loss

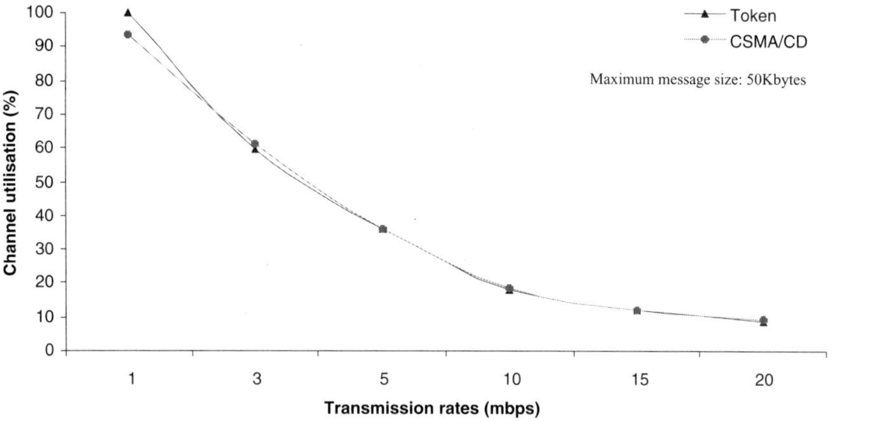

Figure 22. Channel utilisation vs transmission rates for token passing and CSMA/CD LANs.

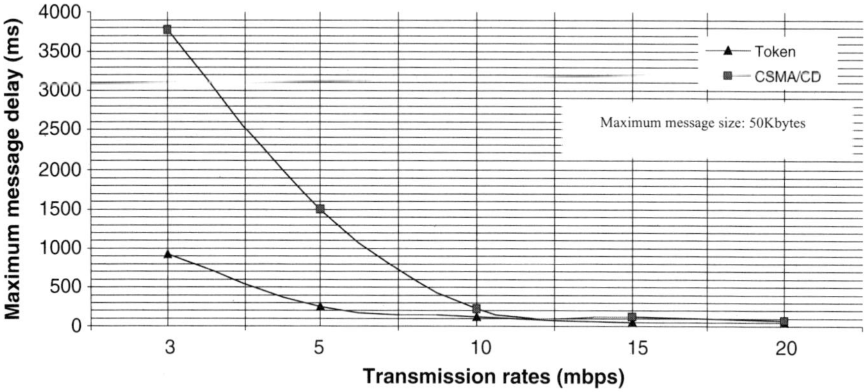

Figure 23. Maximum message delay vs transmission rates for token passing and CSMA/CD LANs.

probability, message delay, and channel utilisation, etc. The factors, which significantly affect the system's performance, are displayed and analysed in graphical form below.

5.2.3.1. CHANNEL UTILISATION (%) AND MAXIMUM MESSAGE DELAY (MS) VS TRANSMISSION RATES (MBPS). Figure 22 and figure 23 indicate the variations of channel utilisation and maximum message delay against transmission rates for both token passing bus and CSMA/CD LANs.

The results are obtained by setting a maximum message size of 50 Kbytes across the network. It indicates that the channel utilisation and the maximum message delay increase rapidly as the transmission rate decreases from the point of 10 mbps. This is a particular problem for the case of the maximum message delay of the CSMA/CD

LAN. Hence, the effect of transmission rates must be taken into account for both LAN protocols.

It is interesting to observe that, for both LAN protocols, the values of their channel utilisation, which corresponds to the same transmission rate between 2 mbps and 20 mbps, are approximately the same. In contrast, for both LAN protocols, the values of their maximum message delay, which corresponds to the same transmission rate (less than 10 mbps), are significantly different. For the example shown in figure 23, at the transmission rate of 3 mbps, which corresponds to a channel utilisation of nearly 60% for the token bus LAN and a channel utilisation of 61% for the CSMA/CD LAN, the maximum message delay is 927 ms and 3776 ms respectively. This indicates that at the same network load, especially for a heavily loaded network, the performance of token bus LAN is much better than CSMA/CD LAN. For a network load of less than 18% (i.e., the transmission rate is more than 10 mbps) there is no significant difference in performance for either type of network. From figure 23, it can be seen that at the transmission rate of more than 10 mbps, the corresponding maximum message delays for the two LANs are very close and relatively small. However, for a transmission rate less than 10 mbps (i.e., a network load of over 18%), there is a big difference in maximum message delay between the two different LAN protocols.

For transmission rates lower than 2 mbps, the difference in maximum message delay between the two LANs increases sharply. When the transmission rate is 1 mbps, the channel utilisation of token bus reaches 100% in 2675 seconds of simulation time; whereas the channel utilisation of CSMA/CD LAN reached 93.71% in about 1200 seconds of simulation time (the simulation collapsed after 2675 and 1200 seconds respectively). The corresponding maximum message delays for both LANs are very different: 1081 seconds and 663 seconds respectively. They are much higher than the shortest machine processing times shown in table 3. This indicates that for both LAN protocols a minimum transmission rate of 2 mbps is essential to successfully operate the PCBA communication system. A cross comparison also shows that at high load the performance of token bus LAN is better than CSMA/CD LAN. This is further illustrated by figure 24.

Figure 24 is a combination of figures 22 and 23, it illustrates the relationship between network load and maximum message delay. It can be seen that at a channel utilisation of over 16 % the maximum message delay starts to increase sharply for the CSMA/CD LAN compared to the token bus LAN. This also confirms the previous studies that under certain circumstances (for instance, at higher network load with a lower network transmission rate) that token passing can be more efficient than CSMA/CD for the PCBA system LAN.

5.2.3.2. CHANNEL UTILISATION (%) AND MAXIMUM MESSAGE DELAY (MS) VS MAXIMUM MESSAGE SIZES (Kb). The maximum message size is an important factor, which affects the performance of the networks. For both LAN protocols, it can be seen from figure 25 that the channel utilisation increases rapidly as the maximum message size increases from 1 Kbyte to 125 Kbytes. Figure 26 shows a comparison of a non-linear variation of maximum message delays against the maximum message size for both LANs. It is

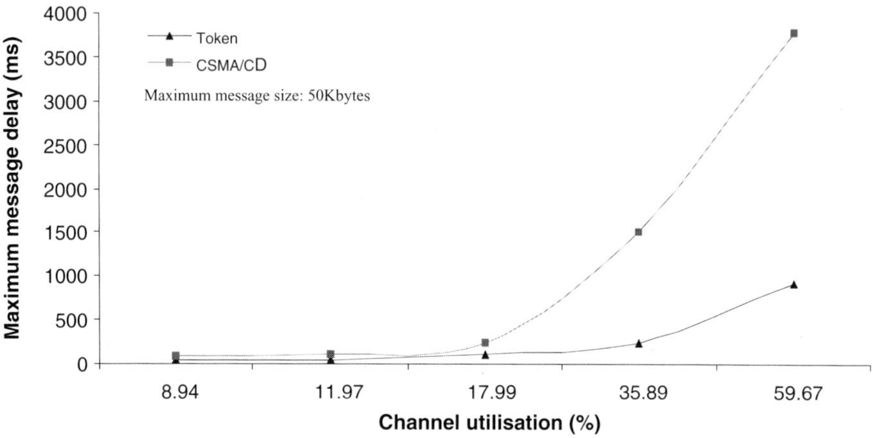

Figure 24. Maximum message delay vs channel utilisation for token passing and CSMA/CD LANs.

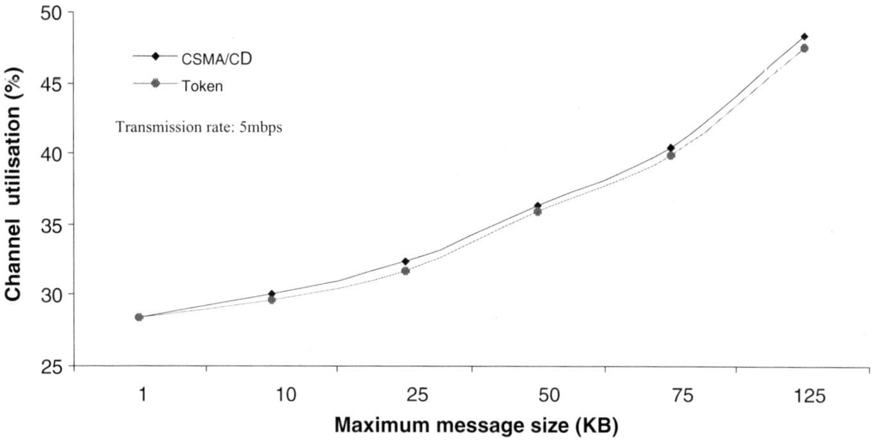

Figure 25. Channel utilisation vs maximum message sizes for token passing and CSMA/CD LANs.

observed that the maximum message delay is greatly affected by the maximum message size that is transmitted between network devices, the affect is significantly different for the different LAN protocols'.

As shown in figures 25 and 26, although the same higher maximum message size results in a higher message delay for the different LAN protocols, the magnitude of the gap between corresponding maximum message delays for different protocols is significantly widened when increasing the maximum message size in the network. For instance, for a maximum message size of 50 Kbytes, the maximum message delay for the token bus LAN is 241 ms with a channel utilisation of 35.89%, compared

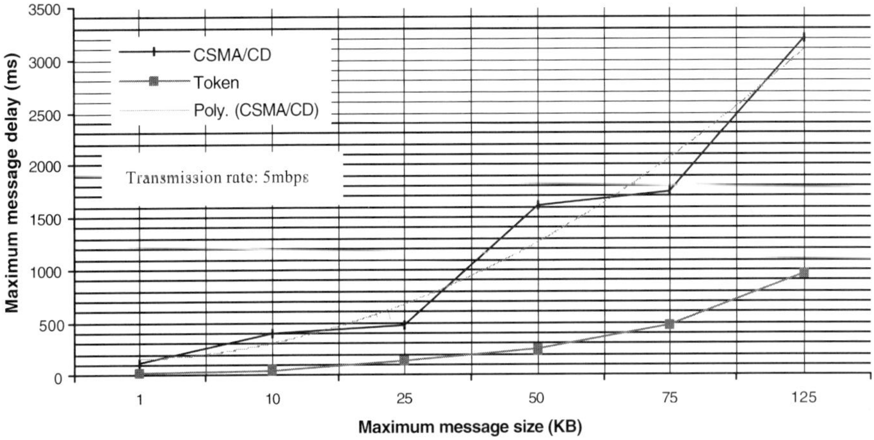

Figure 26. Maximum message delay vs maximum message sizes for token passing and CSMA/CD.

to a maximum message delay of 1616 ms for the CSMA/CD LAN with a channel utilisation of 36.36%. This is further evidence that at the same network load, the token bus LAN has superior performance to the CSMA/CD LAN for the PCBA communication system. This benefit becomes significant when the LAN is heavily loaded.

Furthermore, applying the integrated simulation model of the PCBA system enables designers to make a comparison between the maximum message delay obtained from the COMNET simulation results and minimum tallied machine processing time. From figures 22 and 23 and based on COMNET text-based simulation reports, it shows that at the same maximum message size of 50 Kbytes, the maximum message delay is 4748 ms (89.28% busy) and 927 ms (59.67% busy) for the token bus LAN at 2 mbps (not shown in figure 23) and 3 mbps respectively; and 42701 ms (91.04% busy) and 3776 ms (61.16% busy) for the CSMA/CD LAN at 2 mbps (not shown in figure 23) and 3 mbps respectively. By inspection of the minimum machine processing times shown in table 3, it can be seen that a LAN with a transmission rate of over 3 mbps for both the token bus LAN and CSMA/CD LAN will guarantee that maximum message delay will be less than the shortest workstation (machine) processing time. This ensures all facilities have sufficient time to access to the network during the PCB assembly process.

Moreover, an analysis based on the simulation results concludes that a CSMA/CD LAN with a transmission rate between 5 mbps and 10 mbps has a maximum message delay from 1499 ms to 233 ms, corresponding to a channel utilisation of 36% and 18% respectively, these delays are relatively small, hence performance is reasonable. For a token bus LAN, a transmission rate between 3 mbps and 5 mbps is fast enough to undertake communication duties, and a transmission rate of more than 10 mbps leads to a very small maximum message delay for both LANs. Within this range, the simulation results show no data lost during the transmission across the network. Therefore, it was

Table 5 Token passing-based protocols investigated for implementation of the PCBA network

Protocol standard: IEEE 802.4 and IEEE 802.5
Maximum message size (50 KB)

		Token ring		Token bus	
Data rates (mpbs)	Access method	LAN (%)	Max. del. (ms)	LAN (%)	Max. del. (ms)
1	token	100.00†	—	100.00††	—
3	token	59.57	724.66	5a9.67	927.36
5	token	35.99	293.12	35.89	240.47
10	token	17.97	110.39	17.99	112.12
15	token	11.89	61.12	11.97	51.53
20	token	8.98	44.41	8.94	39.77†

†Results in first 2675 seconds simulation time
††Results in first 2160 seconds simulation time

finally suggested that the PCBA CSMA/CD LAN or the PCBA token passing bus LAN with any transmission rate ranging from 5 mbps to 10 mbps would certainly guarantee the operation without failure of the PCBA manufacturing communication system (this is for a maximum message size of 50 Kbytes in the PCBA network).

Since the operation of token bus and token ring is similar [45], the simulation result for token ring LAN shown in table 5 is extremely close to the result for token bus, hence, the discussion relating to token bus also applies to token ring, though the token ring is not physically suitable for the PCBA communication system.

6. DISCUSSION AND CONCLUSION

As outlined and discussed in section 1, for increasingly highly automated computer-controlled manufacturing systems, successful integration of manufacturing devices and automated equipment using existing communication protocols and networks is crucial to achieve the desired, cost effective, co-ordinated functionality required for CIM systems. As a result, the performance of communication networks has become a key factor for successful implementation of integrated manufacturing systems, particularly, for time-critical applications. Hence, the design and evaluation of manufacturing systems can no longer ignore the performance of the communication environment or conduct a separate investigation without considering the performance of the operational system.

Section 5 presented an assessment of the operational system's aspect for the PCBA system to ensure that the system has no fatal bottlenecks and weaknesses in system operations. It addressed four issues presented in sections 5.2.1 and 5.2.2 respectively, which discussed the impact on logical interactions and interrelationships between operations and information processing systems within the PCBA environment and determined the relative performance merits of the three IEEE 802 standard networks in which the token bus LAN performs best when implemented for the PCBA communication system. The outcome also shows that token bus is better suited to process control applications (since they are time-critical applications) than the CSMA/CD protocol network, which is well suited to standard computer network applications, where the network loading rarely exceeds 8–17%.

A comprehensive review of the current literature reveals the lack of a feasible and practical modelling and simulation method or means that has the ability to investigate manufacturing systems by taking both aspects into account. In fact, there is no single conceptual modelling method or tool available, which can completely model a manufacturing system and easily describe most of its sub-systems due to the high level of complexity of manufacturing systems. It is generally accepted that traditional planning methods and mathematical/analytical modelling techniques are not appropriate to deal with complex manufacturing systems. Nevertheless, manufacturing system's analysts, designers and their clients have an increasingly important requirement for a 'full' system evaluation (particularly for investigation of a highly integrated time-critical manufacturing systems), which will model the basic manufacturing operations and combine the effect of the communication systems.

Therefore, the aim of the research reported herein was to focus on:

The development of an integrated method, in which both the operations and information systems within a manufacturing system could be examined concurrently using the currently developed simulation tools and techniques so that the relevant impact on logical interactions and interrelationships between them could be determined. Moreover, this technique should be implemented based on a real system to test the feasibility of this approach becoming a strategic planning tool for systems analysts and designers to quickly provide a visible preview of the integrated system performance at an early stage in the design process.

The major work of this treatise is to present a methodology that has been developed to examine a manufacturing system by the modelling and simulation of its integrated operational systems and information systems. This approach has been implemented on a relatively complex flexible manufacturing system: a printed circuit board assembly (i.e., PCBA) line; in order to determine its feasibility and capability. The key features of this technique has been demonstrated by analysing and comparing various simulation results (in terms of graphs and tables) that were generated by the established integrated model of the PCBA system using the two powerful simulation-packages that were specially selected for use in this integrated domain.

The research has shown that applying this integrated method allows system designers and analysts to comprehensively predict system behaviour in order to obtain an optimal solution that maximises systems performance. The integrated model can allow users to see the impact on logical interactions and interrelationships between operations and information processing systems within a manufacturing environment so that they can make design judgements that satisfy systems' and production requirements. From this, an optimal system specification can be drawn up.

The research has shown that this approach contributes a useful basis for developing existing modelling frameworks and a practical means of exploring existing modelling simulation methodologies. The research indicates that in principle, this technique is valuable for analysing a wide range of manufacturing systems (CIM systems, FMSs, process control systems, etc.).

Finally, the concept of economic performance control came into being during the 1970s petroleum crisis when industrial circles realised that process control systems that excluded economic variables were not guaranteed to benefit enterprise economic planning. To avoid this difficulty, economic variables must be selected as the ultimate control variables of the control system, and specific costs and market information must be taken as the input that disturbs the control system. However, some of the economic variables are not measurable on-line; therefore, model prediction may be used to generate data for them, but model reliability and system stability are difficult problems. It is wise at present to develop process economic performance display (rather than control) software for industry. This will yield manufacturing profitability with lower economic risk. For example, the economic variable to be displayed for a chemical plant may be instantaneous profit IP:

$$IP = SP - PC$$

where, SP is selling price; PC is production costs, and most components of PC are measurable on-line.

It is widely accepted that in general the economic performance of an enterprise is a function of 8 Ms:

1. Man (Personnel and manpower)
2. Machine (Equipment)
3. Material (including energy)
4. Money (floating capital)
5. Market
6. Method
7. Moment (time)
8. Message (information).

Obviously, the objective of the enterprise is to maximise profit. Therefore, a good system model should optimise response to the above variable. A first step to take is to make available not only technical data, but also instantaneous information on the economic performance of the enterprise concerned, without which decision making is often misguided.

P.S. This work may match the following subject areas:

- New computer technology for enhanced factory modelling and visualisation
- Integration of design with manufacturing planning
- Process modelling in an integrated design and manufacturing environment
- Optimisation techniques for factory design
- Advances in discrete event simulation
- Enterprise resource planning

Keywords:

Manufacturing systems, computer networks, modelling and simulation, integration, FMS, CIM.

REFERENCES

[1] Groover M. P., 2000. *Automation, production systems, and computer integrated manufacturing* (Prentice-Hall, Inc.).

[2] Wong W. M. R., 1993. *Modelling and simulation of the communication protocols used in typical CIM equipment.* Bradford University.

[3] Mansharamani R., 1997. *An overview of discrete event simulation methodologies and implementation.* Sadhana, Vol.22, Part 5, 611–627.

[4] McCarthy I., Frizelle G., Efstathiou J., 1998. *Manufacturing complexity network meeting, University of Oxford.* EPSRC engineering and physical science research council.

[5] Chou Y. C., 1999. *Configuration design of complex integrated manufacturing systems. International Journal of Advanced Manufacturing Technology*, 15:907–913.

[6] AL-Ahmari A. M. A., Ridway K., 1999. *An integrated modelling method to support manufacturing system analysis and design.* Computers in Industry, 38 (1999), 225–238.

[7] O'Kane J. F., Spenceckley J. R., Taylor R., 2000. *Simulation as an essential tool for advanced manufacturing technology problems.* Journal of Materials Processing Technology, 107 (2000), 412–424.

[8] Kim C. H., Weston R., 2001. *Development of an integrated methodology for enterprise engineering.* International Journal of Computer Integrated Manufacturing, 14 (5), 473–488.

[9] Balduzzi F., Giua A., Seatzu C., 2001. *Modelling and simulation of manufacturing systems with first-order hybrid Petri nets.* International Journal of Production Research, 39 (2), 255–282.

[10] Cunha P. F., Dionisio J., 2002. *An architecture to support the manufacturing system design and planning.* Proceedings of the 1st CIRP(UK) Seminar on Digital Enterprise Technology, Durham, UK, 129–134.

[11] Bernard A., Perry N., 2002. *Fundamental concepts of product/technology/process informational integration for process modelling and process planning.* Proceedings of the 1st CIRP(UK) Seminar on Digital Enterprise Technology, Durham, UK, 237–240.

[12] Cantamessa M., Fichera S., 2002. *Process and production planning in manufacturing enterprise networks.* Proceedings of the 1st CIRP(UK) Seminar on Digital Enterprise Technology, Durham, UK, 187–190.

[13] Higginbottom G. N., 1998. *Performance evaluation of communication networks* (Norwood: Artech House, Inc.).

[14] Mitchell F. H., 1991. *CIM systems* (Prientice-hall Ltd.).

[15] Colquhoun G., Baines R., Crossley R., 1993. *A state of the art review of IDEF0.* International Journal of Computer Integrated Manufacturing, 6 (1993), 252–264.

[16] Doumeingts G., Vallespir B., 1995. *Methodologies for designing CIM system: a survey.* Computers in Industry, 25 (1995), 263–280.

[17] AL-Ahmari A. M. A., Ridway K., 1997. *Computerised methodologies for modelling computer integrated manufacturing systems.* Proceedings of 32nd International MATADOR conference, Manchester, 111–116.

[18] Chryssolouris G., Anifantis N., Karagianis S., 1998. *An approach to the dynamic modelling of manufacturing systems.* International Journal of Production Research, 38 (90), 475–483.

[19] Baines T. S., Harrison D. K., 1999. *An opportunity for system dynamics in manufacturing system modelling.* Production Planning & Control, 10 (6), 542–552.

[20] Perera T., Liyanage K., 2000. *Methodology for rapid identification and collection of input data in the simulation of manufacturing systems.* Simulation Practice and Theory, 646–656.

[21] Borenstein D., 2000. *Implementation of an object-oriented tool for the simulation of manufacturing systems and its application to study the effects of flexibility.* International Journal of Production Research, 38 (9) 2125–2142.

[22] Wang Q., Chatwin C. R. et al., 2002. *Modelling and simulation of integrated operations and information systems in manufacturing* ('A' rating awarded), The International Journal of Advanced Manufacturing Technology, Vol. 19, pp. 142–150.

[23] Wang Q., Chatwin C. R. et al. *Comparative dynamic performance of token passing and CSMA/CD LANs for a flexible manufacturing system*, The International Journal of Computer Integrated Manufacturing, in press.

[24] Wang Q., Geha A., Chatwin C. R. et al., 2002. *Computer enhanced network design for time-critical integrated manufacturing plants*, 1st CIRP (UK) International Seminar on 'Digital Enterprise Technology' (DET02), Proceedings of the 1st CIRP(UK) Seminar on Digital Enterprise Technology, Durham, UK, pp. 251–254.

[25] Angelo A. D., Gastaldi M., Levialdi N., 1996. *Dynamic analysis of the performance of a flexible manufacturing systems: a real case application.* Computer Integrated Manufacturing Systems, 9 (2), 101–110.
[26] Fokkert JI. V. Z. D., 1998. *Process flow design for repetitive assembly.* The BETA Research Institute.
[27] Grunow M., 2000. *Simulation-based performance analysis and optimisation of electronics assembly equipment.* International Journal of Production Research, 38 (17) 4247–4259.
[28] Peden C. D., Shannon R. P., Sadowski R. P., 1995. *Introduction to simulation using SIMAN,* System Modelling Corporation (McGraw-Hill, Inc.).
[29] Chan F. T. S., 1992. *Feasibility of modular simulation models for FMSs.* Computer-Integrated Manufacturing Systems, 5 (4), 253–255.
[30] System Modelling Corporation 1998. *ARENA user guides (1994–1998).*
[31] Brooks Roger J., Tobias A. M., 2000. *Simplification in simulation of manufacturing systems.* International Journal of Production Research, 38 (5), 1009–1027.
[32] Kelton W. D., Sadowski R. P., Sadowski D. A., 2001. *Simulation with Arena* (McGraw Hill College Div.).
[33] Ostle B., Turner K. V., Hicks C. R., McElrath G. W., 1996. *Engineering statistics: the industrial experience* (Wadsworth Publishing company).
[34] Arsham H., 2002. *Systems simulation: the shortest path from leaning to applications.* Teching handout. EOF@1995-2002, University of Baltimore, USA.
[35] Chan F. T. S., Jiang B., Tang N. K. H., 2000. *The development of intelligent decision support tools to aid the design of flexible manufacturing systems.* International Journal of Production Economics, 65 (2000), 73–84.
[36] Lee Y. T., 2001. *An overview of information modelling for manufacturing systems integration.* Manufacturing Systems Integration Division and National Institute of Standards and Technology.
[37] Baines T. S., Harrison D. K., 1999. *An opportunity for system dynamics in manufacturing system modelling.* Production Planning & Control, 10 (6) 542–552.
[38] Chou Y. C., 1999. *Configuration design of complex integrated manufacturing systems.* International Journal of Advanced Manufacturing Technology, 15:907–913.
[39] Spathopoulos M. P., Ridder M. de, 1999. *Modelling and distributive control design of a flexible manufacturing system.* Computers in Industry, 38 (1999), 115–130.
[40] Tobaben F., 1997. *WITNESS modelling, simulation, and statistical analysis of an assembly line for Rolls-Royce Motor Cars Ltd.* Project Report, Technical University of Braunschweig.
[41] CACI Products Company, 1998. *COMNET III® reference guide, Release 2.0.*
[42] Pimentel J. R., 1990. *Communication networks for manufacturing* (Prentice-Hall, Inc.).
[43] Ikbal M., Rondeau E., Divoux T., 2001. *Industrial systems communications: design and integration.* International Journal of Computer Integrated Manufacturing, 14 (6), 545–559.
[44] Ikbal M., Rondeau E., Divoux T., 2001. *Industrial systems communications: design and integration.* International Journal of Computer Integrated Manufacturing, 14 (6), 545–559.
[45] Stallings W., 1999. *Data and computer communications* (Prentice-Hall, Inc.).
[46] Carrie A., 1988. *Simulation of manufacturing systems* (John Wiley & Sons Ltd).
[47] Mcginnis L. F., Ammons J. C., et al., 1992. *Automated process planning for printed circuit card assembly.* IIE transactions 24 (4), 19–31.
[48] Little D., Hemmings A., 1994. *Automated assembly scheduling: a review.* Computer Integrated Manufacturing Systems, 7 (1), 51–56.
[49] Choi S. H., Lee S. L., et al., 2000. *The design architecture and implementation of an integrated manufacturing system.* International Journal of Computer Integrated Manufacturing, 10 (1997), 232–244.
[50] G. A. J. van der Vorst Jack, 2000. *Modelling and simulation multi-echelon food systems.* European Journal of Operational Research, 122 (2000), 354–366.
[51] Chryssolouris G., Anifantis N., Karagianis S., 1998. *An approach to the dynamic modelling of manufacturing systems.* International Journal of Production Research, 38 (90), 475–483.
[52] Rao H. A., 1997. *Design methodology and integrated approach for design of manufacturing systems.* Integrated Manufacturing Systems, 8/3 (1997), MCB University Press (ISSN0957-6061) 159–172.
[53] Guest Editorial 2001. *Modelling, specification and analysis of manufacturing systems.* International Journal of Production Research, 39 (2), 159–162.

TECHNIQUES AND ANALYSES OF SEQUENTIAL AND CONCURRENT PRODUCT DEVELOPMENT PROCESSES

MARKO STARBEK, JANEZ GRUM, ALEŠ BREZOVAR, AND JANEZ KUŠAR

1. INTRODUCTION

A company can enter the global market only if it can fulfil the customer needs regarding features and quality of products. Customers are becoming more and more demanding and their requirements are changing all the time. "Customer is the king!" is becoming the motto of today.

In these circumstances only that company can survive on the global market, which can offer its customers the right products in terms of features and quality, products which are produced at the right time and place, at the right quality and at the right price. A product, which is not manufactured in accordance with needs and requirements of the customers, which hits the market too late or is too expensive, will not survive.

When developing a new product the company has to pay special attention to fulfilment of the basic market requirement, i.e. as short new product development time as possible (as short delivery time as possible).

Fierce market competition increases pressure on the companies so that they would hit the market with new products sooner than their competitors. This goal can only be achieved by reduction of product development time, while quality and cost of the product should be taken into account at the same time, which is possible if the concurrent engineering concept is used. The basic idea of the concurrent engineering is concurrent execution of formally sequential activities during new product development process. By executing activities concurrently it is possible to harmonise decisions during the draft phase, which prevents time and engineering changes during manufacturing of

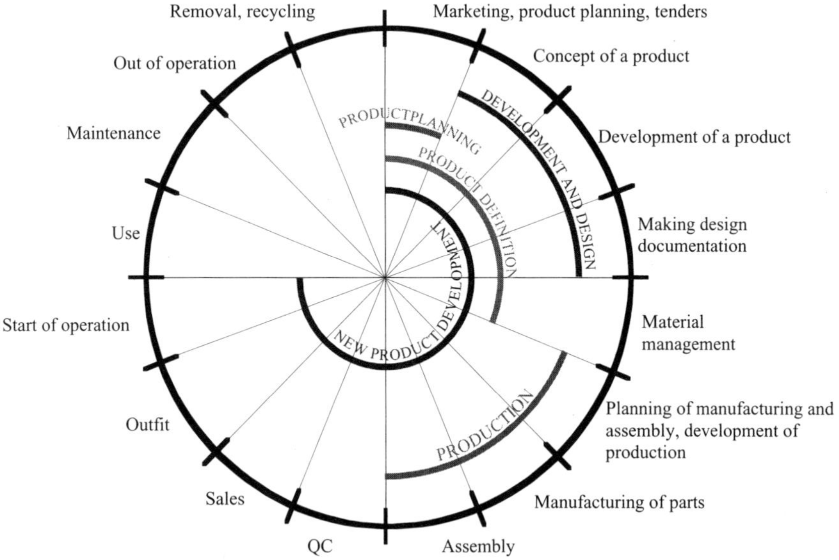

Figure 1. Product development process as a part of the product life cycle.

the product. The motto for successful implementation of the concurrent engineering concept says: "Concurrent engineering starts in the heads of team members."

Several authors [1], [2], [3] have analysed activities in individual stages of new product development processes, and concluded that the volume and contents of product development activities depend on quantity and purpose of the product. There is a substantial difference between new product development activities in individual and mass production [4].

The chapter presents techniques and analyses of sequential and concurrent product development processes, the emphasis being on team work, organisational structures and tools needed for transition from sequential to concurrent product development process. The chapter also presents the results of implementation of concurrent engineering in an SME which produces civil engineering equipment.

2. SEQUENTIAL ENGINEERING

2.1. Sequential product development process

The main feature of sequential engineering is sequential execution of stages in product development process. Figure 1 presents the sequential product development process as a part of the product life cycle.

The next process stage can begin after its preceding stage has been completed. Data on current process stage are collected gradually and they are completed when the stage is finished—then the data are forwarded to the next stage as shown in Figure 2 [1].

Sequential product development time can be calculated as a sum of times needed for individual stages of product development.

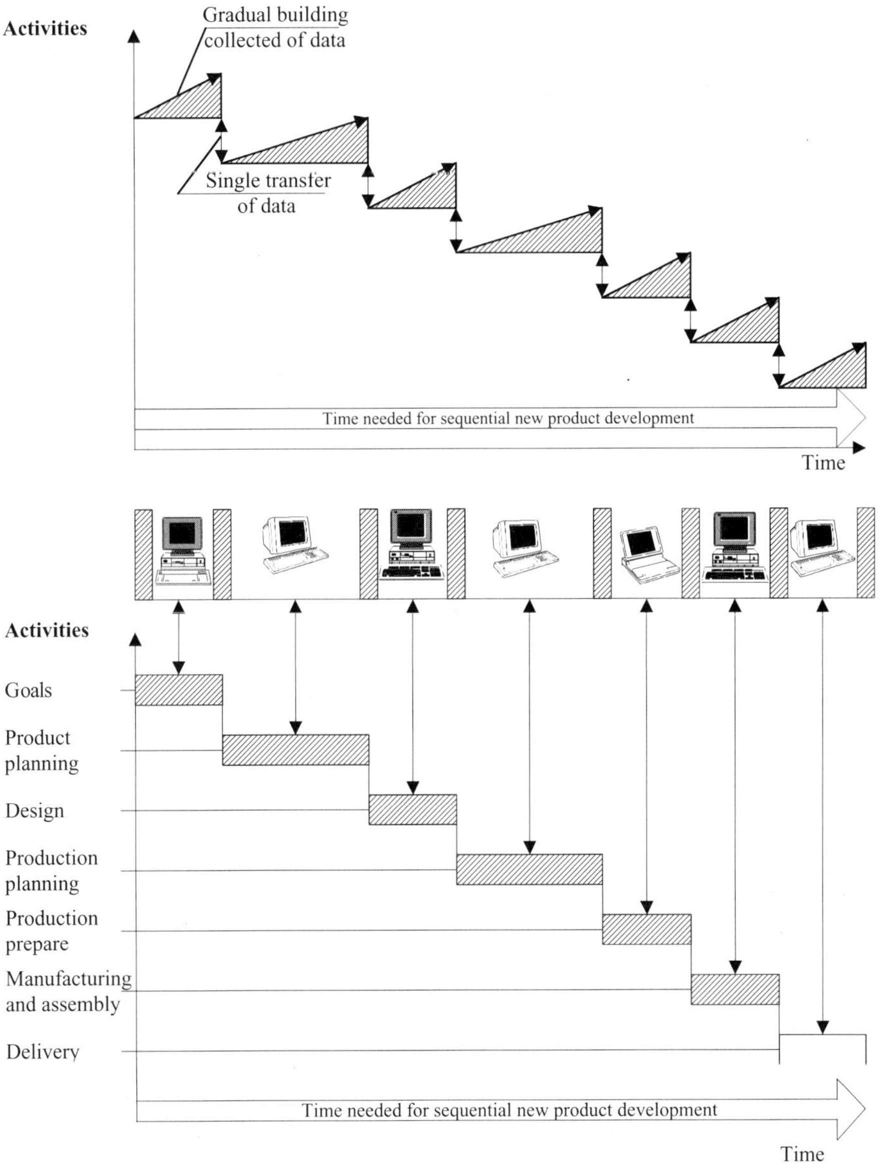

Figure 2. Sequential product development.

2.2. Characteristics of sequential engineering

Three typical types of problems exist in sequential product development:

- *organisational problems* (problems in collaboration, unmotivated employees, requirements and goals are not clearly defined, weak connection between suppliers and customers),
- *problems in product development process* (problems related to explanation of requirements, problems during searching for solutions, problems related to meeting the deadlines),
- *technical and economic problems with products* (problems related to operation of the products, manufacturing problems, environmental protection problems, cost-related problems).

3. CONCURRENT ENGINEERING

3.1. Concurrent product development process

The main feature of concurrent engineering is concurrent implementation of stages in product development process. In this case the next stage can begin before its preceding stage has been completed.

Winner defined concurrent engineering as a "systematic approach to the integrated concurrent product planning and similar processes, including manufacturing and sales" [4].

Ashley defined concurrent engineering [5] as a "systematic approach to integrated product development that emphasizes the response to customer expectations. It embodies team values of cooperation, trust, and sharing in such manner that decision making proceeds with large intervals of parallel working by all life-cycle perspectives early in the process, synchronized by comparatively brief exchanges to produce consensus".

Concurrent engineering is based on eight principles:

First principle: EARLY DETECTION OF PROBLEMS
Problems that are detected early in the product development process can be solved more easily than problems that are detected later.

Second principle: EARLY DECISION MAKING
In early design stages it is much easier to influence the product design than in later stages.

Third principle: SHARING WORK
One man cannot perform several tasks at once, while parallel-connected computers can.

Fourth principle: CONNECTION OF TEAMS
Connection and collaboration within a team is not enough—it is important that there is a connection and collaboration among all teams that strive after a common goal: a customer who is satisfied with the product.

Fifth principle: USING KNOWLEDGE
A knowledgeable and experienced person is still an indispensable decision-making factor.

Sixth principle: GENERAL UNDERSTANDING
Teams work better if they know and understand what other teams do. If one team changes particular parameter then it has to think about how this change will affect other teams.

Seventh principle: OWNERSHIP
Teams will work more enthusiastically if they have some authorisation for making decisions, and if they get some kind of "ownership" of what they have made.

Eighth principle: CONTINUOUS FOCUS ON THE COMMON GOAL
Everybody has to (as much as one can) participate in the fulfilment of the given goal of the company; everybody has to enthusiastically (and yet not competitively) collaborate with other individuals and teams.

3.1.1. Data transfer between activities in concurrent product development process

In concurrent product development the next process stage can begin before its preceding stage has been completed.

Data on the current process stage are collected gradually and forwarded continuously to the next stage. The series of data exchange between the current process stage and the next process stage ends when the data on the current stage has been completed.

Figure 3 presents the principle of concurrent product development process [1].

3.1.2. Loops of concurrent product development process

In concurrent product development there are interactions between individual stages of product development process. Track-and-loop technology was developed for implementation of these interactions [1]. Type of loop defines the type of co-operation between overlapping process stages.

Figure 4 presents types of loops in concurrent engineering with respect to number of interactions between various process stages. 1-T loop means interaction of the process stage with itself, 2-T loop means interaction between two process stages, and 3-T loop means interaction between three process stages. As a general rule, the number of interactions between L process stages is equal to $L \times (L-1)/2$.

Winner [4] proposed the use of 3-T loops, where interactions exist between three stages of product development process.

When 3-T loops are used (Figure 5) the product development process consists of five 3-T loops.

In 3-T loops each loop is defined as an intersection of three mutually covered stages; this can be written as:

Feasibility loop = *Goals* ∩ *Product planning* ∩ *Design*
Design loop = *Product planning* ∩ *Design* ∩ *Production planning*
Production planning loop = *Design* ∩ *Production planning* ∩ *Production*
Production loop = *Production planning* ∩ *Production* ∩ *Manufacturing and assembly*
Manufacturing loop = *Production* ∩ *Manufacturing and assembly* ∩ *Delivery and service*

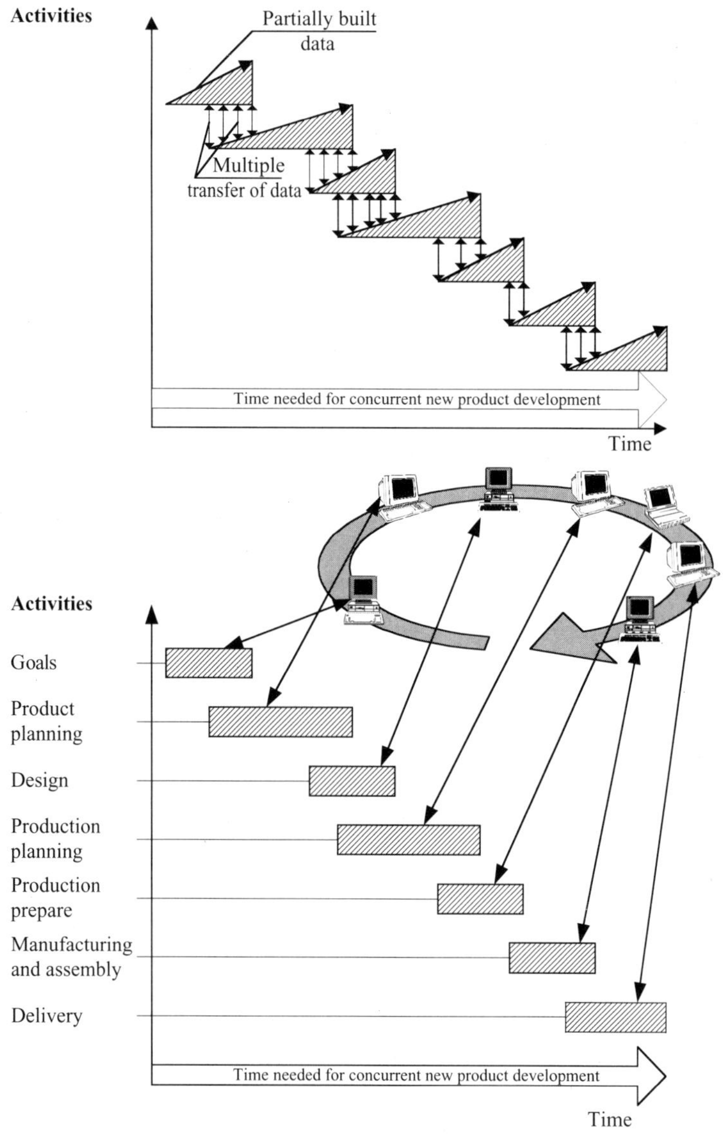

Figure 3. Concurrent product development.

On the basis of the following requirements and restrictions:

- customer requirements,
- geometrical characteristics,
- weight,
- reliability,

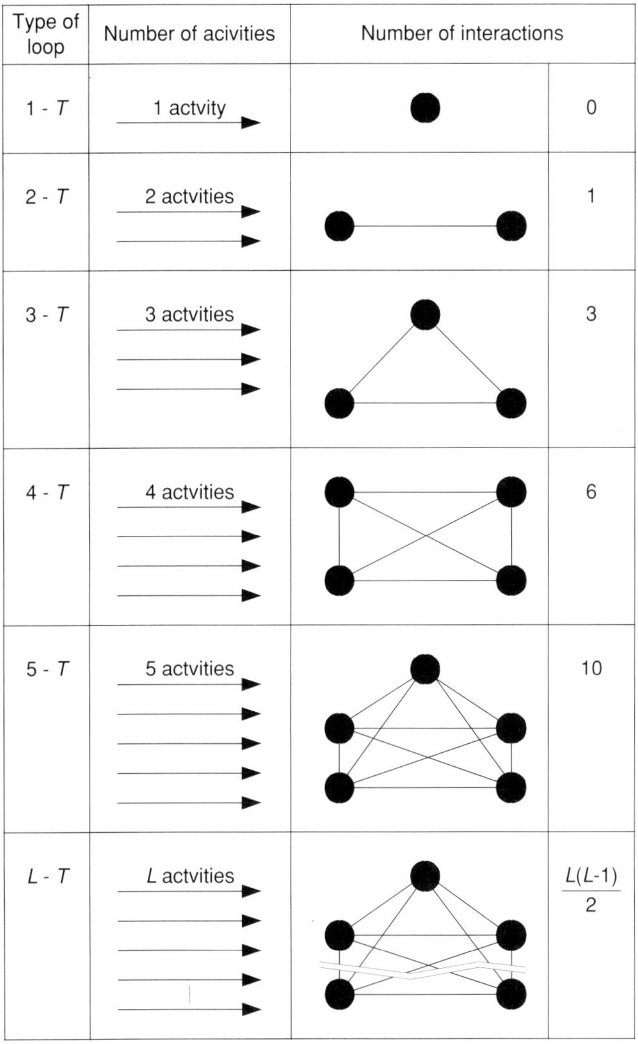
Type of loop
Number of acivities
Number of interactions
1 - T
1 actvity
0
2 - T
2 actvities
1
3 - T
3 actvities
3
4 - T
4 actvities
6
5 - T
5 actvities
10
L - T
L actvities
L(L-1)/2

Figure 4. Number of interaction between product development process stages.

- safety,
- quantity,
- lifetime,
- recycle,
- ecology

input is transformed into output [2] in each loop.

Each transformation loop is carried out in steps, as shown in Figure 6.

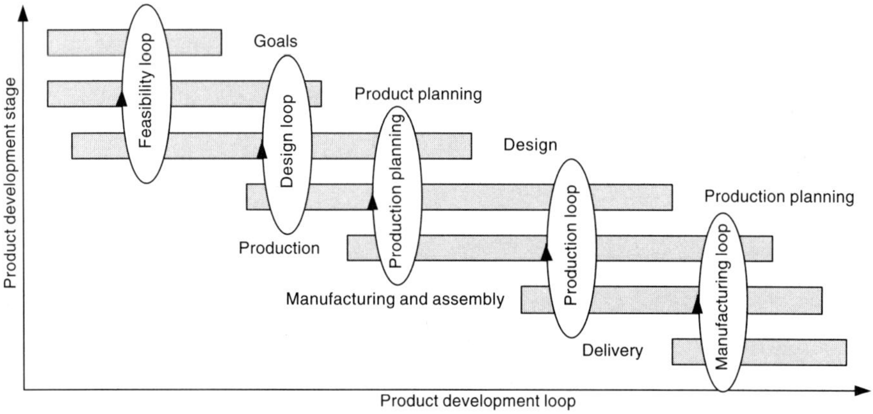

Figure 5. Track and loop process in product development.

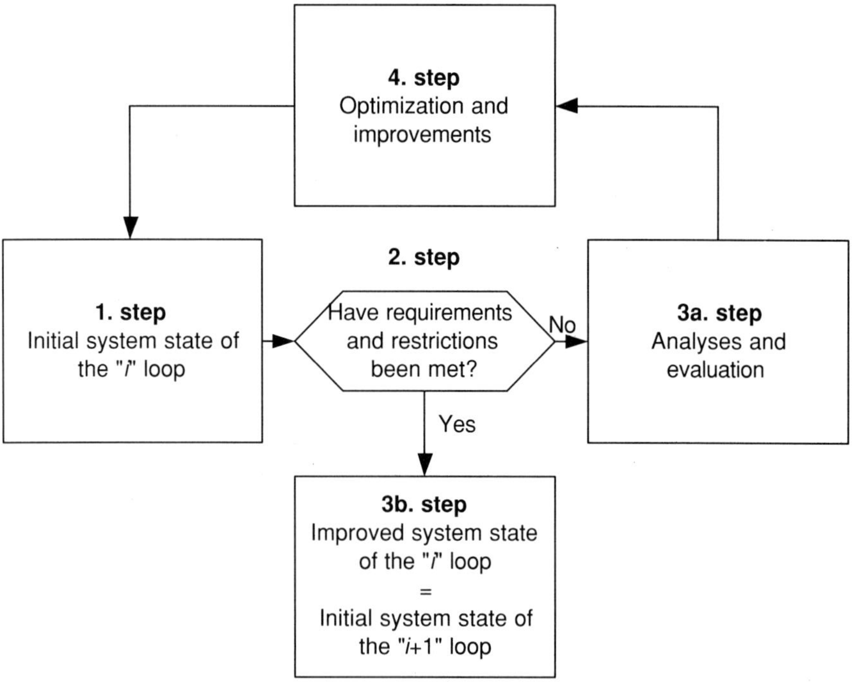

Figure 6. Transformation process in the concurrent engineering loop.

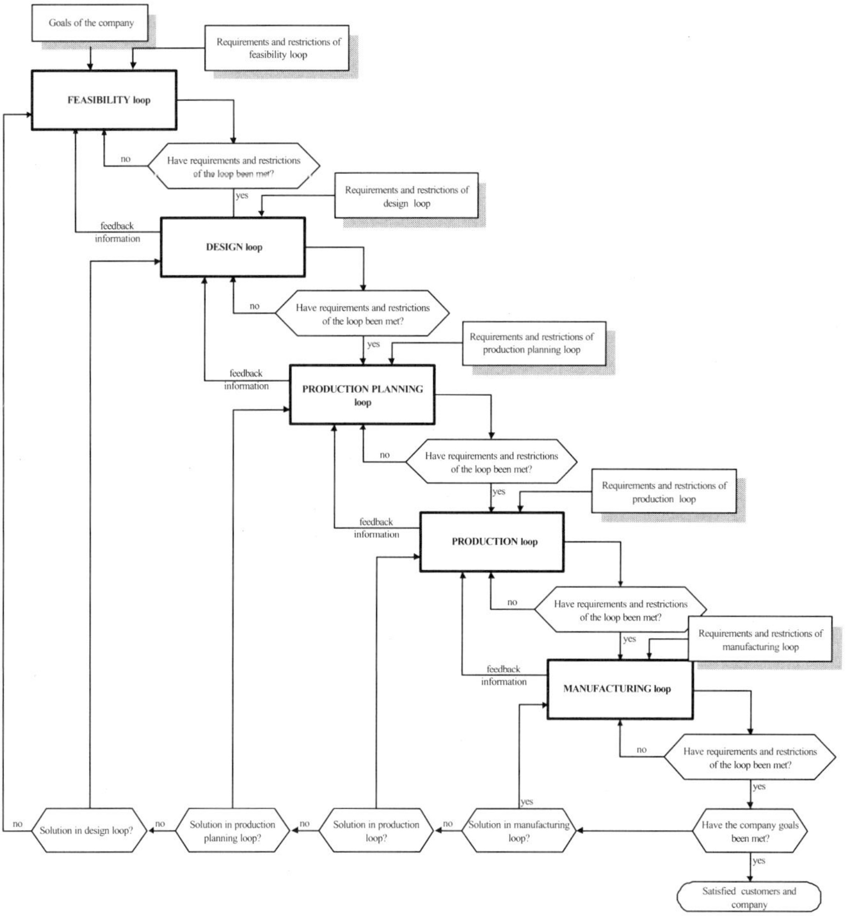

Figure 7. Information flow diagram in the track-and-loop process of product development.

The information flow diagram in the track-and-loop process of product development is shown in Figure 7.

Analysis of the track-and-loop process of product development, as shown in Figures 5 and 7, reveals that the concurrent engineering is not possible without a well-organised team work.

3.1.3. Team work

3.1.3.1. TEAM STRUCTURE IN CONCURRENT PRODUCT DEVELOPMENT PROCESS. We are dealing with team work when a team is oriented towards the solution of a common goal [6]. Team work is an integral part of concurrent engineering as it represents the means for organisational integration.

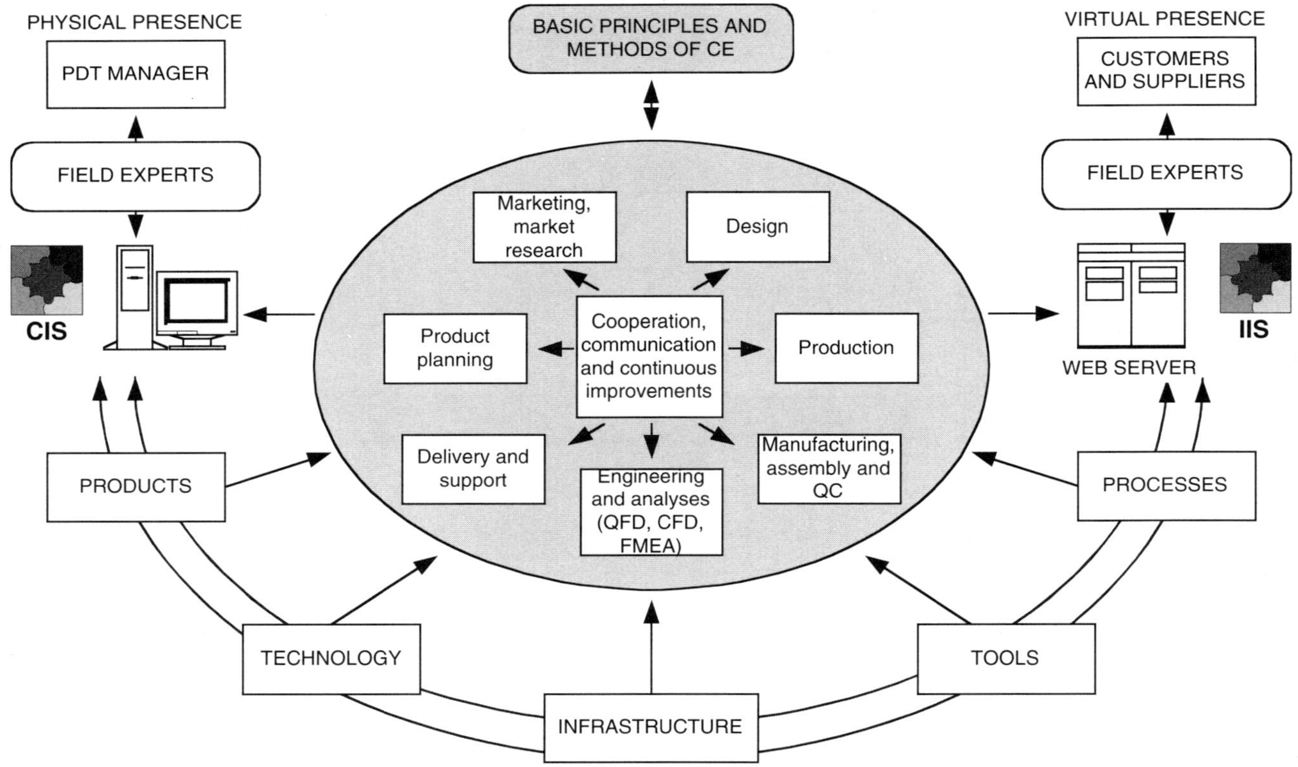

Figure 8. Structure of a multidisciplinary product development team.

Requirements for team work are [1]:

- flexible, unplanned and continuous collaboration,
- commitment regarding achievement of goals,
- communication by exchange of information,
- ability to make compromises,
- consensus in spite of disagreement,
- coordination when carrying out interdependent activities,
- continuous improvements in order to increase productivity and reduce process times.

3.1.3.2. TEAMS IN BIG COMPANY. Concurrent engineering is based on multidisciplinary product development team (PDT) [7], [8]. PDT members are experts from various departments of a company and representatives of strategic suppliers and customers (Figure 8).

Product development team members communicate via central information system (CIS) which provides them with data about processes, tools, infrastructure, technology, and the existing products of the company. Representatives of strategic suppliers and customers—due to their distance from the company—participate in the team just virtually, using the Internet information system (IIS) which allows them to use the same tools and technologies as the team members in the company [8].

In big companies the PDT structure changes in different phases of product development. The team consists of various workgroups in various phases of product development, and each workgroup consists of four basic teams [1]:

- Logical team ensures that the whole product development process is divided into logical units (operations, tasks) and defines interfaces and links between individual process units.
- Personnel team has to find the required personnel for PDT, it trains and motivates the personnel, and provides for proper payment.
- Technology team is responsible for creating strategy and concept. It has to concentrate on quality of products at minimum costs.
- Virtual team operates in a form of computer software and provides other PDT members with data required.

Figure 9 presents the composition of a workgroup in a big company.

The goal of the concurrent engineering is to achieve the best possible collaboration among the four basic teams in a particular workgroup.

The multidisciplinary teams should generally have such a structure that the following goals are achieved:

- clear definition of competence and responsibility,
- short decision paths,
- identification of team members with the product being developed.

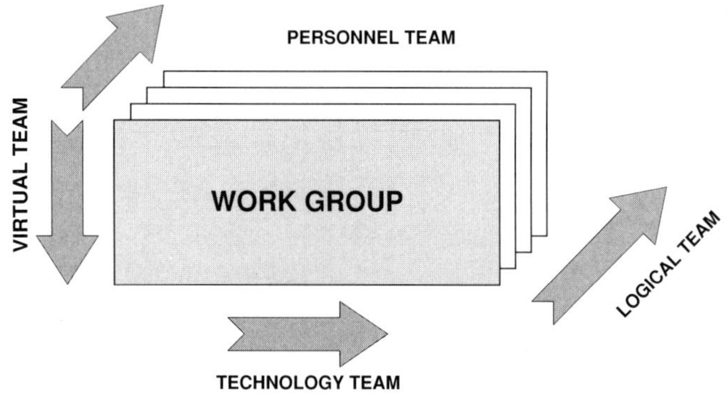

Figure 9. Workgroup in a big company.

A survey of the published works in the field of team structure planning in big companies [1], [9] has revealed that a three-level PDT structure is recommended in big companies, as shown in Figure 10.

Core team consists of the company management and the manager of the level team; its task is to support and control the product development project.

Level team consists of the level team manager and the managers of the participating functional teams in this level (loop); its task is to co-ordinate the goals and tasks of functional teams and to ensure a smooth transition to the next level of product development.

Functional team consists of the functional team manager, experts from various fields in the company and representatives of suppliers and customers; its task is to carry out the tasks given, taking into consideration terms, finance and personnel.

3.1.3.3. TEAM STRUCTURE IN SMEs. Analysis of results regarding setup of workgroups and team structure in big companies has shown that the proposed concept for planning workgroups and structure of teams cannot be used in SMEs as there are too many teams in a workgroup and too many team levels.

When developing a workgroup concept, structure and organisation in SMEs it will therefore be necessary to propose:

- as few workgroup teams as possible,
- as few team levels as possible, and
- appropriate organisation of the company.

Experts of the *Production Systems Institute* made several versions of workgroup composition and team structure, and decided—after evaluation of the proposed versions—that the following seems advisable for SMEs:

- transition from four workgroup teams (personnel, logical, technology, and virtual team) to two teams (logical and technology team);
- transition from the three-level to two-level team structure.

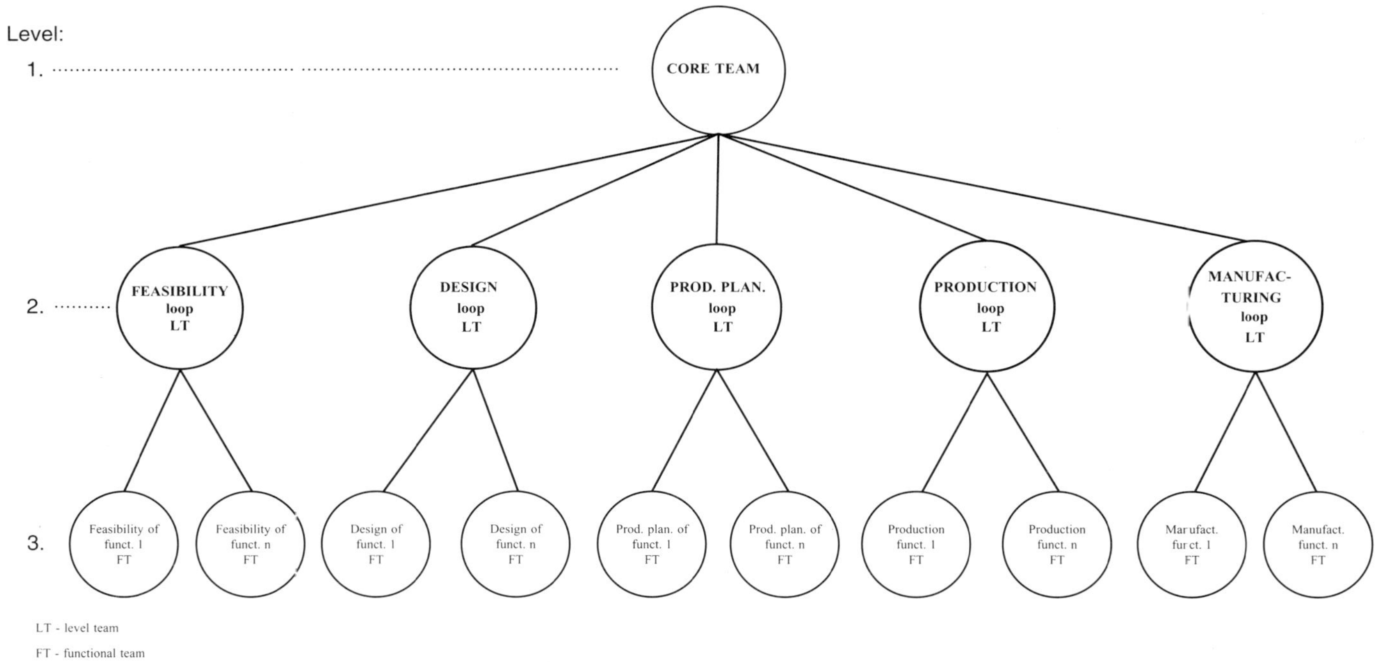

Figure 10. Three-level team structure in a big company.

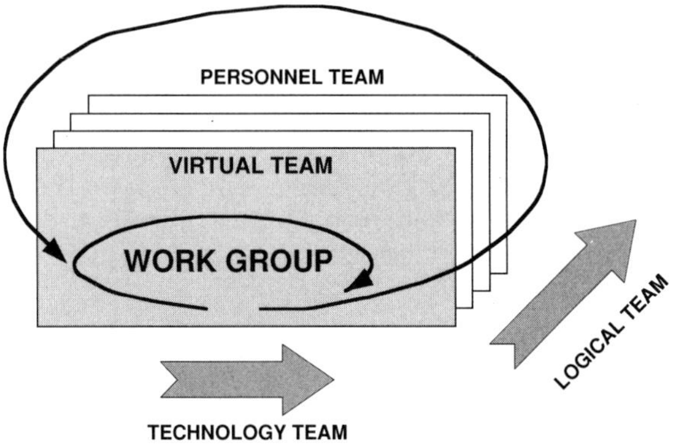

Figure 11. Workgroup in an SME.

In an SME a workgroup therefore consists of just two basic teams (Figure 11):

- logical team ensures that the whole product development process is divided into logical units and that interfaces and links between process units are defined;
- technology team is responsible for providing strategy and concept.

With proper software tools the CIS performs the role of a virtual team (workgroup members should be well trained to use these tools), and project team manager carries out the tasks of the personnel team.

For SME, the transition from a three-level to two-level team structure is planned, as shown in Figure 12.

Core team [10] which supports and controls the product development project consists of:

- core team manager (permanent member),
- department managers (permanent members), and
- project team manager (permanent member).

Project team [10] which carries out the tasks given, taking into consideration terms, finance and personnel consists of:

- project team manager (permanent member),
- experts from various fields in the company and representatives of strategic suppliers and customers (variable members).

The project team in SME is therefore designed similarly as a functional team in a big company, the difference being in that there is just one team and its composition changes in different phases (loops) of product development process.

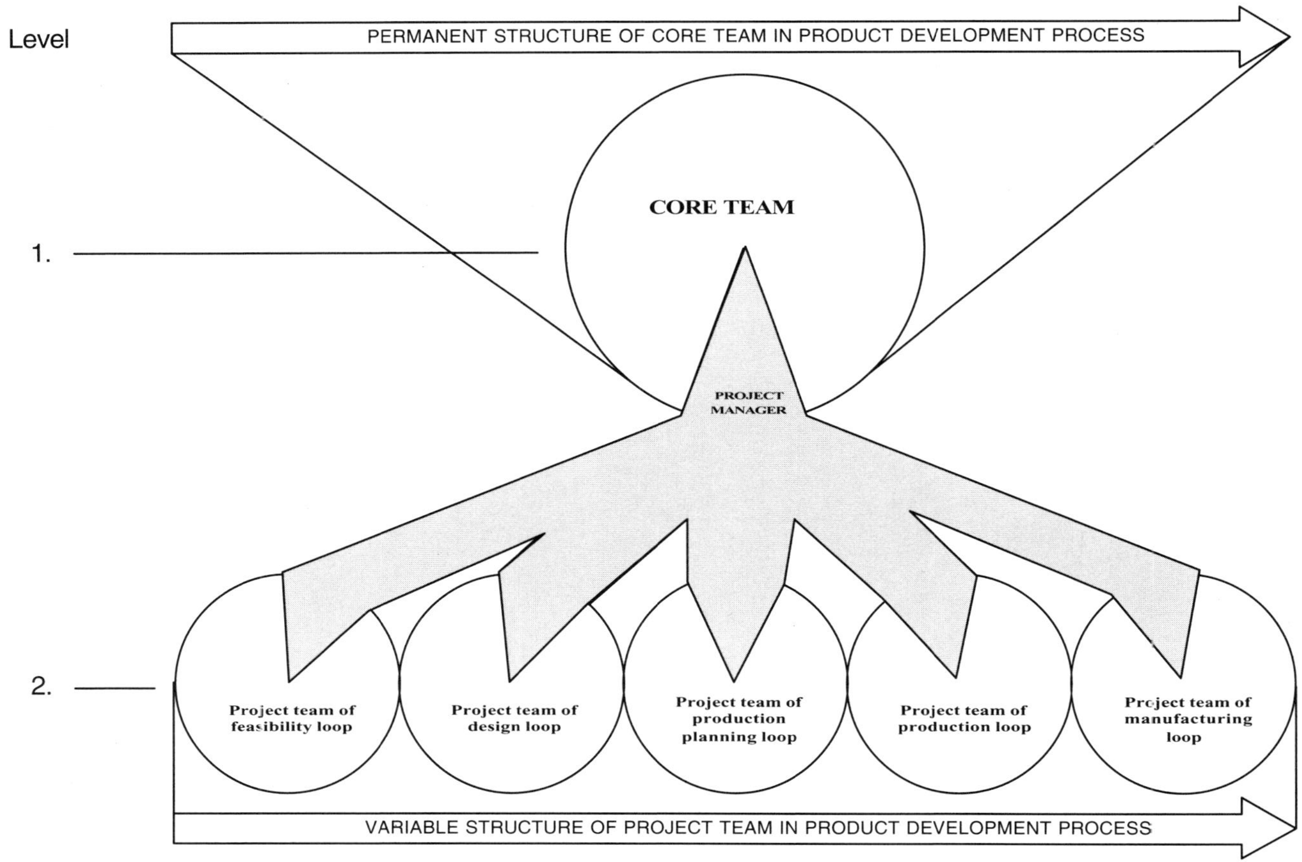

Figure 12. Two-level team structure in SME.

In the feasibility loop the project team should define customer requirements and goals, and make several versions of the product design; the project team should consist of the employees from the marketing, product planning, and design departments, and representatives of strategic customers and suppliers.

In the design loop the project team should provide general solutions regarding the product, product planning and design, its parts and components, development of prototypes, and choice of the most suitable versions from the manufacturing point of view; the project team should consist of the employees from the product planning, design and production planning departments.

In the production planning loop the project team should select the best technology routings for manufacturing of parts and assembling the components (definition of sequence, operations, selection of machines, tools and standard times); the project team should consist of the employees from the design, production planning, and production departments, and strategic suppliers' representatives.

In the production loop the project team should define production type (workshop, cell or product-oriented type of production) and select the optimal layout of production means; the project team should consist of the employees from the production planning department, production, manufacturing and assembly, as well as logistics and delivery.

In the manufacturing loop the project team should take care of prototype tests, supply of required equipment, layout of production means, manufacturing and test of the null series; the project team should consist of the employees from the production department, manufacturing and assembly, quality assurance, warehouse and delivery departments.

3.2. Organisational structures

3.2.1. Functional organisational structure

Functional organisational structure is a centralised organisational structure. It is based on the requirement that the interdependent partial tasks related to a work piece and operations are done in one place (workshop functional type). Therefore, in this organisational structure the areas, sectors, services, departments and workshops are formed, which perform the required special tasks.

So the subordinate employee can have several functional managers besides his line manager. Employee is responsible to his functional managers just for the corresponding functions, while he is responsible to his line manager in the organisational sense. All functional managers on the same hierarchical level have therefore the same subordinate employees.

Operation of a functional structure is complicated so it is necessary to precisely define the responsibilities of the functional managers. An example of organisational scheme in a functional organisational structure is shown in Figure 13.

Advantages of a functional organisational structure:

- division of hierarchical management level on the basis of (business) functions
- specialisation and concentration of knowledge in one place,

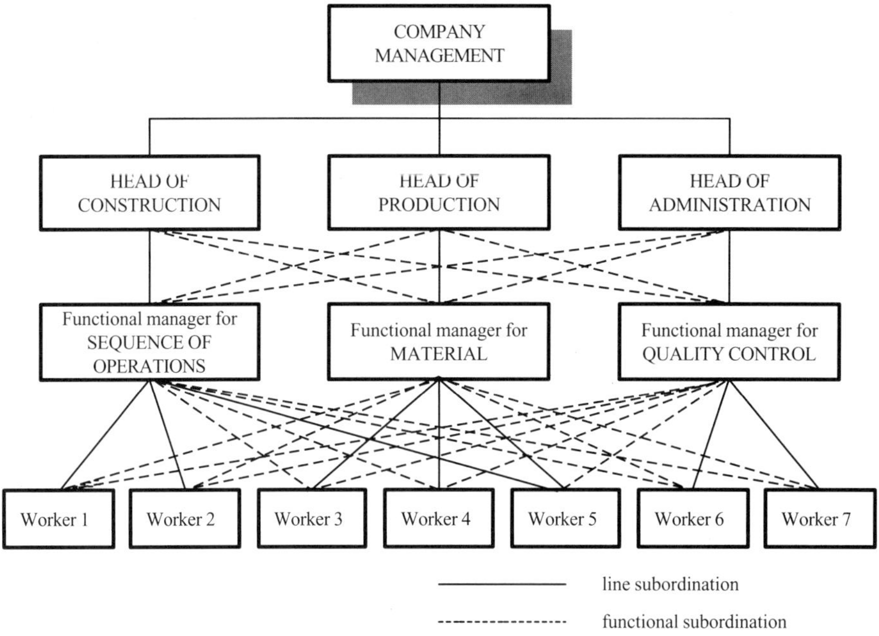

Figure 13. Organisational scheme of a functional organisational structure.

- centralised decision making by means of linear type of management,
- priority is given to expertise,
- it is useful for SMEs with stable production programmes,
- it allows for quick adaptation to changes,
- intensive development of individual functions (concentration of knowledge) and personnel,
- individual function performs specialist operations for the whole company,
- there is less bureaucracy.

Disadvantages of a functional organisational structure:

- coordination between areas is unconnected and unclear,
- there are difficulties in precise definition of working duties and responsibilities of the functional managers,
- communication structure is complicated,
- a lot of coordination is needed when a task should be done which covers several fields,
- working discipline is worse than in linear type of organisation,
- when employees move to a higher hierarchical level, difficulties arise because tasks are not divided on a functional basis any more.

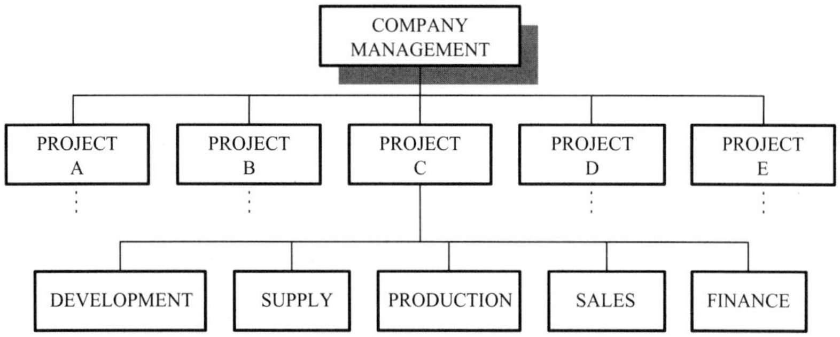

Figure 14. Organisational scheme of a project organisational structure.

In spite of disadvantages the functional organisational structure is still a prevailing form of organisation in companies.

3.2.2. Project organisational structure

Projects are activities that are done just once, and they consist of a series of logically interconnected activities. In order to be accomplished they require time and resources which cause costs.

Project organisational structure is used if the company runs many large projects which are not interconnected. It is formed so that the projects can be finished in the expected time frame, with costs defined in advance, and in accordance with the requirements of the client.

For every project the company forms a fixed organisation, but just for a limited period—the project team (a company within a company), which is completely responsible for execution of the project. Project team starts its mission at the beginning of the project and finishes it when the project is finished. After the completion of the project the team members are employed at other projects or in other departments of the company. An example of organisational scheme in a project organisational structure is shown in Figure 14.

Project organisation is used if one of the following criteria is met:

- the project is large and high funds are involved,
- some of the project parameters are critical, e.g. time for completion of the project, availability of resources, or costs,
- it is the customer's requirement.

Advantages of a project organisational structure:

- planned, harmonised and controlled organisation throughout of the project duration,
- project team is entirely responsible for completion of the project goals and fulfilment of project activities,

- all project-related data are collected and evaluated in a central location,
- ensured are central responsibilities of partners, contractors and employees,
- high level of development flexibility, using internal or external human resources,
- growth, training and education of future project managers,
- high motivation of employees as they participate in exactly defined and interesting tasks.

Disadvantages of a project organisational structure:

- contradictions between project-oriented view and functional dealing with organisational problems,
- disappointment of project managers due to unrealistic goals of the project,
- unsteadiness of team members due to automatic cease of their roles in a project team after a successful completion of the project,
- project managers tend to establish too large project teams, which increases overhead expenses of the project,
- integral project information system should be established, as a part of the information system of the entire company.

3.2.3. Matrix organisational structure

Matrix organisational structure is a combination of functional and project (or product) organisational structures.

In matrix organisational structure a permanent project organisation is not established, only the project team manager is defined who is responsible for the project or for the realisation of the programme (product).

Project team members, selected for accomplishment of the project-related tasks remain in their functional departments (in the organisational sense). Authorisation for work is given to them by their department head, and project-related tasks are given to them by the project manager. The project (product) manager is therefore just a coordinator for the execution of tasks which are (based on his orders) carried out in functional departments. Project team member has two managers: department head (in view of organisational and technical level) and project manager (in view of project tasks).

Matrix organisational structure got its name because of its characteristic shape. An example of simplified organisational scheme in a project matrix organisational structure is shown in Figure 15, and product matrix organisational structure is shown in Figure 16.

Matrix organisational structure is used when there are several concurrent recurring projects being executed, which require common sources of functional departments of the company (multi projects).

Advantages of a matrix organisational structure:

- it is based on a team problem solving,
- clear coordination of tasks,
- project teams temporarily join people from various functional grounds,

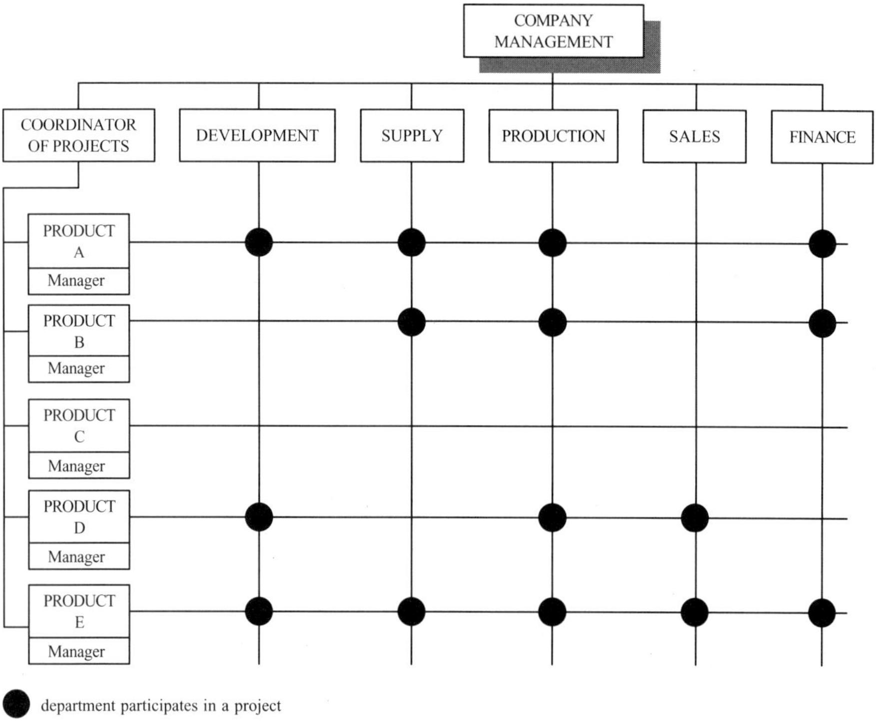

Figure 15. Organisational scheme of a project matrix organisational structure.

- project team structure may change during development of the project (concurrent engineering),
- interdisciplinary links are established in the company so it is very flexible,
- conflicts are solved in teams,
- knowledge is concentrated in functional departments,
- priority is given to expertise.

Disadvantages of a matrix organisational structure:

- it is efficient only if team work is used,
- dual system of management and responsibility (project manager and functional manager),
- large communication needs,
- frequent conflicts and compromises.

3.2.4. Organisational structure of team work in SME

The tasks which are performed by level teams in big companies should be done by the project team manager in SME and he should co-ordinate and tune the goals and

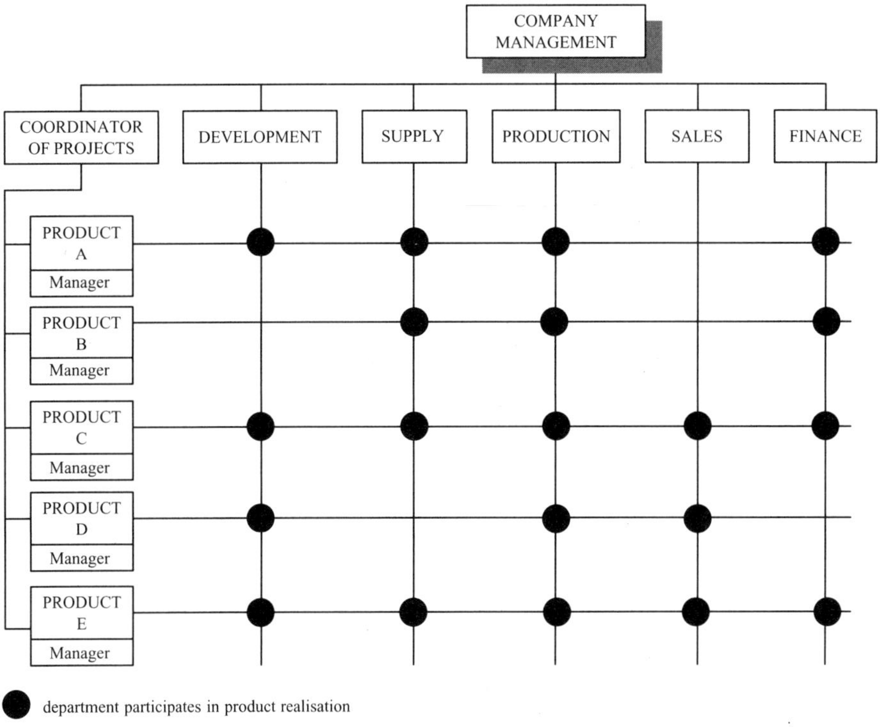

Figure 16. Organisational scheme of a product matrix organisational structure.

activities between the project team and core team, and provide for a smooth transition from one phase (loop) of product development process to another.

In big companies the members of the core, level and functional teams usually use project type of organisation. This type of organisation cannot be used in SMEs as they have too few employees.

Analysis of various organisational structures of companies and teams [11], [12] has shown that in SMEs matrix organisation would be the most suitable for core and project team members (Figure 17).

A member of the core team (with exception of the project team manager) would carry out tasks in his/her department part of his working time (for this work (s)he would be responsible to the general manager of the company), and the rest of his/her working time (s)he would work in the product development project (for this work (s)he would be responsible to the core team manager). A member of the project team (except the project team manager) would carry out the tasks in his/her department part of his/her working time (for this work (s)he would be responsible to department head), and the rest of his/her working time (s)he would work in the product development project (for this work (s)he would be responsible to the project team manager).

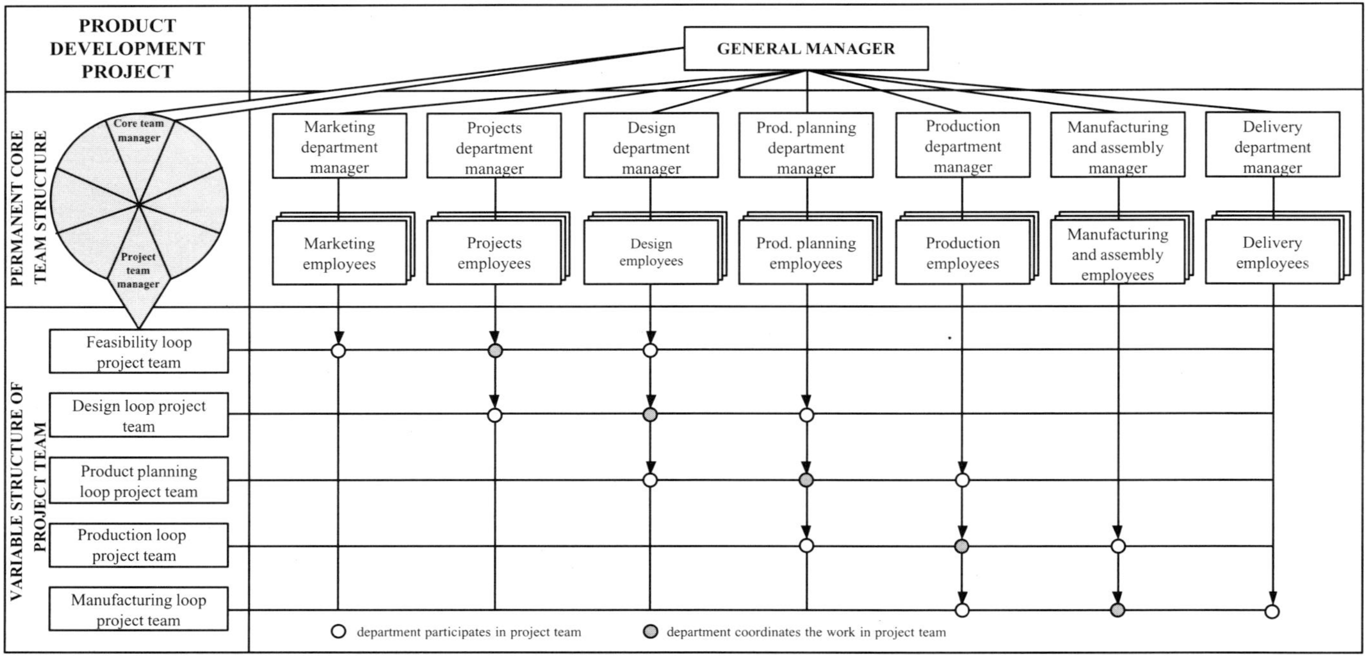
PRODUCT DEVELOPMENT PROJECT
GENERAL MANAGER
PERMANENT CORE TEAM STRUCTURE
Core team manager
Project team manager
Marketing department manager
Projects department manager
Design department manager
Prod. planning department manager
Production department manager
Manufacturing and assembly manager
Delivery department manager
Marketing employees
Projects employees
Design employees
Prod. planning employees
Production employees
Manufacturing and assembly employees
Delivery employees
VARIABLE STRUCTURE OF PROJECT TEAM
Feasibility loop project team
Design loop project team
Product planning loop project team
Production loop project team
Manufacturing loop project team
department participates in project team
department coordinates the work in project team

Figure 17. Ideal matrix organisation in SME.

The project team manager would be excluded from his/her department throughout the duration of the product development project and (s)he would work full time in the project.

3.3. Goals and tools for support of concurrent product development process

Using concurrent engineering, the following goals should be achieved:

- considerably shorter new product development time
- reduced new product development costs
- better quality of new products regarding customer requirements.

a.) Considerably shorter new product development time

Product development time is supposed to be reduced by 50% or more due to the following reasons:

- activities run in parallel
- team members have regular meetings, which allow for fast and efficient exchange of information
- responsibility for all product characteristics is transferred to teams (no time is wasted for searching the one "who is to be blamed for failures").

b.) Reduced new product development costs

Figure 18 presents the diagram of ideal cost curve in sequential and concurrent product development and use.

In sequential development and use of a product we can see that:

- due to sequential activities, product development costs increase evenly
- costs of production and use of a product increase rapidly because of long iteration loops for execution of required modifications and elimination of defects.

In concurrent development and use of a product we can see that:

- product development costs are much higher than in sequential development due to intensive activities during the early development stage (team work)
- costs of production and use of a product are considerably lower than in sequential product development because of short iteration loops for execution of required modifications and elimination of defects.

c.) Better quality of new products regarding customer requirements

Today only those companies are successful which can offer their customers:

- right products,
- of the right quality,
- at the right price and
- at the right time

therefore the companies which are able to adapt to the *requirements of the customers.*

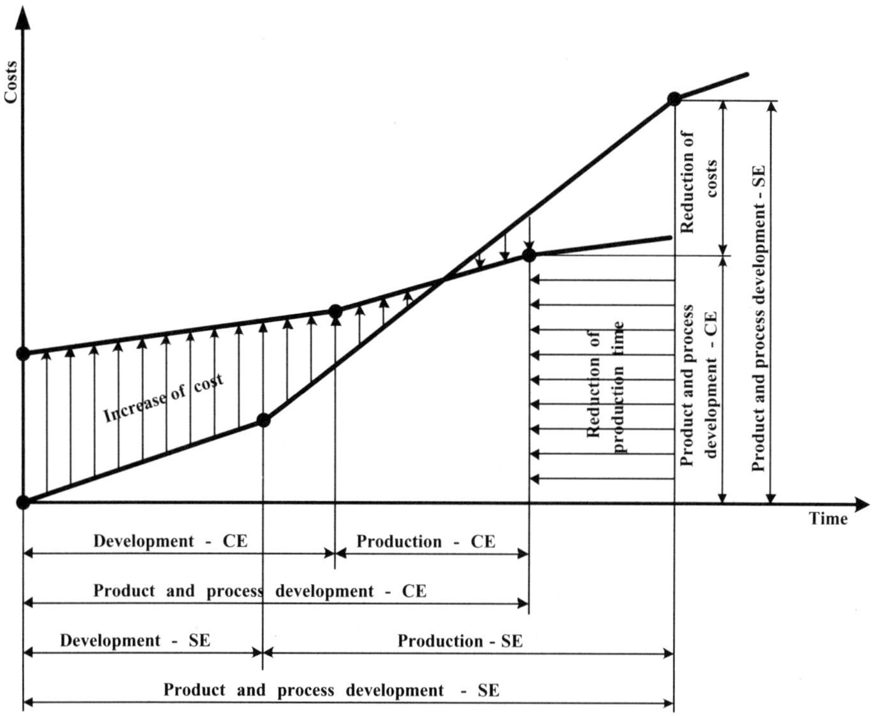

Figure 18. Ideal cost curve in sequential and concurrent product development and use.

Figure 19 presents an overview of the "concurrent engineering tools"; knowledge and use of these tools ensures better quality of products.

3.3.1. Quality Functions Deployment (QFD)

Quality functions deployment method (also known as *House of Quality*) is an important tool of concurrent engineering, which should ensure that all customer requirements will be taken into account and realised during development of the product.

The method [13] was developed in Mitsubishi shipyard in Japanese town of Kobe in 1972. It allows for design of the product development cycle. The method was quickly accepted in other Japanese companies. Toyota made the main contribution to its development and popularity.

In Europe the method is not yet widely used. In USA it appeared in the eighties, mostly related to the Xerox Company.

House of quality is a method that, by using matrices, shows connections between customer requirements and technical capabilities of the company. It is a tool that—in the product development process (as well as during its later improvements)—transforms customer requirements into specific technical solutions—product requirements.

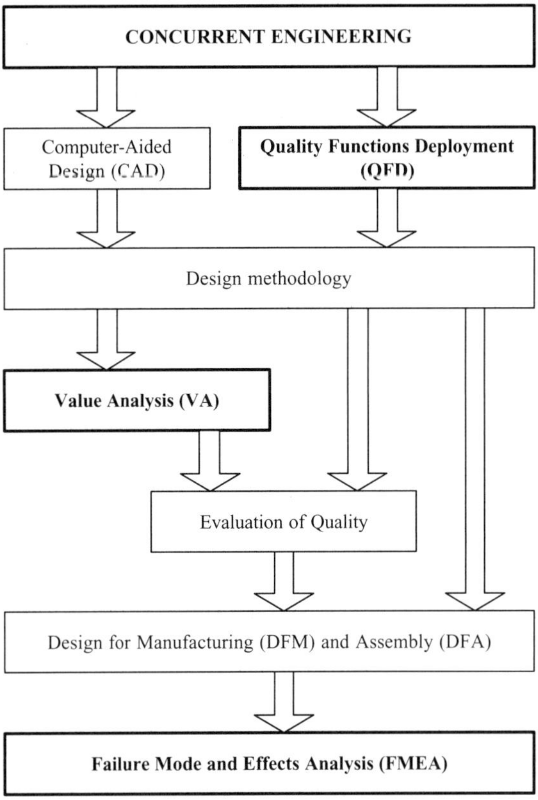

Figure 19. Concurrent engineering tools.

Building a house of quality is a team work and it can be used as a communication tool for team members. The purpose of the method is that the customer participates in development of the product and in its later continuous improvements.

Goetsch and Davis made the following definition [14]: House of quality is a practical tool for designing a product in such a way that it fulfils the customer requirements. House of quality transforms what the customer wants into what the company produces. It allows to define the customer priorities, it seeks innovative approaches for their fulfilment, and improves the process up to its maximum efficiency.

When implementing the QFD method, it is necessary to consider the following rules:

- management has to completely support the implementation of the QFD method,
- QFD implementation project manager should be the team member who is the most experienced in the QFD method usage,
- each meeting of the team should have a precisely defined goal,

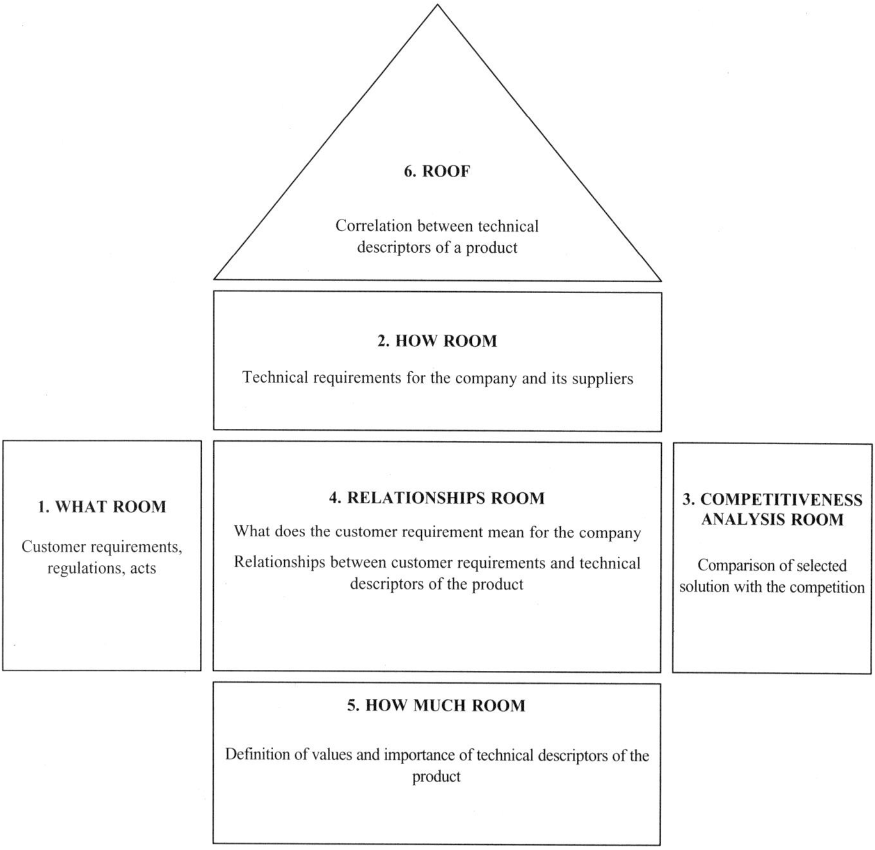

Figure 20. House of quality structure.

- it is necessary to take minutes during every meeting,
- after the meeting the minutes are sent to all team members.

3.3.1.1. HOUSE OF QUALITY STRUCTURE. QFD—quality functions deployment is called a house of quality because of its characteristic shape [13], [15], [16], [17]. It consists of six matrices, called "rooms". House of quality structure is shown in Figure 20.

There are six rooms in the House of quality:

1. WHAT room

This is a list of what the customer wants. Primary, secondary and tertiary requirements are listed. Standards, regulations and acts may also be included.

2. HOW room

This is a list of what the company and its suppliers should do in order to satisfy the customer requirements. It answers the questions of how the customer requirements will be presented in technical descriptors of the product.

3. COMPETITIVENESS ANALYSIS room

It lists current situation of the product in comparison with its competitors, and locations of possible improvements.

4. RELATIONSHIPS room

This is the core of the house of quality. It consists of a relationship matrix between WHAT and HOW rooms (relationships between customer requirements and technical descriptors of the product).

5. HOW MUCH room

This list is used to specify which technical product/process requirements are the most important to satisfy the customer requirements.

6. ROOF of the house of quality

It is presented by a correlation matrix between various technical descriptors of the product.

3.3.1.2. STEPS IN CONSTRUCTING THE HOUSE OF QUALITY. Building a house of quality is simple, yet it requires a lot of effort and efficient team work. Size of the house of quality depends on the number of customer requirements. Authors of the house of quality recommend that this method be used for problems consisting of up to 30 customer requirements and just as many engineering requirements, otherwise the method becomes too complex and unclear.

The house of quality is constructed in 14 steps.

Step 1: Customer requirements

Construction starts by gathering customer requirements. Questionnaires and market research methods are used. The data obtained are classified into primary, secondary and tertiary. The primary ones are general, the secondary ones define the primary ones, and the tertiary ones enable the primary ones.

Step 2: Assigning weights to customer requirements

As customer requirements can be mutually complementary or exclusive, each customer requirement is assigned its relative importance (weight).

Step 3: Technical descriptors of the product

Engineering requirements of the product (HOWs) are defined, which enable meeting the customer requirements (WHATs).

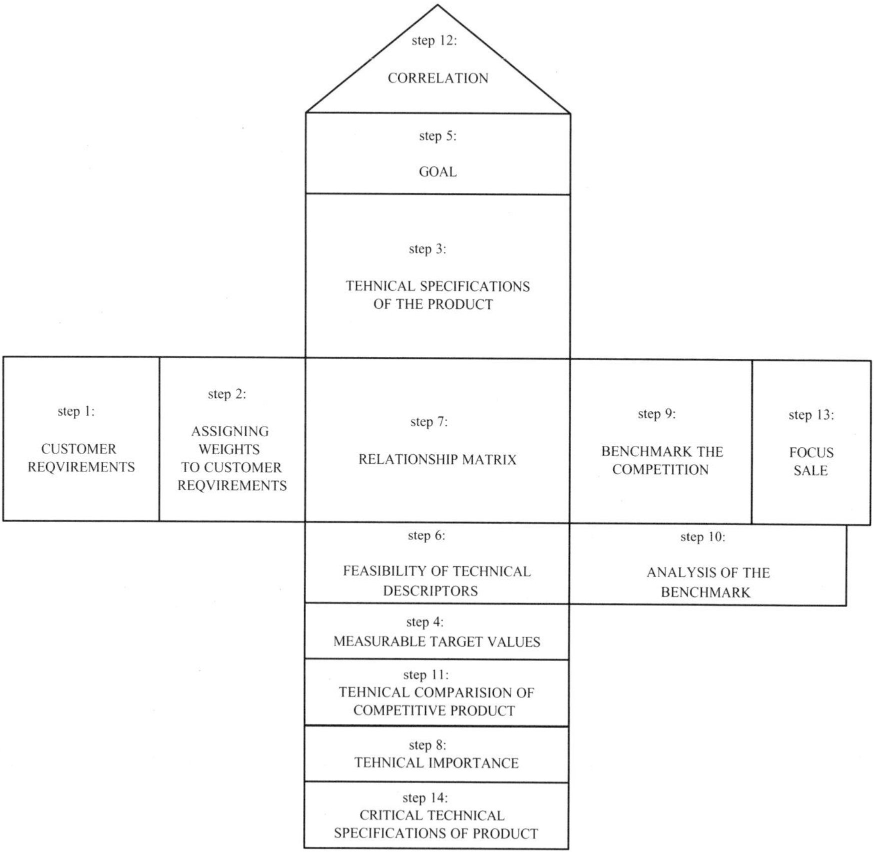

Figure 21. Steps in constructing the house of quality.

When defining engineering requirements the following questions may be useful:

– What is the function and purpose of the product?
– How does the product look like?
– How much does the product cost?
– How will the product be sold?

Step 4: Measurable target values

Measurable target values of technical descriptors of the product are defined (usually these are numerical values; however, they can be defined as a text).

Step 5: Goals

Using an arrow, for each technical descriptor of a product we indicate whether a lower or higher value is desired. Correct value is denoted by 0.

Step 6: Feasibility of technical descriptors

An estimation regarding feasibility of technical descriptors of the product is given on the scale from 1 to 10, 1 being the most easily feasible technical descriptor and 10 being the most difficult one.

Step 7: Relationship matrix

Central part of the house of quality is filled with data. Relationship matrix defines how the technical descriptors of the product (HOWs) are related to the customer requirements (WHATs). There are four possible relationships:

– strong relationship – weight of 9,
– moderate relationship – weight of 3,
– weak relationship – weight of 1,
– no relationship (empty cell) – weight of 0.

Practical use has shown that for successful solution of the problems it is suitable that less than half of the matrix cells be filled in.

After the data have been filled into the matrix, checks have to be made whether each customer requirement has interaction with at least one technical descriptor. If there is no interaction a new technical descriptor has to be defined, which fulfils the customer requirement. If all cells in a matrix column (technical descriptors of the product) are empty then this particular descriptor is not important.

Step 8: Technical importance

For each technical descriptor of the product its absolute and relative technical importance is calculated. Absolute technical importance is calculated using the equation:

$$ATI = \sum_{i=1}^{n} (VR_i \times I_i)$$

ATI – absolute technical importance
VR_i – value of the relationship of the i-th customer requirement
I_i – importance of the i-th customer requirement
n – number of all customer requirements

Technical importance with highest absolute (relative) importance obtains the highest rank, which means that it has the highest influence on satisfying the customer requirements.

Step 9: Benchmark the competition

In this step the competitiveness room is filled in. Current design of the product is compared with competitive products (our and competitive products are rated on a 1 to 5 scale). Benchmark is carried out on the basis of questionnaire the customers and by other market research methods.

Step 10: Analysis of the benchmark

The points obtained in step 9 are summed up for our and competitive products.

Step 11: Technical comparison of competitive products

Fulfilment of technical descriptors of our and competitive products is rated on the scale from 1 to 5.

Step 12: Correlation

Correlation matrix shows interactions of technical descriptors of the product. Interactions can be:

– strong negative – symbol =,
– negative – symbol –,
– positive – symbol +,
– strong positive – symbol ++.

Correlation matrix makes the roof of the house of quality.

Step 13: Sales focus

Those customer requirements are defined which are best fulfilled by our product (in comparison with the competitors). When fulfilling these requirements we take care that we keep ahead of the competition.

Step 14: Critical technical descriptors of the product

Those technical descriptors of the product are defined that achieve the highest absolute (relative) values (using e.g. ordinal ranking from 1 to 8). Those technical descriptors mostly influence the fulfilment of customer requirements.

3.3.1.3. EXTENDING THE HOUSE OF QUALITY. House of quality is a method for finding interactions between product functions and customer requirements. House of quality is extended in such a way that technical descriptors of the product in existing house of quality (HOWs) become requirements in new house of quality (WHATs). First a relationship between technical descriptors of the product and properties of parts is found (second house of quality), then between properties of parts and key process operations (third house of quality) and finally between the key process operations and production requirements (fourth house of quality).

An example of such an extension of a house of quality is shown in Figure 22.

3.3.1.4. ADVANTAGES OF USING THE HOUSE OF QUALITY. There are several benefits if a company uses the house of quality method, especially in the fields of improving the competitiveness and quality. They are expressed in:

- *Focus on the customer*
  Every company that introduced TQM has to be focused on the customer. House of quality allows for collecting input and feedback data from customers, these data are transformed into a collection of customer requirements and they become target values that the company has to achieve.

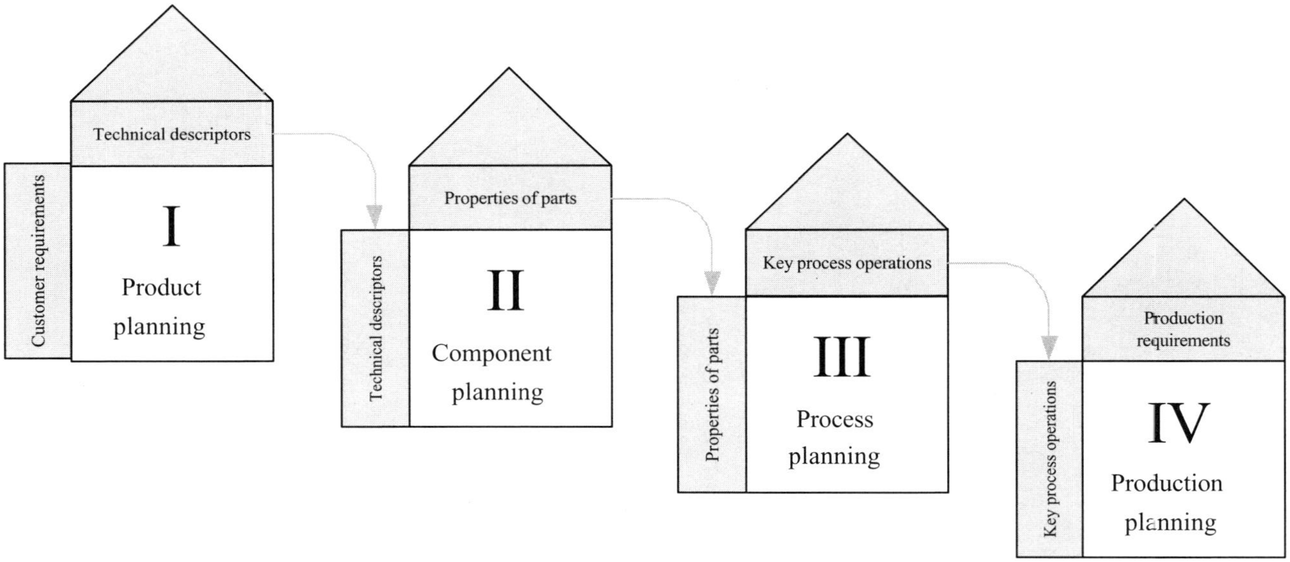

Figure 22. Extension of the house of quality.

- *Better use of time*
  House of quality reduces product development time because it shows the most important and clearly defined customer requirements. Therefore time is not wasted to develop features which are of no interest to the customer.
- *Team work*
  As a method, the house of quality is oriented towards a team work. All decisions are results of a consensus of team members.
- *Consistent documentation*
  One of the results of the house of quality is an exhaustive document, which combines all data about processes and shows how they complement when satisfying the customer requirements. Document is being continuously updated as new data are obtained. In order to successfully plan new products and improve existing ones it is necessary to note daily information on customer requirements.

3.3.2. Value analysis

L. D. Miles wrote that value analysis [18] is an organised creative method whose task is to show exactly and efficiently the unnecessary costs—i.e. the costs, which neither contribute to the quality, usefulness or life-time of a product nor to its aesthetic function or other characteristics desirable by the customer.

Value analysis is a system which allows solutions of complex problems which cannot be completely or partially transformed into an algorithmic form. It consists of combined actions of the following system elements:

- management,
- method and
- mode of operation
- with their simultaneous mutual impact; the goal being to optimise the end result.

Value analysis is a professionally applied, function-oriented, systematic team approach used to analyse and improve value in a product, facility design, system or service—a powerful methodology for solving problems and/or reducing costs while improving performance/quality requirements.

Value analysis is a systematic method which can be used in order to reduce the costs of a product or service. It is a creative process, a systematic searching for facts and alternatives, whose purpose is to reduce costs to a minimum in each phase of product life-cycle [19].

The concept and techniques of value analysis are called basic when dealing with "economy decisions". Proper use of value analysis ensures better results when searching for and reducing unnecessary costs. However, as any other tool, value analysis can be improperly used which means that we do not obtain desired results. Considering the fact that the method has been successfully used in the industry for more than 40 years we can conclude that improper use is usually the one that obtains unsatisfactory results.

Value analysis is not a substitution for design-engineering and production-engineering knowledge—it is an excellent systematic approach to use this knowledge.

Value analysis is an aid, which allows the company to preserve or increase its competitiveness on the market.

At the beginning value analysis was used only in mass production (and in great extent it still is used today). However, the attempts to use value analysis in small-series production (or even in individual production) were extremely successful. It is obvious that it is more sensible to use value analysis if quantity or price of the analysed object increases [20], [21].

Today value analysis is limited neither to a product manufactured in mass- or individual production nor to the size of the company or the industry. Objects of value analysis can be:

- products,
- production systems,
- administration,
- organisation.

Selection of the object of value analysis depends on business decisions, supported by proper analyses.

According to VDI 2222 [22], value analysis of a product can be used in all three key phases of product development:

- development,
- design,
- production.

Naturally, the most benefits are obtained from the value analysis if it is used in the design phase. The sooner in product development value analysis is used in order to find economic solutions, the higher the benefits will be.

In the design phase the value analysis deals with products which exist only as drawings, models or prototypes—things which are not yet in production. In the production phase a value analysis of products on the market is made.

Graphical presentation of value analysis presents clearly why it is so important to use it early in the product development phase—see Figure 23.

Goals of research made by value analysis arise from the goals of the company [21]. Depending on strategic orientation, the goals of the market research are:

- increase of profit,
- increase of usefulness for the customer,
- achieving competitive advantages.

The results of value analysis are usually presented as reduced costs. Additional benefit is that customer requirements are fulfilled well, and thus competitive advantage is achieved.

Using value analysis an optimum between producer costs and customer benefits is expected:

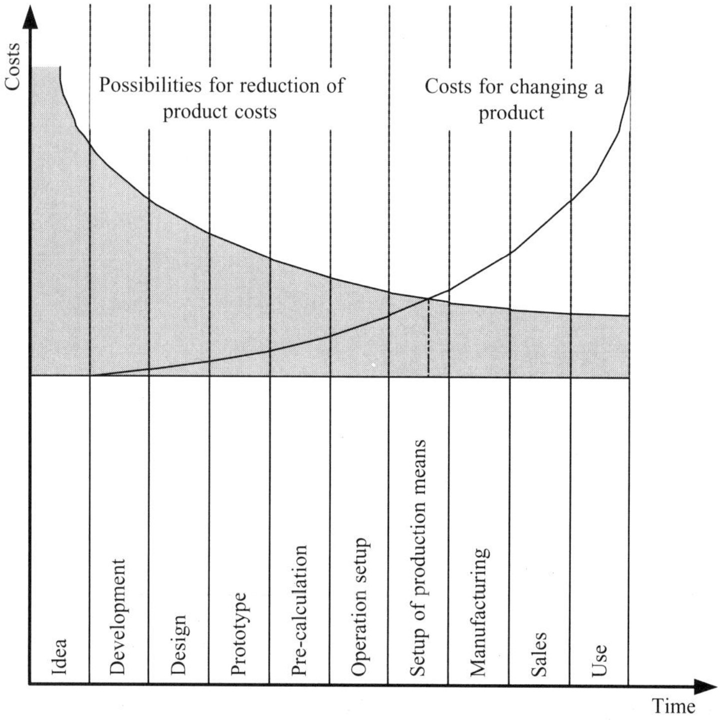

Figure 23. Reduction of product costs with value analysis in different phases of product life cycle [22].

- increase of usefulness for the customer was shown in 80% of all researches,
- reduction of throughput time up to 50%,
- reduction of costs up to 20%.

Depending on the goals the costs may be reduced, or the number of functions may be increased, or the quality may be improved or the processes may be sped up.

Value analysis research should increase productivity and increase value for the end user. 90% of all researches revealed an increase of quality in spite of reduced production costs; the remaining 10% revealed that the same quality was retained.

In addition to quantitative results, value analysis brings several additional benefits to the company:

- Employees' thinking is oriented towards goals, costs and functions.
- All participants are motivated to give their contribution to achieve success.
- Collaboration inside the company is improved.
- Capabilities of team work are improved.
- Creativity of all employees is used.

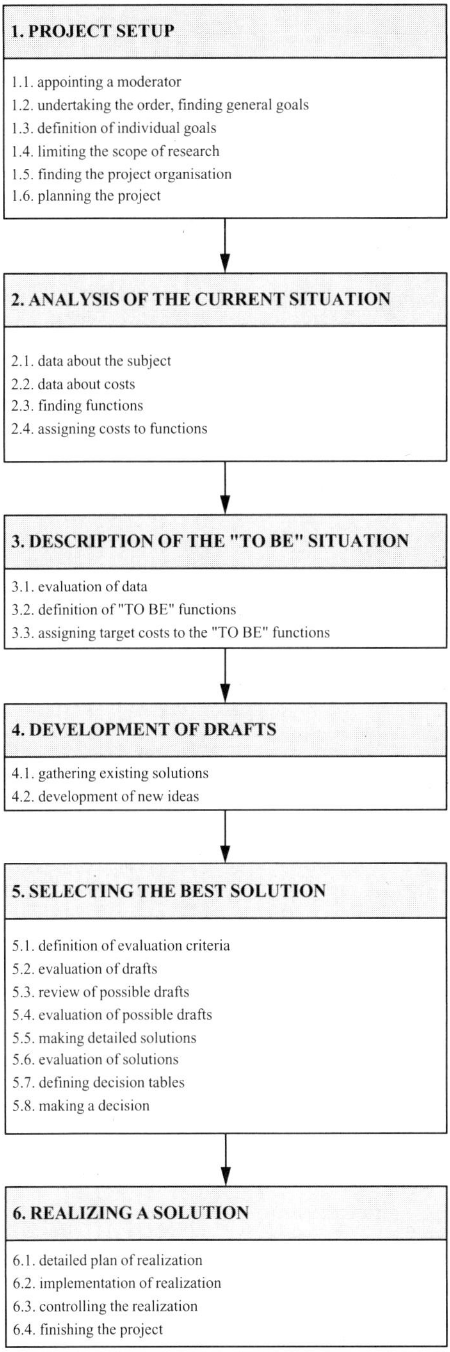

Figure 24. Value analysis method (DIN 69910).

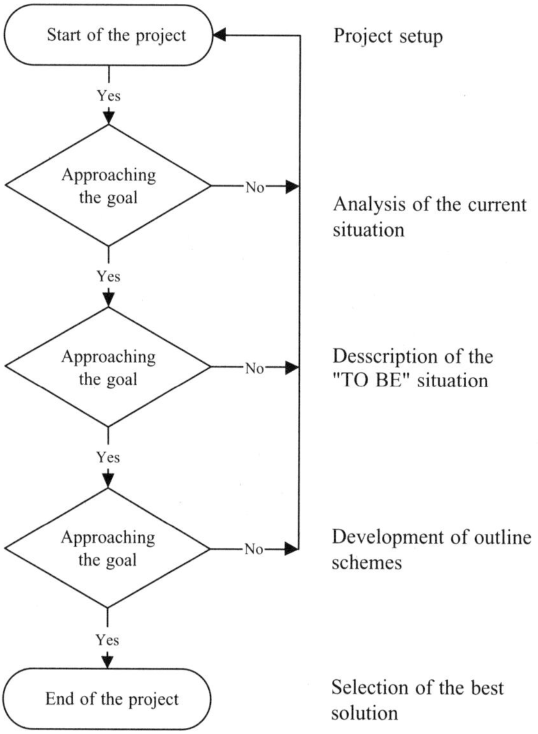

Figure 25. Iteration model of value analysis.

Value analysis method is standardised in DIN 69910 [23] and consists of 6 steps (Figure 24). Steps are divided into sub-steps, which can be repeated in several iterations (Figure 25).

Sub-steps can be mixed or can be repeated in several iterations.

3.3.3. Failure Mode and Effects Analysis (FMEA)

Failure Mode and Effects Analysis (FMEA) is a method of preventive quality assurance. The goal of the FMEA method is to find and prevent possible failures during product development and manufacturing.

Failures that arise during production or use of the product cause high costs. Because of them the company often loses its reputation in view of the customers.

FMEA is a target-oriented method which allows us to find possible failures on time. Risks as results of failures are evaluated, and corrective measures are developed to prevent failures. FMEA goals are:

- evaluation of effects and consequences of events, which will be caused by each failure found in the system,
- definition of value or criticalness of each failure with respect to the proper function of the system and influence on the reliability and/or safety of the process,

Table 1 Types of FMEA

	Object of analysis	Elements of FMEA	When?	Responsibility
System FMEA	Superior product/ system (e.g. car)	Project of a product	Project of a product after manufacturing	Development
Design FMEA	Important component	Design documentation	Design documentation after manufacturing	Design
Process FMEA	Manufacturing process steps (e.g. casting)	Manufacturing plans	Plan after manufacturing	Manufacturing planning
FMEA of joint-ventures, suppliers	Service steps	Plans of services	Plan after service	Planning a service

- finding the failures in accordance with the possibility of their detection, diagnosing and testing,
- estimation of required corrective measures.

In various product development phases there are four types of FMEA; all together they form a complete system:

- *system FMEA* defines functionality of individual system components with respect to the complete system and interconnections between individual components (e.g. operation of the engine, gearbox and drive shaft at the gearbox);
- *design FMEA* is used for finding possible failures of individual component in design, manufacturing and assembly;
- *process FMEA* researches possible sources of failures in production process,
- *service FMEA* is used for joint-ventures and suppliers.

Types of FMEA and their basic features are shown in Table 1. Their common feature is the same approach. Differences between FMEA types are visible especially in the design phase and in definition of a goal, which corresponds to their execution.

Although it makes sense to use all types of FMEA, in practice most often design and process FMEA are used; they are divided as shown in Figure 26.

Using FMEA has the following advantages [24]:

- It helps at selection of alternative design solutions with high reliability and safety already in early development phase.
- It identifies possible failures and their effects, which influence efficiency of product functions.
- Program of tests is made in development phase, before final confirmation of design.
- Criteria for definition of production process, supply and service are developed.
- Failures are documented as future references in order to help us in failure analysis during use, and when dealing with design changes.
- It is a basis for finding priorities of corrective actions.

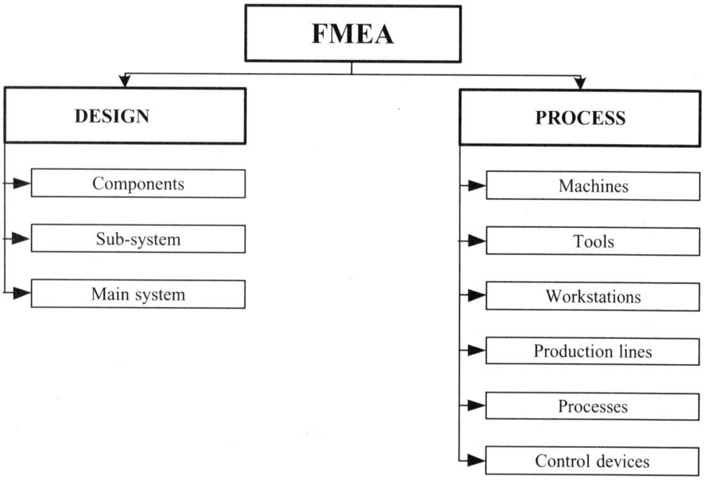

Figure 26. Division of design and process FMEA.

FMEA is a preventive technique which allows for a systematic study of causes and effects of failures before design is finished. The product is analysed (on a system or lower level) from all possible points of view which may lead to failures. For each possible failure, effects on entire system are estimated; their severity and their frequency of occurrence are defined.

Drawbacks of FMEA:

- It is difficult to perform FMEA for complex systems which perform several functions and consist of many components.
- FMEA results do not take into account human errors. Human errors usually appear in a certain sequence during the system operation. Yet, the FMEA can find the components which are the most sensitive to human factors.

Execution of the FMEA is in the competence of the company management whose task is to:

- define the requirement for FMEA execution
- define the goal
- define the limits of problem solving
- define the deadline for execution of the task
- form the workgroup.

Setup and execution of FMEA is a result of a team work. Figure 27 presents the composition of a workgroup, responsible for execution of the FMEA analysis.

This method is divided into several working steps [25]. Figure 28 presents a form for execution of the method, where individual steps, which follow each other in a sequence, are shown.

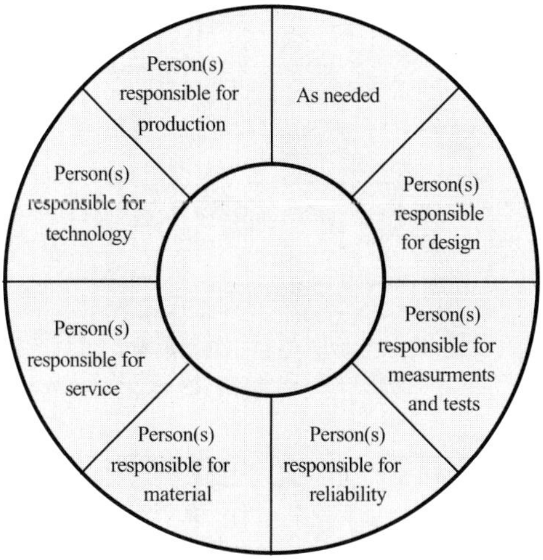

Figure 27. Composition of a workgroup.

The header of the form is first filled out with the basic data required for clear definition of the product. The form is then filled out in four steps:

Step 1: Failure analysis

According to the FMEA type used (system, design or process) it is necessary to define system or design functions and individual production process steps. Possible failures, their effects and sources of failures are analysed in detail.

Step 2: Risk assessment

For each possible reason of failure *the probability of its arising* (risk factor N) is estimated and assigned a value from 1 (not probable) to 10 (highly probable).

For each cause of failure the *influence* or *meaning of the failure for customers* is estimated (risk factor V). It is important for the customer that the product works well so the estimation from 1 (no consequences) to 10 (great consequences) is used.

For each source of failure the *probability of finding the failure* is estimated (risk factor O). The range of estimation is from 1 (high probability) to 10 (not probable).

In order to define the total risk of possible cause of failure the *preventive risk number* (PRN) is calculated as a product of estimated values for the N phenomenon, influence V and finding the failure O:

$$\text{PRN} = \text{N} \times \text{V} \times \text{O}$$

The value of PRN is between 1 (no risk) and 1000 (very high risk). However, the PRN value is not enough. If reasons for failures are sorted by PRN it is possible to define priority for their elimination. High-PRN reasons can be eliminated by introducing corrective measures into the product and production process.

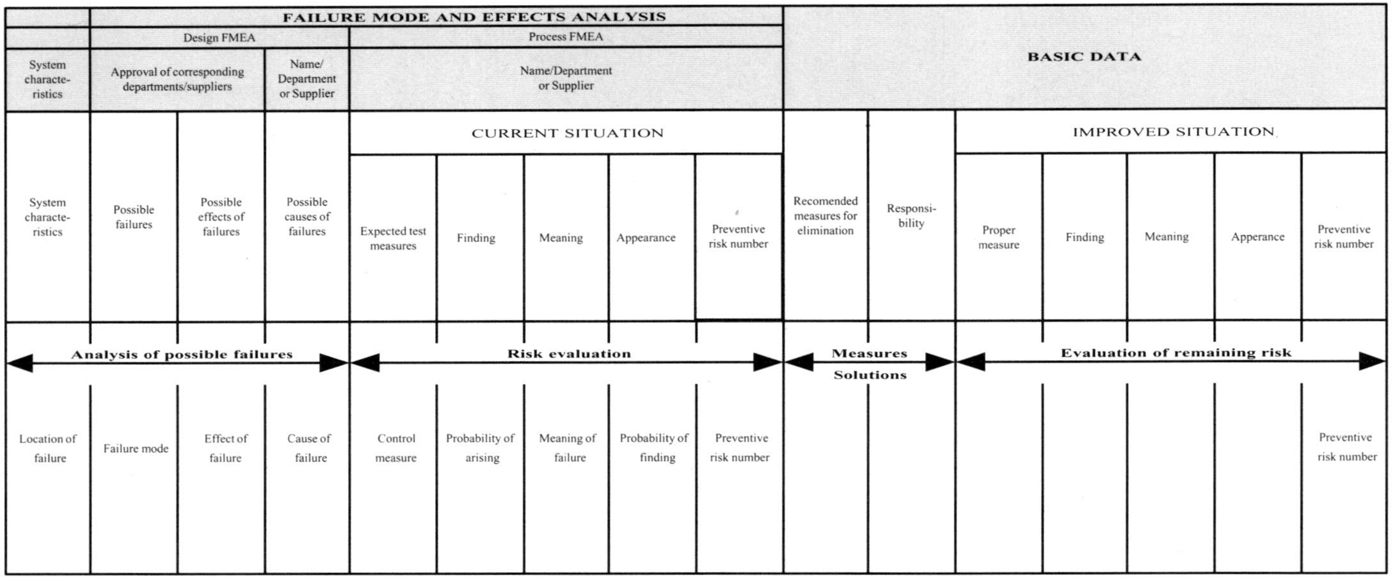

Figure 28. Form of the FMEA method.

Figure 29. The VEPER mini-loader.

Step 3: Measures for optimisation of product design

With respect to individual risk assessments (the value of PRN) it is possible to introduce appropriate corrective measures and improvements into the product design. This can be done on the company level or just in a particular department.

Step 4: Assessment of results

Using the above-mentioned procedures and measures it is possible to correct individual deficiencies. These improvements have to be re-evaluated regarding possible failures (step 2 has to be repeated (PRN calculation)).

4. SAMPLE CASE OF INTRODUCTION OF CONCURRENT ENGINEERING IN AN SME

An SME which produces civil engineering equipment decided to develop a mini-loader (Figure 29).

Mini-loader development process ran in two phases:

1. Analysis of customer requirements (i.e. market analyses) and construction of the house of quality.
2. Plan and execution of mini-loader development project using the concurrent engineering principle.

4.1. Building a house of quality

In order to build a house of quality the company management formed a team whose members were from the following departments:

- marketing and sales,
- development and product planning
- design,
- production process
- production
- QC/QA,
- supply and
- external member (designer).

Head of marketing department was selected as a project team manager.

Before starting the construction of the house of quality for the mini-loader, the team members were informed on details about the product, possible customers, domestic and global competitors, and manufacturing costs.

After preliminary activities had been finished the team members performed all 14 steps in construction of the house of quality, which is shown in Figure 30.

Analysis of the house of quality for the mini-loader led the team members to some important conclusions:

1. The mini-loader, produced by the company, fulfils the following customer requirements better than its competitors:

   - it is lower and narrower than competitive products,
   - it has a recognisable design (influence of external designer),
   - it can be transported on a trailer,
   - it consumes less fuel,
   - it is cheaper than competitive products.

   In comparison with the competition, the product is worse regarding the following three requirements:

   - its components are of worse quality,
   - delivery time is much longer,
   - maintenance is more demanding.

2. The mini-loader, produced by the company, fulfils the following technical descriptors better than its competitors:

   - engine power,
   - size and weight of the mini-loader,
   - volume of the ladle,
   - selection of colour,
   - cost of materials used.

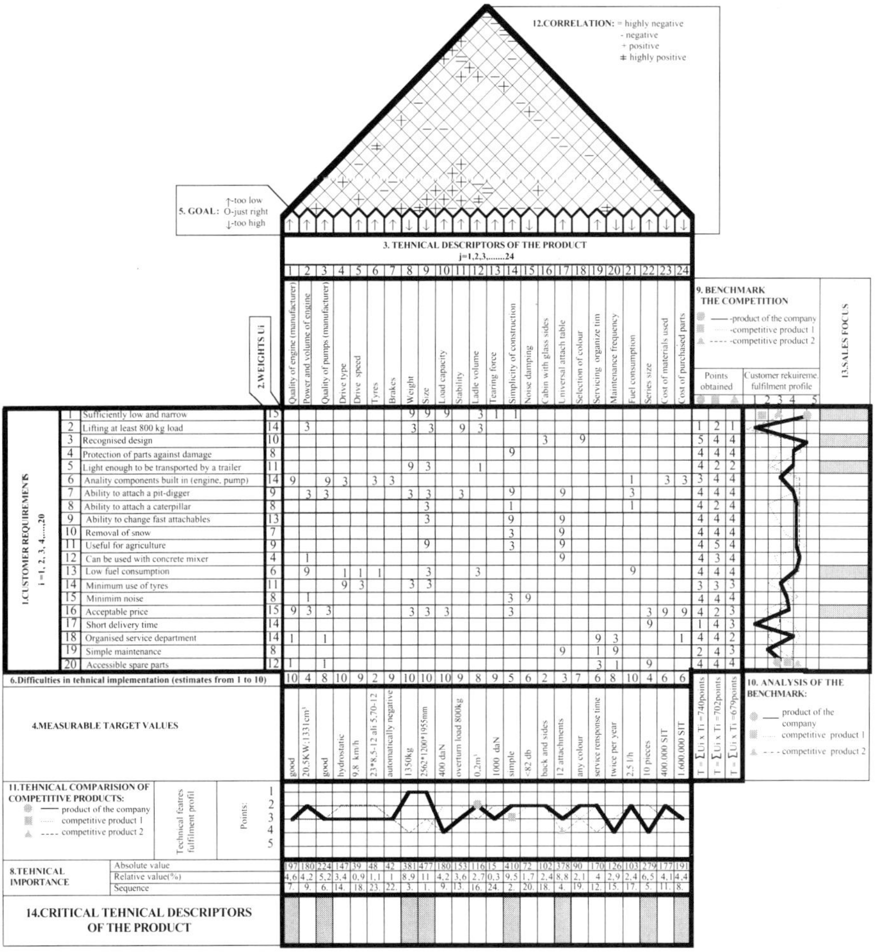

Figure 30. House of quality for the mini-loader.

The product is worse regarding the following technical descriptors:

- smaller load capacity,
- smaller tearing force,
- maintenance frequency,
- too small lot size.

3. A highly positive correlation exists between the following pairs of technical descriptors of the product:

- engine power and load capacity,
- weight and size,

- stability and tearing force,
- organisation level of the service department and maintenance frequency.

Highly negative correlation exists between:

- quality of engine and cost of purchased parts,
- engine power and maintenance frequency,
- quality of pump and cost of purchased parts,
- load capacity and design simplicity,
- stability and design simplicity.

4. In further development of the mini-loader it will be necessary to pay special attention to the following technical descriptors:

    - size of mini-loader,
    - construction simplicity,
    - weight of mini-loader,
    - universality of connection plate,
    - lot size,
    - quality of pump,
    - quality of engine,
    - evaluation of purchased parts.

The results of team work with an emphasis on the construction of the house of quality for the mini-loader were presented to the company management; it was stressed that this was the first one of four houses of quality which should reveal how the product fulfils the customer requirements.

The company management and the team members discussed the results obtained and decided that the team should proceed with the construction of the other three houses of quality:

- house of quality for planning parts and components,
- house of quality for production process planning, and
- house of quality for manufacturing and assembly planning.

Four Houses of quality for the mini-loader will be used in order to gradually transfer customer requirements from the product to its components and parts, from components and parts to production processes, and from production processes to manufacturing and assembly.

4.2. Project of concurrent product development process

4.2.1. Goals of the project and project team

The company decided to develop a new mini-loader in a project style. The goal of the project was development of mini-loader and implementation of the concurrent engineering in the company.

In order that the company could switch to the concurrent development of mini-loader it was necessary first to decide about the structure and composition of concurrent product development teams.

The company management decided to form a two-level team structure (core and project teams).

In order to get the best structure of both teams two creativity workshops were organised with the general manager, his assistant and nine department managers participating.

Results of the first creativity workshop have shown that the core team should consist of eleven company employees:

- general manager who would manage the core team,
- nine department managers,
- assistant general manager who would manage the project team.

All core team members will be permanent members; core team composition will therefore not change within the mini-loader development time.

4.2.2. *WBS of the project and responsibility matrix*

The second creativity workshop was organised in order to define stages of mini-loader development process and their corresponding activities, as well as responsibilities of departments to carry out those activities. For the new mini-loader development project a WBS structure of the project was made, as shown in Figure 31.

For execution of project activities, responsibilities were assigned to department heads and company employees, as presented in responsibility matrix (Table 2).

4.2.3. *Structure of a project team for execution of concurrent engineering loops*

Results of the second creativity workshop and selection of the project team manager allowed for the definition of the project team structure in individual loops of the mini-loader development, as shown in Table 2. Changeable structure of the project team in loops of the mini-loader development is shown in Table 3.

Project team manager will be a permanent team member, while experts from nine departments of the company and representatives of designers, suppliers and customers will be variable team members.

After the structure of the core and project teams had been defined, it was possible to form a two-level team structure for mini-loader development (Figure 32).

4.2.4. *Time and structural plan of the project*

Up to now the producer of mini-loaders has developed new products sequentially. Analysis of the past results of sequential development of mini loaders has shown that the average development time for a particular product was four years. In these days the market demands short delivery terms of products and short development times. In order to reduce the mini-loader development time (and thus get a competitive advantage) the company decided to concurrently develop a new type of mini-loader.

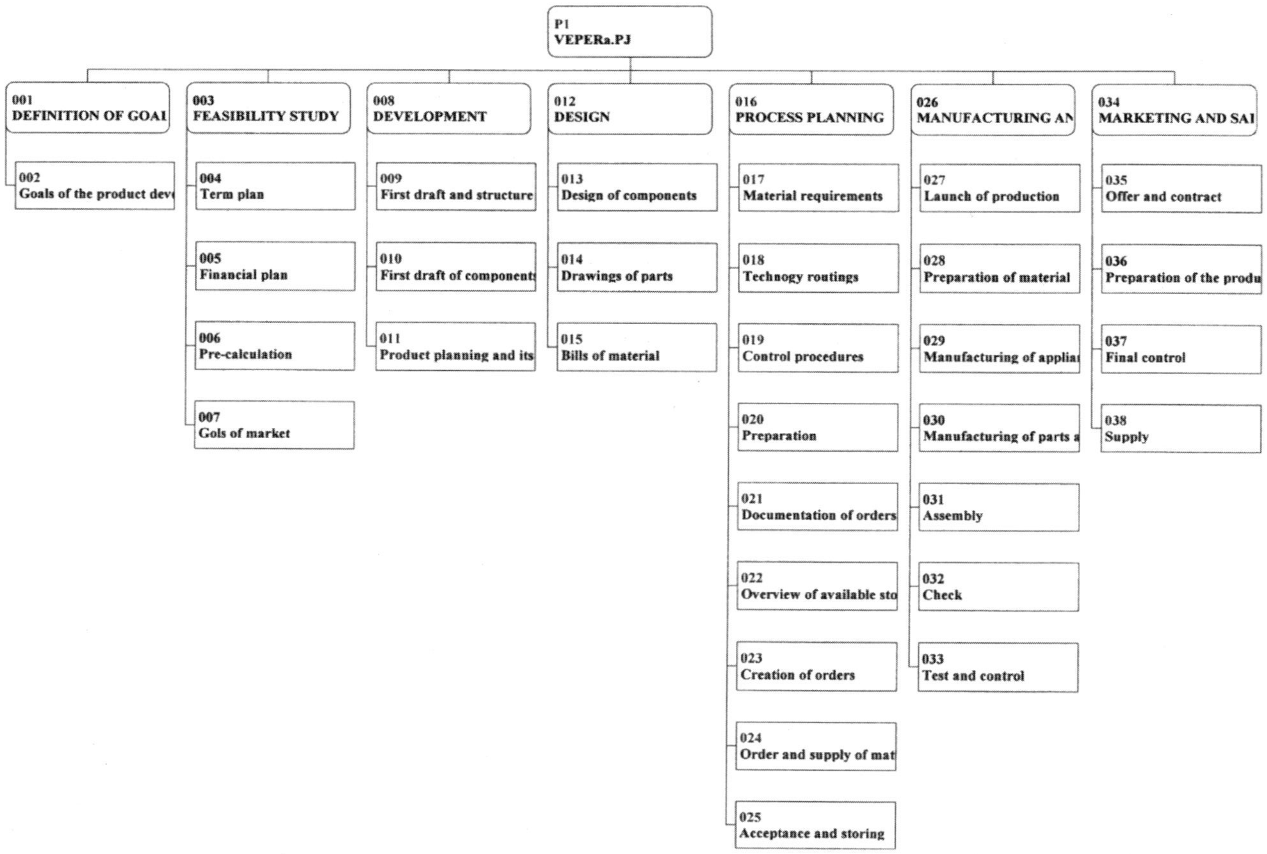
P1
VEPERa.PJ
001
DEFINITION OF GOAI
002
Goals of the product dev
003
FEASIBILITY STUDY
004
Term plan
005
Financial plan
006
Pre-calculation
007
Gols of market
008
DEVELOPMENT
009
First draft and structure
010
First draft of component
011
Product planning and its
012
DESIGN
013
Design of components
014
Drawings of parts
015
Bills of material
016
PROCESS PLANNING
017
Material requirements
018
Technogy routings
019
Control procedures
020
Preparation
021
Documentation of orders
022
Overview of available sto
023
Creation of orders
024
Order and supply of mat
025
Acceptance and storing
026
MANUFACTURING AN
027
Launch of production
028
Preparation of material
029
Manufacturing of applia
030
Manufacturing of parts a
031
Assembly
032
Check
033
Test and control
034
MARKETING AND SAI
035
Offer and contract
036
Preparation of the produ
037
Final control
038
Supply

Figure 31. WBS of the mini-loader development project.

Table 2 Responsibility matrix of the mini-loader

Stage No:	Description of product development stage:	Department: / Employees: / Planned activities within the stage:	Development and planning dept.		Design dept.	Technology dept.		Supply dept.		Production		Marketing and sales dept.		Financial dept.	Quality dept.	Informat. unit	Delivery	Shaping
			Development	Prod. planning	Design	Prod. proc. plan	Logistics	Supply	Cooperation	Prepare	Manufacturing	Marketing	Sales					
1	Definition of goals	Goals	\\\	\\\								\\\						
2	Feasibility study	Term plan	///	///		///		///				///	///			///	///	
		Financial plan											\\\	\\\		\\\		
		Pre-calculation		///		///		///					///	///		///		
		Goals of market						\\\				\\\	\\\					
3	Product planning	First draft of the product	///	///								///						///
		First draft of components	\\\	\\\	\\\							\\\						\\\
		Planning of the product	///	///														
4	Design	Design of components	\\\	\\\	\\\											\\\		
		Drawings of parts	///	///	///	///										///		
		Bills of material		\\\	\\\	\\\	\\\	\\\								\\\		
5	Process planning	Material requirements			///	///	///	///								///		
		Technology routings				\\\				\\\						\\\		
		Control procedures				///	///			///					///	///		
		Preparations			\\\	\\\				\\\								
		Documentation of orders				///										///		
		Overview of stock					\\\								\\\	\\\		
		Creation of orders					///	///								///	///	
		Order of material					\\\	\\\		\\\						\\\	\\\	
		Acceptance and storing					///	///							///	///	///	
6	Manufacturing and assembly	Launch of production					\\\			\\\	\\\					\\\		
		Preparation of material					///			///	///					///		
		Manufacturing of appliances				\\\				\\\	\\\					\\\		
		Manufact. of components				///			///	///	///					///		
		Assembly				\\\				\\\	\\\							
		Check				///				///	///							
		Test and control								\\\					\\\			
7	Marketing and sales	Offer and contract			///	///				///	///		///	///	///	///		
		Preparation of the product			\\\	\\\				\\\	\\\							
		Final control	///							///	///		///		///			
		Supply				\\\					\\\		\\\			\\\		

Table 3 Project team structure in individual loops of the mini-loader development

Loop number	DESCRIPTION OF THE LOOP:	STAGES, INCLUDED IN THE LOOP:	PROJECT TEAM MEMBERS																	TOTAL No OF PROJECT TEAM MEMBERS
			PROJ.T EAM MANAGER	DEVELOPMENT	PRODUCT PLAN.	DESIGN	PROD. PROC. PLAN	LOGISTICS	SUPPLY	COOPERATION	OPERATIVE PREP.	MANUFACTURING	MARKETING	SALES	FINANCE	QUALITY	INFORMAT. UNIT	DELIVERY	SHAPING	
1.	FEASIBILITY LOOP	- definition of goals - feasibility study - planning	X	X	X	X	X		X				X	X	X		X	X	X	12
2.	PROJECT LOOP	- feasibility study - planning - design	X	X	X	X	X	X	X				X	X	X		X		X	12
3.	DESIGN LOOP	- planning - design - process planning	X	X	X	X	X	X	X		X		X			X	X	X		12
4.	PROCESS PLANNING LOOP	- design - process planning - manufact. and assembly	X	X	X	X	X	X	X	X	X	X				X	X	X		13
5.	MANUFACTU-RING AND ASSEMBLY LOOP	- process planning - manufact. and assembly - marketing and sales	X	X		X	X	X	X	X	X	X		X	X	X	X	X		14

A creativity workshop was organised with all members of the core team participating. They were asked to estimate or define the following:

- duration of individual stages (activities) in the concurrent product development process;
- possible connections between stages (activities);
- types and planned times of overlapping stages (activities).

Results of the core team work during mini-loader development are shown in Table 4.

The data on times, connections and overlapping of stages (activities) in concurrent mini-loader development (shown in Table 4) are the input data for the CA—SPJ software which was used to design the Gantt chart of the development process of the new type of mini-loader (Figure 33).

Analysis of the Gantt charts of the existing sequential and the planned concurrent development of the new mini-loader has shown that if the company shifts from sequential to concurrent engineering, it will be able to launch a new mini-loader in 25 months instead of four years as before—which would considerably improve the competitiveness of the company.

The success of the concurrent mini-loader development process mostly depends on the effectiveness of work of the project team in the product development loops, and therefore activities in future will be directed towards a detailed organisation and co-ordination of the project team members during individual loops of product development.

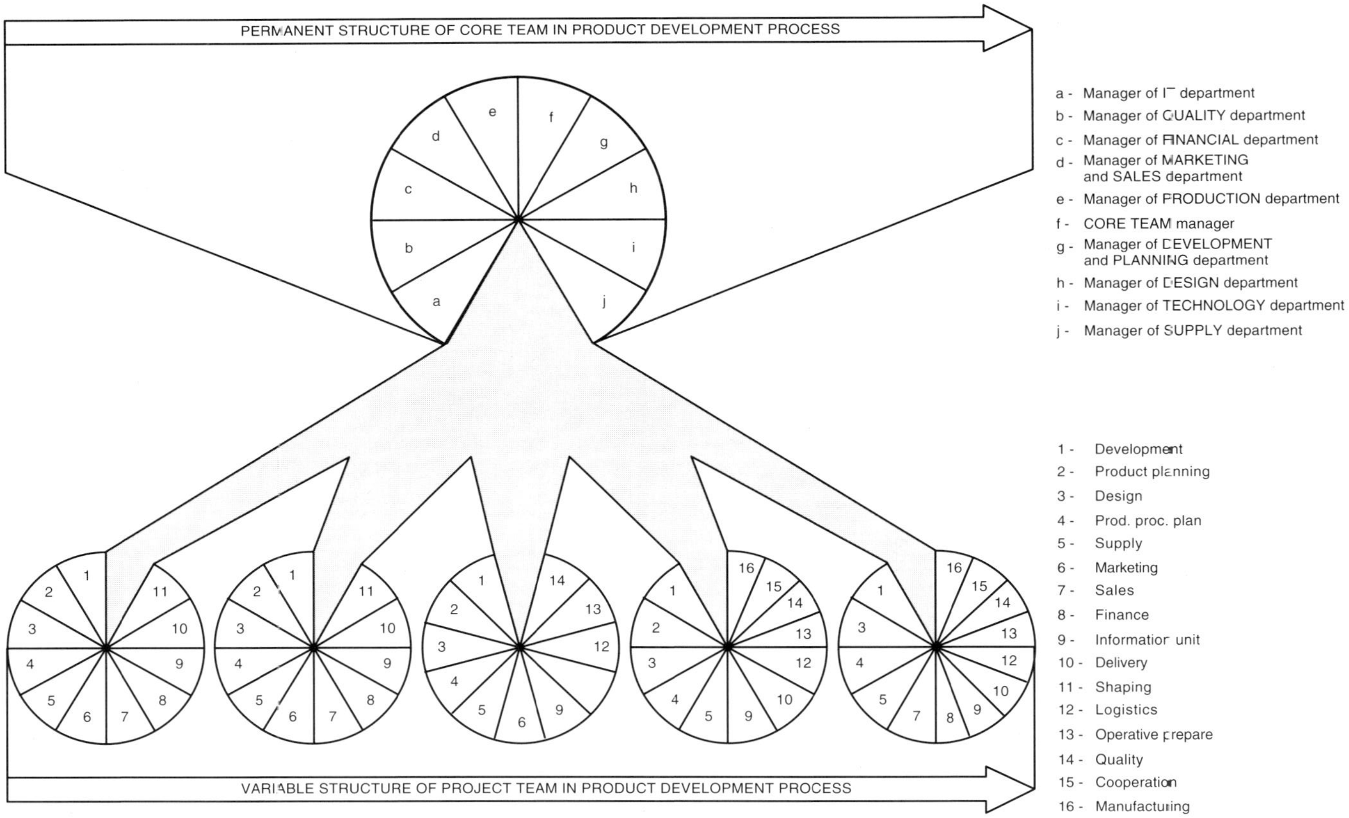
PERMANENT STRUCTURE OF CORE TEAM IN PRODUCT DEVELOPMENT PROCESS
a - Manager of IT department
b - Manager of QUALITY department
c - Manager of FINANCIAL department
d - Manager of MARKETING and SALES department
e - Manager of PRODUCTION department
f - CORE TEAM manager
g - Manager of DEVELOPMENT and PLANNING department
h - Manager of DESIGN department
i - Manager of TECHNOLOGY department
j - Manager of SUPPLY department
1 - Development
2 - Product planning
3 - Design
4 - Prod. proc. plan
5 - Supply
6 - Marketing
7 - Sales
8 - Finance
9 - Information unit
10 - Delivery
11 - Shaping
12 - Logistics
13 - Operative prepare
14 - Quality
15 - Cooperation
16 - Manufacturing
VARIABLE STRUCTURE OF PROJECT TEAM IN PRODUCT DEVELOPMENT PROCESS

Figure 32. Two-level team structure during mini-loader development.

Table 4 Duration of activities, types, and times of overlapping activities during mini-loader development

Stage id.	DESCRIPTION OF PRODUCT DEVELOPMENT STAGE	Planned activities within the stage	Activity id.	Activity duration estimation [months]	Preceding activity id	Type of overlap FS	Type of overlap SS	Type of overlap FF	Time of overlap [months]
1	Definition of goals	Goals	2	3	-				
3	Feasibility study	Term plan	4	13	2		x		1
		Financial plan	5	12	2		x		2
		Pre-calculation	6	19	5		x		1
		Goals of market	7	10	4			x	0
					5			x	0
8	Product planning	First draft of the product	9	4	2		x		2
		First draft of components	10	4	9		x		1
		Planning of the product	11	9	9		x		3
12	Design	Design of components	13	5	9		x		3
					11		x		0
		Drawings of parts	14	8	10		x		3
		Bills of material	15	9	9		x		3
16	Process planning	Material requirements	17	8	9	x			0
					10		x		3
					14		x		0
					15			x	0
		Technology routings	18	11	13		x		3
		Control procedures	19	13	18		x		1
		Preparations	20	5	19		x		1
		Documentation of orders	21	14	18		x		0
		Overview of stock	22	3	19		x		0
					21		x		1
		Creation of orders	23	4	20		x		0
		Order of material	24	5	17		x		5
					22		x		2
		Acceptance and storing	25	7	24		x		1

26	Manufacturing and assembly	Launch of production	27	11	19			x	0
					21			x	0
					24		x		0
		Preparation of material	28	6	25		x		1
					27		x		2
		Manufacturing of appliances	29	8	7	x			0
					14	x			0
					20		x		4
		Manufact. of components	30	4	24			x	3
		Assembly	31	5	30			x	2
		Check	32	4	29			x	0
					31			x	1
		Test and control	33	4	32			x	0
34	Marketing	Offer and contract	35	11	28		x		0
		Preparation of the product	36	4	32		x		0
					33		x		0
		Final control	37	2	6			x	0
					33			x	0
		Supply	38	3	35			x	1
					37			x	2

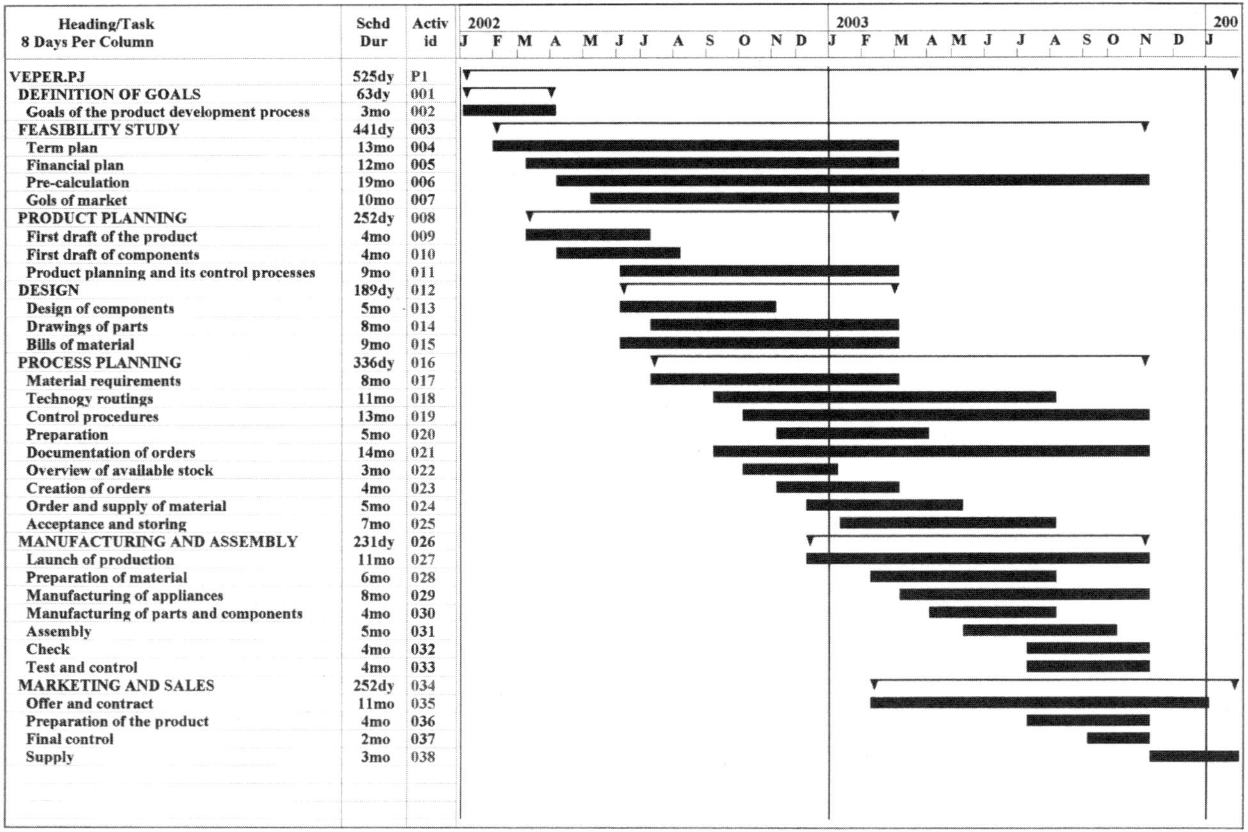

Heading/Task
8 Days Per Column
Schd Dur
Activ id
2002
2003
200
J F M A M J J A S O N D J F M A M J J A S O N D J
VEPER.PJ 525dy P1
DEFINITION OF GOALS 63dy 001
Goals of the product development process 3mo 002
FEASIBILITY STUDY 441dy 003
Term plan 13mo 004
Financial plan 12mo 005
Pre-calculation 19mo 006
Gols of market 10mo 007
PRODUCT PLANNING 252dy 008
First draft of the product 4mo 009
First draft of components 4mo 010
Product planning and its control processes 9mo 011
DESIGN 189dy 012
Design of components 5mo 013
Drawings of parts 8mo 014
Bills of material 9mo 015
PROCESS PLANNING 336dy 016
Material requirements 8mo 017
Technogy routings 11mo 018
Control procedures 13mo 019
Preparation 5mo 020
Documentation of orders 14mo 021
Overview of available stock 3mo 022
Creation of orders 4mo 023
Order and supply of material 5mo 024
Acceptance and storing 7mo 025
MANUFACTURING AND ASSEMBLY 231dy 026
Launch of production 11mo 027
Preparation of material 6mo 028
Manufacturing of appliances 8mo 029
Manufacturing of parts and components 4mo 030
Assembly 5mo 031
Check 4mo 032
Test and control 4mo 033
MARKETING AND SALES 252dy 034
Offer and contract 11mo 035
Preparation of the product 4mo 036
Final control 2mo 037
Supply 3mo 038

Figure 33. Gantt chart of the concurrent development of a new type of mini-loader.

5. CONCLUSION

Global market requires short product development times, and therefore small companies are forced into transition from sequential to concurrent product development.

As the basic element of the concurrent product development is team-work, the chapter pays special attention to the formation and structure of teams in a small company. Research has led us to the conclusion that a workgroup in a small company should consist of just two teams (logical and technology team) instead of four ones, and that a two-level team structure (permanent core team and variable project team) is more suitable for small companies.

In order to reach these goals the companies will have to shift from individual to team work, implement the known methods for quality management of products and processes, and finally organise the process of concurrent engineering for new product implementation with emphasis on:

- Computer-aided design (CAD)
- Quality functions deployment (QFD)
- Design methodology
- Value analysis (VA)
- Evaluation of quality
- Design for manufacturing (DFM) and assembly (DFA)
- Failure mode and effects analysis (FMEA)

The proposed concept of team formation in a small company has been tested in a sample case of team composition in a mini-loaders producing company.

First the permanent core team structure and then the variable project team structure have been defined. The team of company department's managers accomplished activities of construction house of quality for product.

With the construction of the first house of quality, which refers to product planning, the voice of the customer has not yet reached the lowest level of product planning (manufacturing and assembly); the team will have to build another three houses of quality for the mini-loader:

- house of quality for planning parts and components,
- house of quality for production process planning, and
- house of quality for manufacturing and assembly planning.

Construction of the four houses of quality for the mini-loader will enable the team to gradually transfer the requirements and wishes of the customer from product to its components, from components to production processes, and from production processes to manufacturing and assembly.

Team work and construction of houses of quality are important elements of concurrent product implementation: the first one is a means for organisation integration and the second one provides for the fulfilment of customer's requirements.

The team of company department's managers finally constructed a project of concurrent product development into company. Results of project has shown that if the company shifts from sequential to concurrent engineering, it would be able to launch a new mini-loader in 25 months instead in 48 months as before.

REFERENCES

[1] Prasad B., 1996: Concurrent Engineering Fundamentals, Volume I. Integrated Product and Process Organization, New Jersey. Prentice Hall PTR, pp. 216–276.
[2] Duhovnik J., Starbek M., Dwivedi S. N., Prasad B., 2001: Development of New Products in Small Companies, Concurrent Engineering: Research and Applications, Volume 9, Sage Publications, pp. 191–210.
[3] Ehrlenspiel K., 1995: Integrierte Produktentwicklung, Carl Hanser Verlag, München Wien, pp. 144–180.
[4] Winner R. I., 1988: The Role of Concurrent Engineering in Weapons System Acquisition, IDA Report R-338, Alexandrija, VA: Institut for Defence Analysis.
[5] Ashley S., 1992: DARPA initiative in Concurrent Engineering, Mechanical Engineering, Vol 114, No. 4 pp. 54–57.
[6] Schlicksupp H., 1977: Kreative Ideenfindung in der Unternehmung, Watter de Gruyter, Berlin New York, pp. 152–165.
[7] Starbek M., Kušar J., Jenko P., 1988. The Influence of Concurrent Engineering on Launch-to-Finish Time, The 31th CIRP International Seminar on Manufacturing System, Berkeley, USA.
[8] Starbek M., Kušar J., Jenko P., 1999: Building a Concurrent Engineering Suport Information System, The 32nd CIRP International Seminar on Manufacturing System, Division PMA, Katholieke Universitet Leuven, Belgium.
[9] Bullinger H. J., Wagner F., Warschat J., 1994: Ein Ansatz zur Zulieferer-Integration in der Produktentwicklung, Datenverarbeitung in der Konstruktion 1994, VDI-Verlag, Düsseldorf.
[10] Duhovnik J., Starbek M., Dwievedi S. N. Prasad B., 2003. Development of innoative products in a small and medium size enterprise, Int. J. of Computer Applications in Technology, Vol. 17, No. 4, pp. 187–201.
[11] Bullinger H. J., Warnecek H. J., 1996: Neue Organisationsformen in Unternehmen, Springer-Verlag, Berlin Heidelberg New York.
[12] Draft R. L., 1998: Organizational Theory and Design, Cincinnati South Western College Publ.
[13] Gevirtz C. D., 1994: Developing New Product With TQM, Mc Graw-Hill, Inc, New York, pp. 101–114.
[14] Goetsch, David, L. 1994: Introduction to total quality: quality, productivity, competitiveness, New York, Macmillan, cop. 1994.
[15] Erhlenspiel K., 1995: Integrierite Produktentwicklung, Carl Hanser Verlag, Munchen Wien, pp. 144–180.
[16] VDI- Gesellschaft, 1994: Wege zum erfolgreichen Qualitatsmanagement in der Produktentwicklung, VDI Verlag, Düsseldorf, pp. 67–79.
[17] Prasad B., 1996: Concurrent Engineering Fundamentals, Volume II Integrated Product Development, Now Jersey: Prentice Hall PRT, pp. 1–51.
[18] Miles, L. D. 1961: Techniques of Value Analysis and Engineering, McGraw-Hill Book Company, Inc.
[19] N. N., 1991: Wertanalyse; Idee, Methode, System, VDI-Verlag GmbH., 4. Auflage, Düsseldorf.
[20] VDI 2801, 1970: Wertanalyse – Begriffsbestimmungen und Beschreibung der Methode, Hrsg. VDI.
[21] VDI 2802, 1971:Wertanalyse-Vergleichsrechnung, Hrsg. VDI.
[22] VDI 2222, 1972: Konstruktionsmethodik BL. 2, Konzipieren technisher Produkte, VDI.
[23] DIN 69910, 1973: Wertanalyse-Begriffe, Methode, Hrsg. Deutscher Normenausschuß.
[24] Strancar, D., Krizman, V., 2000: FMEA – seminar papers, SIQ Ljubljana.
[25] Stamatis, D. H., 1995: Failure Mode and Effect Analysis: FMEA from theory to execution, ASQ Quality Press, Milwaukee, Winsconsin.

DESIGN AND MODELING METHODS FOR COMPONENTS MADE OF MULTI-HETEROGENEOUS MATERIALS IN HIGH-TECH APPLICATIONS

KE-ZHANG CHEN AND XIN-AN FENG

1. INTRODUCTION

With rapid developments of high-tech in various fields, there appear more critical requirements for special functions of components/products. For example, the thermal deformation of satellite's paraboloid antenna (10 meters in diameter) should be controlled within 0.2 mm in order to work well under the environment with large variations in temperature ($-180^{\circ}C \sim 120^{\circ}C$). To fulfil it, its thermal expansion coefficient should be close to zero. Another example is that Poisson's ratios of sensors should be negative in order to increase their sensitivities to hydrostatic pressures. If Poisson's ratio of a sensor can be changed from an ordinary value of 0.3 to −1, its sensitivity will be increased by almost one order of magnitude. The third example is about the cylinders of vehicular engines or pressure vessels. They are subjected to a high temperature/pressure on the inside while the outer surface is subjected to ambient conditions. It is desirable to have ceramic on the inner surface due to its good high temperature properties while it is also desirable to have metal away from the inner surface owing to its good mechanical properties. Joining the two materials abruptly will lead to stress concentration at the interface. A gradual change of constituent composition is thus required. But, the components made of homogeneous materials rarely possess all these special functions mentioned above. Recently attention has focused on heterogeneous materials, including composite materials, functionally graded materials, and heterogeneous materials with a periodic microstructure.

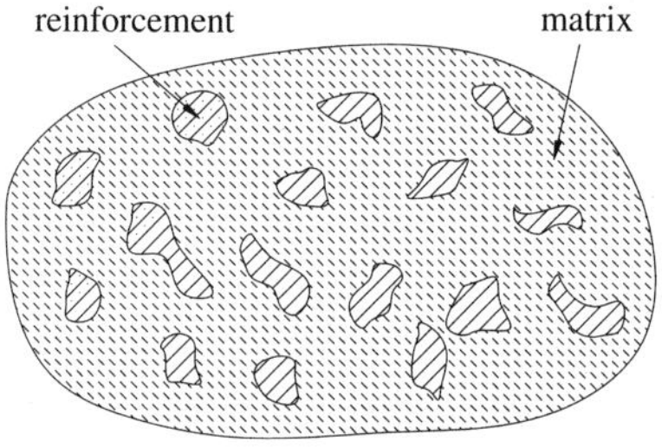

Figure 1. Composite material.

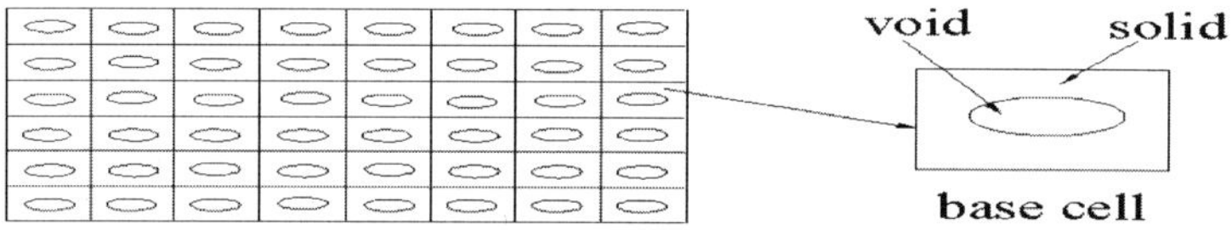

Figure 2. Heterogeneous material with a periodic microstructure.

In the most general case, a composite material [1–3] consists of one or more discontinuous phases distributed in one continuous phase as shown in Figure 1. The continuous phase is called the matrix and may be resin, ceramic, or metal. The discontinuous phase is called reinforcement or inclusions and may be fibers or particles. The inclusions are used to improve certain properties of materials or matrices, such as stiffness, behavior with temperature, resistance to abrasion, decrease of shrinkage. For instance, particles of brittle metals (such as tungsten, chromium, and molybdenum) incorporated in ductile metals can improve their properties at higher temperatures while preserving their ductility at room temperatures; and elastomer particles can be incorporated in brittle polymer matrices to improve their fracture and shock properties by decreasing their sensitivity to cracking.

Functionally graded materials [4, 5] are used to join two different materials without stress concentration at their interface. Gradation in properties from one portion to another portion can be determined by material constituent composition. The volume fraction of one material constituent should be changed from 100% on one side to zero on another side, and that of another material constituent should be changed the other way round. These functionally graded materials can help reducing thermal stress, preventing peeling off of coated layer, preventing micro-crack propagation, providing high-temperature and impact resistant capability, etc.

A heterogeneous material with a periodic microstructure [6–10] is described by its base cells, which is the smallest repetitive unit of material and comprises of a material phase and a void or softer material phase, as shown in Figure 2. It should be emphasized that the microscopic length scale is much larger than molecular dimensions

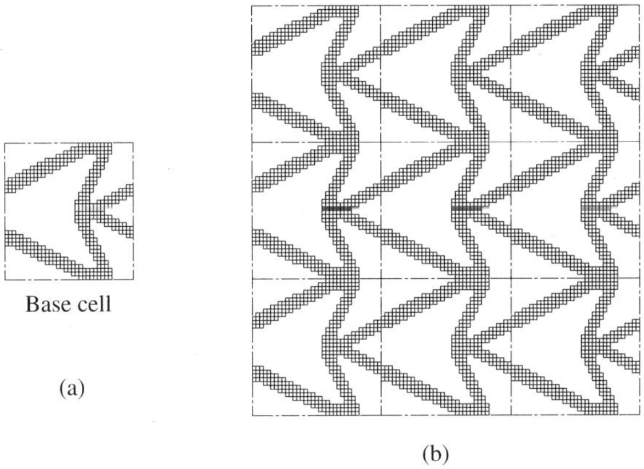

Figure 3. Topology for the material with Poissin's ratio: −0.8.

but much smaller than the component size. The material with a special microstructure may have special properties, such as zero thermal expansion coefficient and negative Poisson's ratio. Its effective properties are determined by the topology of its base cell and the properties of its constituents, and can be predicted by the homogenization theory [9, 10]. In other words, its effective properties or the values of its property characteristics can be changed by designing various topologies of its base cell. With the homogenization theory, the topology of its base cell for required properties can be designed using topology optimization [9, 10]. Its design domain is the base cell, which is discretized by four-node quadrilateral finite elements. The design variables are the density of material in each finite element. The design goal is to minimize the error in obtaining the prescribed elastic properties for several loading cases. For instance, we may specify the elastic properties of a material with Poisson's ratio: −0.8 and solve the optimization problem for a quadratic base cell discretized by 1600 quadrilateral finite elements, each representing one design variable. The resulting topology can be obtained and shown in Figure 3(a) [6]. The base cell is repeated as shown in Figure 3(b), where the mechanism is seen more clearly. When the material is compressed horizontally, the triangles will collapse and result in a vertical contraction, which is the characteristic behavior or performance of a material with negative Poisson's ratio.

However, currently there exists no systematic and effective method for designing the components made of **multi** heterogeneous materials according to the functional requirements from their high-tech applications. The history of materials development has followed the sequence from process to properties and to performance or applications. Human discovered materials naturally produced from volcanic actions and then found suitable uses for them. A simple mixture of clay, sand and straw produced a composite, which was found to have some good properties and then used as building materials by the oldest known civilizations. Even in the case of plastics, the processing techniques such as the polymerization process and incorporation of fibers in polymers were done first, followed by characterization of material properties and microstructures. After their attractive properties (e.g., the considerably low ratio of weight to strength, high corrosion and thermal resistance, high toughness, and low cost) were identified, they have then been used in various fields, such as aerospace, transportation, and other branches of civil and mechanical engineering. Therefore, the conventional component design method is always to first choose a kind of material, and then design the configuration of a component and check whether the component can satisfy the functional requirements. For multi heterogeneous components, however, the design process has to be reversed according to Axiomatic Design theory [11, 12], i.e., from functional requirements in high-tech application to material properties to microstructures and/or constituent compositions and to process. It can be developed under the guidance of Axiomatic Design.

2. DESIGN METHOD FOR THE COMPONENTS MADE OF MULTI HETEROGENEOUS MATERIALS

2.1. Design procedure

According to Axiomatic Design, design involves the continuous processing of information between and within four distinct domains: the consumer domain, the functional domain, the physical domain and the process domain. Customer needs are established in the consumer domain and then are formalized in the functional domain as a set of functional requirements (FRs) that govern the solution process. The creation of a synthesized solution is through the mapping process between the FRs that exist in the functional domain and the design parameters (DPs) that exist in the physical domain. The DPs in the physical domain are then mapped into the process domain in terms of process variables (PVs). The customer domain of multi heterogeneous component design is where the desired performances of the component in high-tech application are specified. These desired performances are its customer attributes (CAs). In the functional domain, its FRs are the configuration of component and the properties of materials in different portions of the component, which can provide the desired performances specified in customer domain. These FRs are satisfied by choosing the microstructure and/or constituent composition of materials and the optimal parameters of the component's geometric shape, which are its DPs in the physical domain. Finally, its PVs in the process domain specify how the desired microstructure and/or constituent composition and geometric parameters can be created. Figure 4 shows the design process for multi heterogeneous components in terms of the four domains of the design world.

According to Figure 4, mapping from customer domain to functional domain is the mapping from the component's performances required in high-tech application to the component's configuration and the properties of materials applied in the component. Mapping from functional domain to physical domain is the mapping from the required component's configuration and the required properties of materials applied in the component to the material microstructure and/or constituent composition and the optimal geometric parameters of the component. Mapping from physical domain to

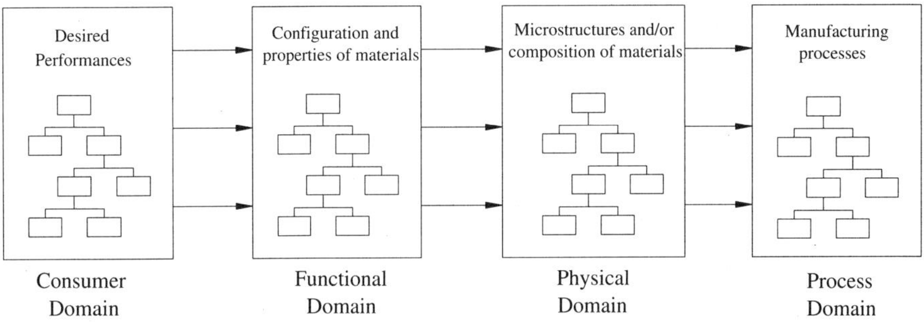

Figure 4. Design process for multi heterogeneous components in terms of the four domains of the design world.

process domain is the mapping from the material microstructure and/or constituent composition and the optimal geometric parameters of the component to the process variables for manufacturing the physical component.

The mapping process between two adjacent domains can be summarized as the mapping process between the design requirements (DRs) ('What we want to achieve') and design solution (DSs) ('How we achieve them'). When mapping from FRs to DPs, the FRs are the design requirements (DRs), and DPs are the design solution (DSs). But when mapping from DPs to PVs, the DPs become the design requirements (DRs), and PVs are the design solution (DSs). For the design with only one objective function or design requirement (DR), the DR does not involve the independent requirement and can reach its optimum by adjusting its corresponding DSs. Therefore, Optimization Design [13] is very effective in this case. But, for the design with multiple objective functions (DRs) that are controlled by the same set of DSs, it is not very effective because the same set of DSs cannot control all DRs to reach their optimums at the same time. When one adjusts the same set of DSs to let the second DR, for example, to reach its optimum, the first optimized DR will be changed. Therefore, one must go back to adjust DSs to optimize the first DR; this in turn changes the second optimized DR. In this case, the most important DR is usually selected as an objective function and the others are eliminated, or different weights are assigned to the different objective functions to form one composite objective function. For the former, it becomes a one-DR problem and Optimization Design is very effective for determining the optimums of both the DR and its corresponding DSs as explained above. But the other DRs have not been optimized. For the latter, although the composite objective function is one DR, the optimization results are for the artificial DR, not for the real DRs, and thus rather unconvincing because different designers may give different weights to the same objective function according to their knowledge base [14]. Therefore, a coupled design is a bad design, and it is significant to apply Axiomatic Design to make DRs to satisfy the Independent Axiom, i.e., a perturbation in a particular DS must affect only its referent DR without affecting other DRs. When they are not coupled with each other, Optimization Design can be then applied very effectively to determine the optimized DSs for each real DR of the design problem, because different real DRs are now controlled by different DSs and can reach their optimums at the same time.

For a component made of a homogeneous material or single heterogeneous material, as mentioned above, its design method is always to first choose a kind of material, and then design the component configuration and check whether the component can satisfy the functional requirements. If the initial material is found not to be suitable after checking, another material can be selected, according to the most important portion of the component, without changing its configuration since it is allowed not to make full use of the material of non-important portion. Therefore, its geometric design is not coupled with its material design. But the components made of **multi** heterogeneous materials are used in high tech and have many rigorous requirements or constraints. As mentioned above, their design processes have to be reversed, i.e., from functional requirements in high-tech application to component configuration to material properties and to material microstructures and/or constituent compositions. Some functional requirements of a component made of multi heterogeneous materials can be satisfied by changing either the component's configuration or material properties in different portions of the component, because these functions will be changed if we either change the component's configuration or change the materials of the component. Thus, their geometric design and material design are coupled with each other. Different configuration or geometric designs will require different material selections, and different material selections of each portion will also influence the shape and dimensions of the component and the material selection for other portions. Therefore, many factors are coupled with each other and their designs become very complicated. It is necessary to apply Axiomatic Design to design the design procedure to decouple them. Otherwise, it is very difficult to obtain good design or optimums for all the DRs as described above.

The elements and workflow of design method developed, under the guidance of Axiomatic Design, for the components made of multi heterogeneous materials are shown in Figure 5 and explained as follows:

First, the performance requirements (i.e., CAs) of the component to be designed are carefully analyzed and can be divided into two groups. The first group (CA_1) should be satisfied by the component's configuration (FR_1), and the second group (CA_2) should be met by the properties of materials in different portions of the component (FR_2). The former is geometric design, and the latter is material design. Its design equation, according to Axiomatic Design, can be obtained as follows:

$$\begin{Bmatrix} CA_1 \\ CA_2 \end{Bmatrix} = \begin{bmatrix} X & 0 \\ X & X \end{bmatrix} \begin{Bmatrix} FR_1 \\ FR_2 \end{Bmatrix} \tag{1}$$

where X represents a non-zero element and 0 represents zero element. From the equation obtained, it can be seen that the design matrix at this level is a triangular matrix, which indicates that the design is a decoupled design [11, 12] and the independence

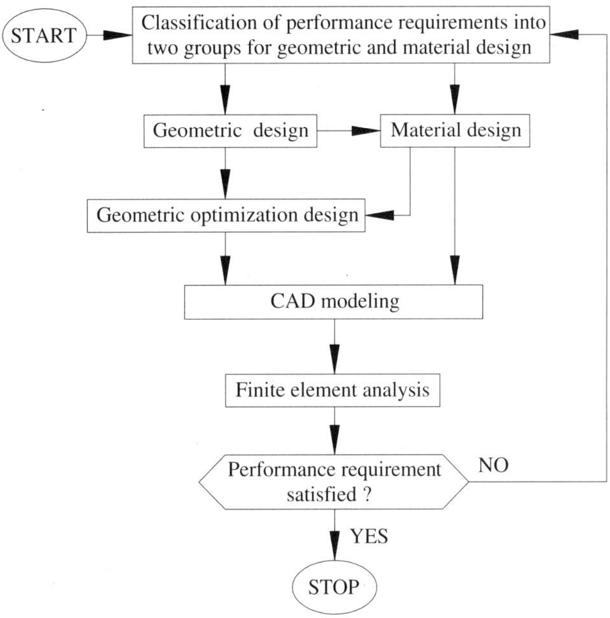

Figure 5. Elements and workflow of design method.

of the CAs can be assured if the FRs are adjusted in a particular order: FR_1 first and then FR_2. Therefore, it is reasonable and necessary that geometric design should be done first and followed by determining material properties. That is, according to CA_1, a 3D variational geometric model [15, 16] of the component (FR_1) can be first built by using conventional design method with the aids of advanced computer-aided design system. Based on the model, the material properties in different portions of the component (FR_2) will then be determined in a certain way.

When mapping from FRs to DPs, if configuration optimization is implemented first to obtain optimized geometric parameters, the design equation will be as follows:

$$\begin{Bmatrix} FR_1 \\ FR_2 \end{Bmatrix} = \begin{bmatrix} X & X \\ X & X \end{bmatrix} \begin{Bmatrix} DP_1 \\ DP_2 \end{Bmatrix} \tag{2}$$

since different material selection scheme will result in different optimal geometric parameters of the component as analyzed above. It can be seen, from Equation (2), that the design matrix is neither a diagonal nor a triangular matrix, which indicates that the design is a coupled design and does not satisfy Independence Axiom [11, 12]. This procedure cannot be accepted and should be reverse. That is, the material selection is implemented first to obtain optimized material microstructures and/or constituent compositions (DP_2), and followed by geometric optimization design to obtain the optimal geometric parameters (DP_1). The design equation can become:

$$\begin{Bmatrix} FR_2 \\ FR_1 \end{Bmatrix} = \begin{bmatrix} X & 0 \\ X & X \end{bmatrix} \begin{Bmatrix} DP_2 \\ DP_1 \end{Bmatrix} \tag{3}$$

It can be seen, from the equation obtained, that the design matrix at this level is also a triangular matrix and Independent Axiom can be met if the DPs are adjusted in a particular order: DP_2 first and then DP_1. Therefore, it is reasonable and necessary that material selection should be done first and followed by geometric parameter optimization.

It is normal to have many suitable design schemes satisfying FR_2. For instance, some material properties required can be satisfied by many different materials, such as composite, functional graded materials, or heterogeneous material with a periodical microstructure. Even for the same type of materials selected, say functional graded materials, there are some different material constituent compositions that can satisfy the requirement concerned. Accordingly, material design optimization is first implemented to determine the optimal material constituent compositions and material microstructures for different portions of the component. Based on the material design, the geometric parameters can be optimized further. After that, a CAD model with the information of both configuration and materials can be created for the component, and finite element analysis method can be applied to analysis whether all the performance requirements are satisfied or not. If the performance requirements are satisfied, the design is over. If not satisfied, their CAs need to be analyzed again, and the above procedure will be repeated until all the requirements are satisfied. The final CAD model can be used for manufacturing the multi heterogeneous component, e.g., using layered manufacturing methods.

Thus, it can be summarized that the design procedure for the components made of multi heterogeneous materials should go through: (1) geometric design ($CA_1 \rightarrow FR_1$), (2) material design ($CA_2 \rightarrow FR_2 \rightarrow DP_2$), and (3) geometric parameter optimization ($FR_1 \rightarrow DP_1$). Since the first and the third steps are conventional geometric design that is well developed, there is no need to further introduce them in this chapter. But material design is new and must be developed in details.

2.2. Material design

The elements and workflow of material design method ($CA_2 \rightarrow FR_2 \rightarrow DP_2$) developed for the components made of multi heterogeneous materials are shown in Figure 6. Its design procedure is explained as follows:

Step 1: Create 3D variational geometric model for the component

The 3D variational geometry model [15, 16] of the component should be first built with the aids of current advanced CAD/CAE software. The reason for using variational model is that the modification of its geometric parameters or model can be simplified after material design. After material design, only few variables need to be optimized or

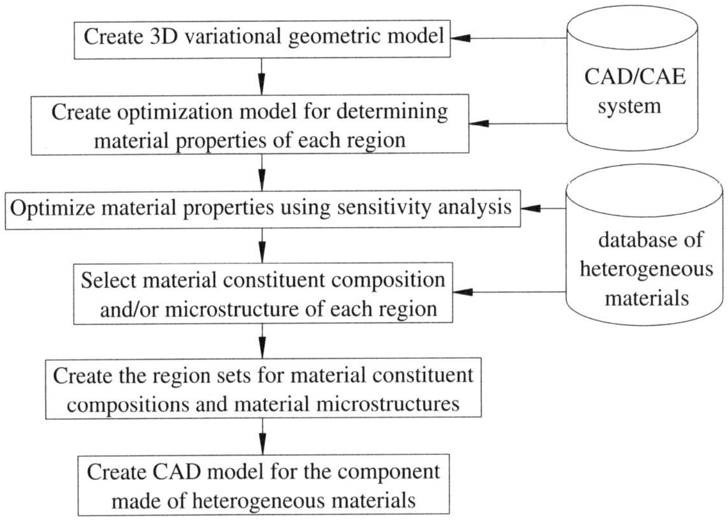

Figure 6. Elements and workflow of material design method.

modified and other parameters will be modified automatically by computer according to the relationships between these parameters and the variables.

This model should meet both the first type of performance requirements (CA_1) and the constraints of the component (e.g., its overall dimension and its relationship dimension with other components in assembly), and has suitable variables for geometric parameters and functional relationships between the variables and other dimensions of the component. This work belongs to conventional geometric design and is used as the input of material design.

Step 2: Create optimization model for determining material properties of each region in the component

Based on the 3D variational geometric model made, the component will be divided into several portions or regions for selecting the optimal material constituent composition and/or microstructure. The partitioning can be implemented by using any commercial Finite Element Analysis (FEA) [17] software since current FEA software all has this function. The number of regions depends on the component to be designed since different components will have different shapes and requirements. But the guideline for it is that the number of regions is small since, normally, there are not many different types of material constituent compositions and/or microstructures in a component. The approach is designed to (a) select one kind of material for the component first, (b) analyze the component's performance using finite element analysis method, and (c) find out the regions having larger response to the component's performance. Based on the result, the geometric model of the component will be modified by (i) increasing the size of those having larger responses where more material regions will be created by means of preprocessor program [17] of finite element analysis in CAE software, and (ii) reducing the size of those having less response where less material regions will be created. The relationships will then be made between their partial nodal coordinates and the variables of the component's geometric parameters, so that its geometric parameters can be optimized after material design.

Effective material properties include mechanical properties (e.g., hardness, bulk and shear modulus), thermal properties (e.g., coefficient of thermal expansion and coefficient of thermal conductivity), electrical properties (e.g., electric conductivity and dielectric constant), optical properties, and chemical properties (e.g., diffusion constant). The performance requirement of component can involves one of them or some of them (e.g., both small coefficient of thermal expansion and high mechanical strength), and should be optimized by material design for each region. The objective function for optimization model is the functional relationship between the component's performance and the material properties of regions created, and can be in the forms of analytical expression or implicit expression that can be determined by finite element model. The constraints for optimization model normally involve its manufacturability, affinity of two materials in the adjacent regions, and/or physical properties of component.

Step 3: Optimize material properties using sensitivity analysis and steepest descend method

The sensitivity analysis [18] of material properties is to determine the changing rates of response quantities (i.e., component's performances) due to variations in design variables (i.e., material properties in different regions). If objective function is in the form of mathematical equations, the sensitivity analysis is to evaluate the partial derivative of component's performances with respect to material properties in each region. If objective function is an implicit expression determined by finite element model, the sensitivity analysis is to create global stiffness matrix for each performance, and to determine the changing rates of the performance due to variations in the material properties of each region. Based on the sensitivity analysis, the optimal values of material properties will be obtained for each region using Steepest Descend Method [13].

Step 4: Select material constituent compositions and/or microstructures

According to the results of optimization, suitable materials can be selected for each region from the database of heterogeneous materials. Normally, there are many suitable materials. Thus, Genetic Algorithms [19–20] will be applied to find the optimal scheme that can satisfy both constraints and the best performances.

Step 5: Create the region sets for material constituent compositions and material microstructures respectively

The regions with the same or similar material constituent compositions and material microstructures can be combined together into a larger region. Thus, the component

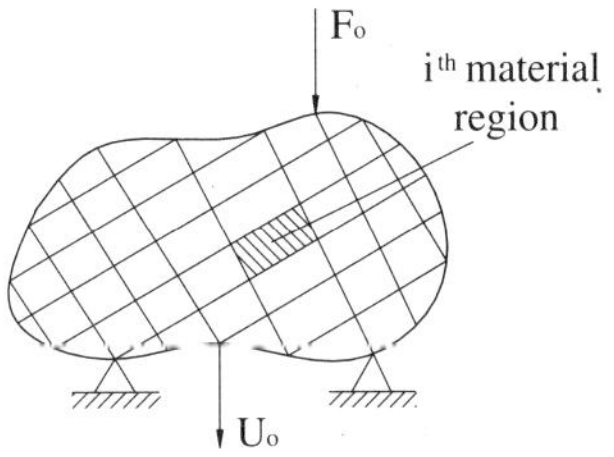

Figure 7. A simply supported component made of heterogeneous materials.

consists of several larger regions for different material constituent compositions, which form a region set, and comprises several larger regions for different material microstructures, which form another region set.

Step 6: Create CAD model for the component made of multi heterogeneous materials

After the above steps, all the information needed for creating CAD model have been obtained. The information includes two region sets, the code name of material constituent composition for each region, the code name of material microstructure for each region. According to these code names, the information, such as material constituent composition function, geometric model of inclusion, and inserting function, can be obtained from the database of heterogeneous materials. The method for CAD modeling will be introduced in Section 3. After its CAD model is created, the optimal geometric parameters of the component can be further obtained using optimization design method [13], which belongs to conventional geometric design and are not illustrated in this chapter. The following sections will introduce the elements of material design method in more details.

2.3. How to determine the optimal material properties needed in different regions

As mentioned in the previous section, the optimal properties of materials needed in different portions of a component can be determined using sensitivity analysis and steepest descend method. Sensitivity analysis is the method for obtaining the changing rates of response quantities due to variations in design variables. In this case, the design variables are the material properties of different portions in a component, and the response quantity is the objective performance of the component. For instance, a simply supported component made of heterogeneous materials shown in Figure 7 is subject to a vertical load (F_0). Its design variables are the relevant material properties of different regions in the component, and its response quantity is its response displacement (U_0). The procedure of determining the optimal properties of materials needed in different portions of a component based on sensitivity analysis and steepest descend method can be explained as follows:

Step 1: Create optimization model

The optimization model for selecting materials in different regions can be written as follows:

$$\left.\begin{array}{l} \text{Minimize} \quad U_0 = f(B) \\ \text{Subject to the constraint:} \\ \qquad g_u(B) \le 0, \quad u = 1, 2, \ldots, m \\ \qquad h_v(B) = 0, \quad v = 1, 2, \ldots, p \end{array}\right\} \tag{4}$$

where $U_0 = (u_1, u_2, \ldots, u_k)^T$ and is the objective performance vector of the component; k is the number of objective performences; $B = \left(b_1^{(1)}, b_2^{(1)}, \ldots, b_{C1}^{(1)}, b_1^{(2)}, b_2^{(2)}, \ldots, b_{C2}^{(2)}, \ldots, b_1^{(n)}, b_2^{(n)}, \ldots, b_{Cn}^{(n)}\right)$; and $b_j^{(i)} (i = 1, 2, \ldots, n, j = 1, 2, \ldots C_i)$ is the j-th material property in the i-th region.

Step 2: Determine material sensitivity for each region

If the objective function is in the form of mathematical equations, the sensitivity ($s_j^{(i)}$) of the j-th material property of the i-th region with respect to the objective performance of the component can be obtained by:

$$s_j^{(i)} = \frac{\partial U_0}{\partial b_j^{(i)}} \tag{5}$$

If the objective function is an implicit expression determined by finite element model, the procedure of obtaining the sensitivity is as follows:

(a) Derive the global stiffness matrix $[K]$ for the component
To simplify the illustration, each material region is a finite element. The component is first divided into an equivalent system of finite elements with associated nodes and the most appropriate element type. According to each type of response quantities (e.g., displacement) of the component, the stiffness matrix of each finite element can be obtained and assembled into the global stiffness matrix of the component. Thus, its equilibrium equation can be given as follows:

$$[K]U = F \tag{6}$$

where $[K]$ is the global stiffness matrix of the component, U is the displacement vector of the nodal points of the component, and F is the external load vector of the component.

(b) Derive the sensitivity of the j-th property in material property vector of the i-th region with respect to the objective performance of the component

The global stiffness matrix of the component can be considered as a function of the j-th property in material property vector of the i-th region, and its equilibrium equation can be rewritten as:

$$\left[K\left(b_j^{(i)}\right)\right]U = F \tag{7}$$

Implicit differentiation of Eq. (7) with respect to the variable, $b_j^{(i)}$, yields

$$\left[K\left(b_j^{(i)}\right)\right]\frac{\partial U}{\partial b_j^{(i)}} = \frac{\partial F}{\partial b_j^{(i)}} - \frac{\partial\left[K\left(b_j^{(i)}\right)\right]}{\partial b_j^{(i)}}U \tag{8}$$

Since the load does not vary with the material property, the first item on the right side of Eq. (8) is equal to zero. Thus, the equation can be rewritten as:

$$\frac{\partial U}{\partial b_j^{(i)}} = -\left[K\left(b_j^{(i)}\right)\right]^{-1}\frac{\partial\left[K\left(b_j^{(i)}\right)\right]}{\partial b_j^{(i)}}U \tag{9}$$

(c) Partition the global stiffness matrix
The displacement vector can be partitioned as:

$$U^* = \begin{Bmatrix} U_0 \\ U_i \\ U_q \end{Bmatrix} \tag{10}$$

where U_0 is sub-vector of displacement for objective performances, U_i is the sub-vector of nodal displacement of the i-th region, and U_q is the sub-vector consisting of other displacement. Thus, the global stiffness matrix and the external load vector can be partitioned according to the sequence of U as:

$$\left[K^*\left(b_j^{(i)}\right)\right] = \begin{bmatrix} \left[K_{00}\left(b_j^{(i)}\right)\right] & \left[K_{0i}\left(b_j^{(i)}\right)\right] & \left[K_{0q}\left(b_j^{(i)}\right)\right] \\ \left[K_{i0}\left(b_j^{(i)}\right)\right] & \left[K_{ii}\left(b_j^{(i)}\right)\right] & \left[K_{iq}\left(b_j^{(i)}\right)\right] \\ \left[K_{q0}\left(b_j^{(i)}\right)\right] & \left[K_{qi}\left(b_j^{(i)}\right)\right] & \left[K_{qq}\left(b_j^{(i)}\right)\right] \end{bmatrix} \tag{11}$$

and

$$F^* = \begin{Bmatrix} F_0 \\ F_i \\ F_q \end{Bmatrix} \tag{12}$$

(d) Approximate the sensitivity by finite differences
The most challenging task here is to evaluate the derivatives of the stiffness matrix with respect to the design parameters. Normally, this is done by approximating

them by finite differences [21]. Thus, Eq. (9) can be mathematically stated as:

$$\left\{\begin{array}{c}\frac{\partial U_0}{\partial b_j^{(i)}} \\ \frac{\partial U_i}{\partial b_j^{(i)}} \\ \frac{\partial U_q}{\partial b_j^{(i)}}\end{array}\right\} = -\left[K^*\left(b_j^{(i)}\right)\right]^{-1} \frac{\Delta\left[K^*\left(b_j^{(i)}\right)\right]}{\Delta b_j^{(i)}} U^*$$

$$= -\left[K^*\left(b_j^{(i)}\right)\right]^{-1} \frac{\left[K^*\left(b_j^{(i)} + h_j^{(i)}\right) - K^*\left(b_j^{(i)}\right)\right]}{h_j^{(i)}} U^* \tag{13}$$

where $h_j^{(i)}$ is perturbation step length for the j-th material property of the i-th region. Therefore, the sensitivity ($s_j^{(i)}$) of the j-th material property of the i-th region with respect to the objective performance of the component can be obtained from Eq. (13) as:

$$s_j^{(i)} = \frac{\partial U_0}{\partial b_j^{(i)}} \tag{14}$$

All the sensitivities can then be assembled into a sensitivity vector S as:

$$S = \left(s_1^{(1)}, s_2^{(1)}, \ldots, s_{C1}^{(1)}, s_1^{(2)}, s_2^{(2)}, \ldots, s_{C2}^{(2)}, \ldots, s_1^{(n)}, s_2^{(n)}, \ldots, s_{Cn}^{(n)}\right)^{\mathrm{T}} \tag{15}$$

Step 3: Search for the optimal material property vector of different regions of the component

Optimization can be implemented according to Steepest Descend Method [13]:

(a) Start with an initial point B_1. Set the iteration number as $k = 1$.
(b) Find the search direction $-S_k$ using sensitivity analysis as introduced above.
(c) Determine the optimal step length h_k in the direction $-S_k$ and set

$$B_{k+1} = B_k - h_k S_k \tag{16}$$

(d) Test the new point, B_{k+1}, for optimality. The new objective performance of the component can be estimated by:

$$U_0 = f(B_{k+1}) \tag{17}$$

or U_0 can be obtained from Eq. (10), where

$$U^* = [K^*(B_{k+1})]^{-1} F^* = [K^*(B_k - h_k S_k)]^{-1} F^* \tag{18}$$

After the new values of material properties (B_{k+1}) are obtained, check both if there are suitable material microstructures and/or constituent composition for them in the database of heterogeneous materials and if the response quantities (i.e., component's performances) are improved. If the answers for both checks are "yes", set the new iteration number $k = k + 1$ and go to step (b). The above procedure from step (b) will be repeated until the improvement of objective performance of the component is smaller than a threshold. If the answer for any of the two checks is "no", the optimization process is over. The last material property vector of different regions in the component is the optimal material property vector of different regions of the component.

2.4. How to select material constituent composition and microstructure

After the material properties of each region in the component are determined as introduced above, the suitable material constituent composition and microstructure can be selected for each region from the database of heterogeneous materials that is designed using IDEFIX notation [22] as shown in Figure 8. Commercial tools are readily available for constructing IDEFIX diagrams and generating database structure.

According to IDEFIX notation, in Figure 8, the square box indicates an independent entity, which can exist on its own as its name suggests; the rounded box represents a dependent entity, which can exist only if some other entities also exist; and the name of entity is listed above the box. The top portion of the box contains primary key attributes, the lower portion contains the remaining attributes, and the notation "FK" denotes a foreign key. The lines are labeled with relationship type names. A solid line between two entities denotes an idetifying relationship type, and a dashed line represents a non-identifying relationship type. The solid ball denotes many multiplicity (zero or more), the lack of a symbol indicates a multiplicity of exactly one, and a line with a solid ball at one end represents a one-to-many relationship. The large circle with two lines underneath denotes generalization. The attribute next to the circle is called a discriminator and indicates whether each heterogeneous material record is elaborated by material constituent composition or material microstructure.

2.4.1. Select material constituent compositions from the database of material constituent composition

There are two types of operations for it: from code name (C.N.) to properties and from properties to code name (C.N.).

(a) Based on the code name of material constituent composition, retreive its material constituents, the code name of constituent composition function, the properties of material constituents, manufacturing technology & equipments, application fields, and application examples.
(b) Based on the optimal material properties determined using above method, search for the code name of material constituent composition which has the properties close to or a bit higher than the optimal properties determined. Then, based on the

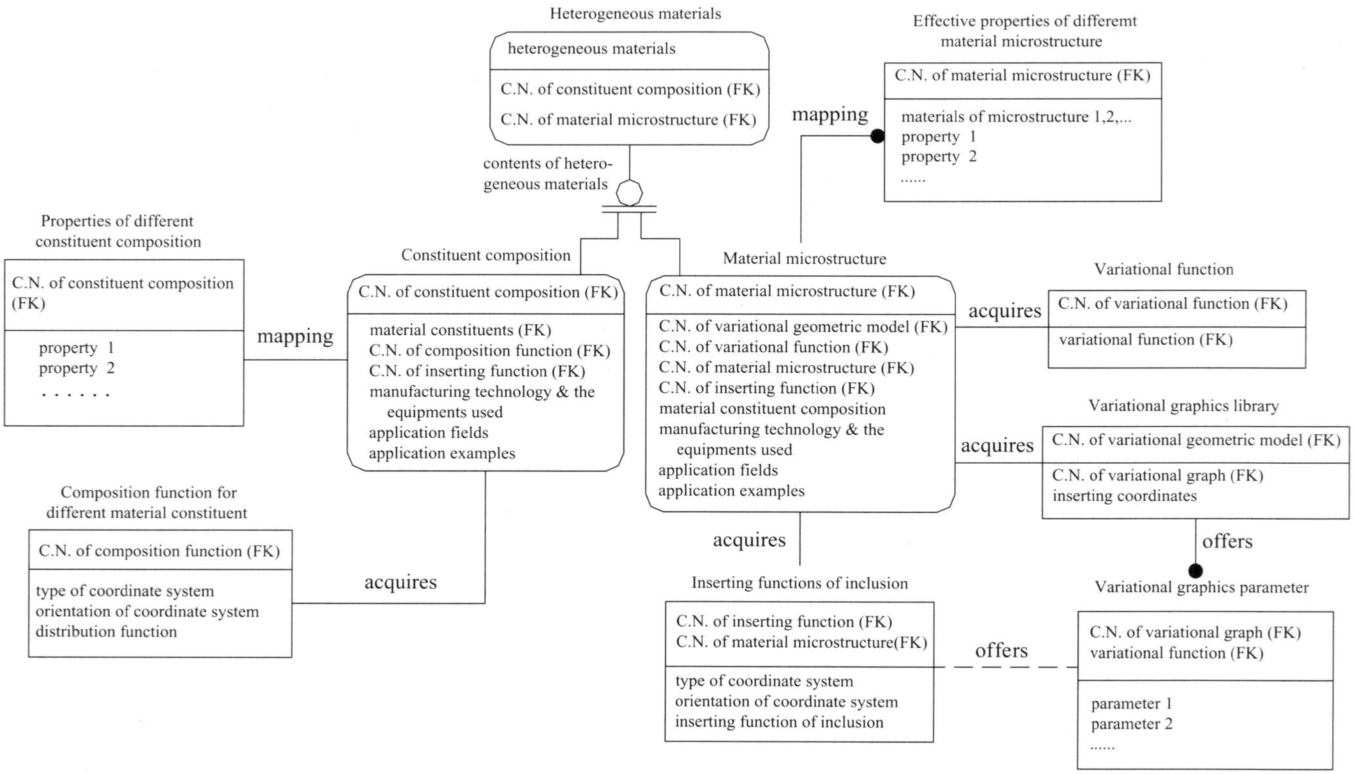

Figure 8. Database of heterogeneous materials designed using IDEFIX.

code name of material constituent composition, retreive its material constituents, the code name of constituent composition function, the properties of material constituents, manufacturing technology & equipments, application fields, and application examples.

Since, normally, there are more material constituent compositions which satisfy the requirement from the optimal material properties determined, they all should be found out.

2.4.2. Select material microstructures from the database of material microstructure

There are also two types of operations for it: from code name (C.N.) to properties and from properties to code name (C.N.).

(a) Based on the code name of material microstructure, retreive the code name of variational geometric model of microstructure, the code name of its inserting function, the type of heterogeneous materials (composite or heterogeneous material with a periodic microstructure), effective properties of material, manufacturing technology & equipments, application fields, and application examples.
(b) Based on the optimal material properties determined using above method, search for the code name of material microstructure which has the properties close to or a bit higher than the optimal properties. Then, based on the code name of material microstructure, retreive its code name of variational geometric model of microstructure, the code name of its inserting function, the type of heterogeneous materials (composite or heterogeneous material with a periodic microstructure), effective properties of material, manufacturing technology & equipments, application fields, and application examples.

Since, normally, there are also more material microstructures which satisfy the requirement from the optimal material properties determined, they all should be found out.

2.5. How to generate two material region sets

After the selection from the databases, there appear many suitable material constituent compositions and material microstructures for each region of the component. Among them, the most suitable one should be selected with good material affinities for adjacent regions, the lowest material cost, and the lowest manufacturing cost. As far as the material constituent composition is concerned, the regions with similar material constituent composition can be aggregated into a larger region, and thus the component can be divided into several regions which form a set of material constituent composition regions (C_1). For the material microstructure, the regions with similar material microstructure can also be combined into a larger region, and thus the component can also be divided into several regions which form another set of material microstructure regions (C_2). This work is implemented using Genetic Algorithms [19, 20] and explained as follows:

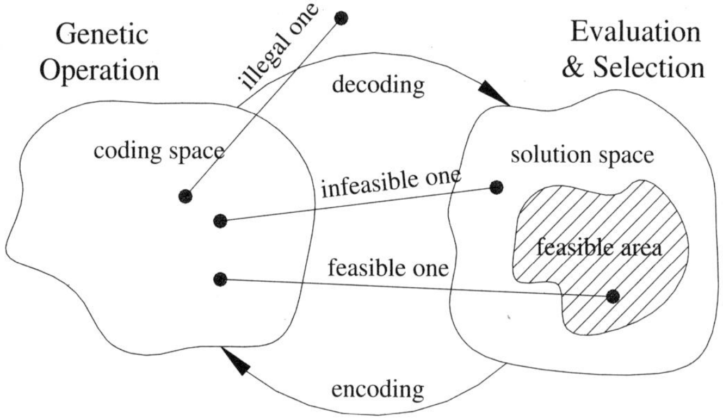

Figure 9. Mapping between coding space and solution space.

(1) Encode decision variables

If there are n regions in a component and m_i material choices for the i-th region, the decision variables or solutions (i.e., the material constituent compositions and material microstructures of different regions of a component) are encoded as a string, called chromosome, which have n bits and a decimal value ($1\sim m_i$) for the i-th bit, and can be represented as:

$1\sim m_1$	$1\sim m_2$	$1\sim m_3$	......	$1\sim m_i$	......	$1\sim m_n$

(2) Determine the size of population

The coding space of chromosomes covers total population (TP), which is very large and can be calculated by $\Pi_{i=1}^{n} m_i$. The size of initial population should have less chromosomes, which are randomly generated. The number (L) of chromosomes in the initial population is determined, according to the TP, by:

$$L = \begin{cases} TP, & \text{if } TP < 20 \\ 0.2 \times TP, & \text{if } TP \geq 20 \text{ and } L > 20 \\ 20, & \text{if } TP \geq 20 \text{ and } L \leq 20 \end{cases} \qquad (19)$$

(3) Evaluation

The dicision variables represented by the chromosome can be an illegal one, infeasible one, or feasible one as shown in Figure 9. All the genetic operations are implemented in the coding space, and the evaluation and selection are in the solution space. Mapping between the two spaces is through encoding and decoding. If the solution or decision variables is outside the solution space, it must be an illegal one, which cannot be

Table 1 Database for the affinity of materials

Material A		Material B		Affinity of materials $k_j^{(i)}$
Code No.	Price	Code No.	Price	

evaluated and has to be eliminated. The chromosomes in the coding space defined by this paper can always be mapped to the solution space, and no illegal one will be generated. The infeasible one is the solution which cannot satisfy constraints from manufacturing technology, materials etc., and is outside the feasible area. The feasible one is the solution which meets the constraints, but must not be an optimal solution.

The objective function for deriving optimal solution is represented by fitness. The fitness value for the i-th chromosome is calculated by:

$$f_i = \frac{1}{m_i}\sum_{j=1}^{m_i} k_j^{(i)} + k_1 \sum_{j=1}^{n} [V_j(C_j + M_j)]^{-a} + P_i \tag{20}$$

In Eq. (20), the first item is for evaluating the material affinity of adjacent regions in the i-th chromosome, where m_i is the number of boundaries of adjacent regions in the i-th chromosome and $k_j^{(i)}$ is the material affinity value of the j-th boundary in the i-th chromosome. If the material affinity of two adjacent regions is poor, there must be stress concentration at the interface between the two regions. The material affinity can be a value within (0, 1), and can be searched from its database, the structure of which is represented by Table 1. If the material of a region is the same as that of one of its adjacent regions, the material affinity for the adjacent regions is 1. If the material affinity cannot be found from the database, the materials of the two adjecant regions cannot be connected together and the value for the material affinity will be −100 for penalty of not satisfying material constraint.

The second item in Eq. (20) is for evaluating the material cost and manufacturing cost, where C_j is the price per unit volume of material in the j-th region and can be searched from the database represented by Table 1, V_j is the volume of the j-th region, M_j is the manufacturing cost per unit volume for the j-th region and can be searched from the database about manufacturability, the structure of which is represented by Table 2, and n is the number of regions in the component. The coefficients k_1 and a are used to adjust the weight of items. The database of manufacturability includes the types and models of layered manufacturing machines, the types and number of materials to be added, the minimal possible size of inclusions, and material manufacturing cost per unit volume.

The third item in Eq. (20) is for penalty of not satisfying manufacturability constraints, where P_i is the the penalty value of the i-th chromosome. The material constituents selected should be able to be manufactured using corresponding layered

Table 2 Database for manufacturability

Type of layered manufacturing machine	Model of layered manufacturing machine	Type of the materials to be added	Number of the material to be added	Minimal possible size of inclusions	Material manufacturing cost per unit volume

manufacturing machines. When there is a suitable machine found from the database represented by Table 2, P_i is equal to zero. If there is no suitable machine found, the penalty (P_i) of the i-th chromosome will be –100.

(4) Selection

The first generation of population is selected ramdonly from the initial population using a roulette wheel approach [19].

(5) Crossover operation

After the first generation is obtained, genetic operations involve crossover and mutation to yield offspring. Crossover operates on two chromosomes at a time and generates offspring by combining both chromosomes' features. But it should avoid inbreeding since the crossover between two similar chromosomes is not useful for efficient evolution. The degree of homology between two chromosomes may be estimated by calculating the evolutional distance between genes of two chromosomes. Since the evolutional distance between genes of two chromosomes is not easy to be calculated, an alternative method has been developed in this paper. The degree of homology is determined based on "family tree". For example, the first generation has twelve chromosomes, 1.1 to 1.12, as shown in Figure 10. The second generation after genetic operation and selection has twelve chromosomes: 1.1~1.5, 1.7~1.9, 1.11, 2.1~2.3. The chromosomes 2.1–2.3 are three offsprings generated and the 1.6, 1.10, 1.12 have been eliminated. Chromosomes 1.1 and 2.1 form a family; and chromosomes 1.2, 2.2, and 2.3 form another family. The third generation after another genetic operation and selection has twelve chromosomes: 1.1~1.3, 1.5, 1.8, 1.9, 1.11, 2.1~2.3, 3.2, 3.3. The 3.1–3.3 are three offsprings generated and the 1.4, 1.7, and 3.1 have been eliminated. Chromosomes 1.2, 2.2, and 2.3 form a family, and Chromosomes 1.1, 1.9, 2.1, 3.2, and 3.3 form another family. The chromosomes with cross in Figure 10 are eliminated through selections. Chromosome 1.11, for instance, has no consanguinity relationship with chromosome 3.2 which is in another family, so that they should be given a priority for crossover. After evolution for many many generations, all the chromosomes in population may have consanguinity relationships with each other. The degree of homology between two chromosomes is measured by the number of evolutional paths between them. For example, the number of evolutional paths between chromosome 1.2 and 2.2 is 1, and that between chromosome 2.1 and 3.3 is 3. Sometimes, there are several different routes between two chromosomes. In this case,

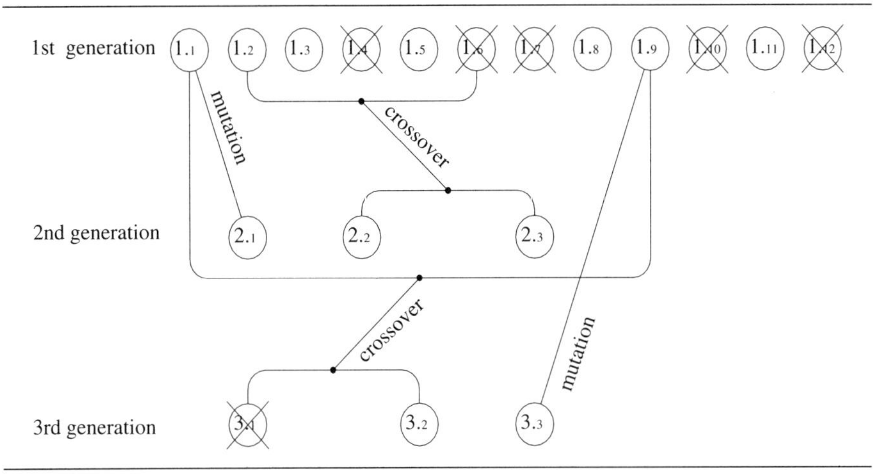

Figure 10. Family tree.

the route with less number of evolutional paths is selected for measuring their degree of homology.

If there are n chromosomes in a population, the number of possible pairs for crossover can be calculated by:

$$S = C_n^2 = \frac{n\,!}{2(n-2)\,!} \tag{21}$$

The probability of crossover for the i-th pair of chromosomes is determined by:

$$P_c^{(i)} = \frac{G_i}{\sqrt{k + G_i^2}} \tag{22}$$

where G_i is the degree of homology between the chromosomes in the i-th pair, and k is a positive real number which is used to adjust the sensitivity of G_i with respect to the probability of crossover. When there is no consanguinity relationship between two chromosomes, let G_i be infinity and thus $P_c^{(i)}$ is equal to 1.

After the probabilities of crossover for all the pairs of chromosomes are determined, each probability can be normalized by:

$$P_c^{(i)*} = \frac{P_c^{(i)}}{\sum_{i=1}^{S} P_c^{(i)}} \tag{23}$$

The cumulative probability for the i-th pair of chromosomes can then be obtained by:

$$q_c^{(i)} = \sum_{i=1}^{i} P_c^{(i)*} \tag{24}$$

Based on their cumulative probability, a roulette wheel can be constructed. The selection process begins by spinning the roulette wheel for $(0.2L)$ times; each time, a pair of chromosomes is selected for a new population in the following way:

Step 1. Generate a random number r from the range [0, 1].
Step 2. If $r \leq q_c^{(1)}$, then select the first pair of chromosomes; otherwise, selecte the i-th pair of chromosomes such that $q_c^{(i-1)} < r \leq q_c^{(i)}$.

For each pair of chromosomes selected, for instance:
Parent 1:

X_1	X_2	...	X_j	X_{j+1}	...	X_k	X_{k+1}	X_{k+2}	...	X_n

Parent 2:

Y_1	Y_2	...	Y_j	Y_{j+1}	...	Y_k	Y_{k+1}	Y_{k+2}	...	Y_n

generate two random numbers, j and k ($j < k$), from the range (1~n), and exchange the segments bounded by the crossover points represented by the two random numbers to create two new chromosomes called offspring:
Offspring 1:

X_1	X_2	...	Y_j	Y_{j+1}	...	Y_k	X_{k+1}	X_{k+2}	...	X_n

Offspring 2:

Y_1	Y_2	...	X_j	X_{j+1}	...	X_k	Y_{k+1}	Y_{k+2}	...	Y_n

(6) Mutation

New chromosomes or offspring can also be formed using a mutation operator, which involves modification of the values of genes in a chromosome and increases the variability of a population. In the case when fitness functions of chromosomes in a population converge to a small range or local optimum, it is difficult for crossover to generate offspring with more improved fitness function values, but mutation can play an important role for it. In fact, that fitness functions of chromosomes in a population converge to a small range means that more and more similar chromosomes have been obtained. The similarity of two chromosomes indicates that the two chromosomes have the same genes in some same bits. A population can be divided into several groups according to their similarities. The similarity of the i-th group can be represented by the product of the number (G_i) of bits with same genes and the number (C_i) of chromosomes in the group. Some chromosomes may be similar to more groups, but they can only belong to the groups they are most similar to. The group with more similarity should have priority for mutation. In order to find global optimum rapidly, probability of mutation can be adjusted using the following formula:

$$p_m^{(i)} = \frac{C_i G_i}{\sqrt{k + (C_i G_i)^2}} \tag{25}$$

where k is a positive real number and is used to adjust the sensitivity of $C_i G_i$ with respect to the probability of mutation. Using the same roulette wheel approach as that used for crossover, 10% of chromosomes will be selected for mutation. Since the same genes the chromosomes of a group have in the same bits is possibly the local optimal one, a gene (e.g., the k-th gene) is randomly selected from these same genes and its value is replaced with a value randomly selected from the range ($1\sim m_k$) for its possible material constituent compositions and material microstructures.

(7) Reproduction

The reproduction is performed on enlarged sampling space [19]. After crossover operations, offspring with 40% population has been generated. With mutation operations, offspring with 10% population has also been obtained. Therefore, the parent and the offspring have 150% population in total and form an enlarged sampling space. It is easy to implement evolution based on enlarged sampling space [19]. After the genetic operations, check whether there are the same chromosomes among the parent and the offspring. If yes, keep one of them and eliminate the others. Then, an elitist selection scheme is used. The chromosome with the highest fitness function value among the parent and the offspring is selected as an elitist and copied directly into the new population of next generation. With this operation, nature's survival-of-the-fittest mechanism can be guaranteed. The other chromosomes are selected by a roulette wheel selection scheme. A roulette wheel is a wheel on which each chromosome in the parent and the offspring is represented by a slot with slot size proportional to its fitness function values.

(8) Stop criterion

After the second generation is generated, the above crossover, mutation and reproduction operations will be repeated until the best chromosome is obtained. Since genetic operation is implemented randomly, its fitness is not always increased continuously. It is not correct to stop the optimization process when there is no increment or improvement for the fitness after a new generation is obtained. Therefore, a threshold is used for the number of generations that have the same best chromosomes. That is, if $n_i - n^*$ is greater than a threashold $q = 20$, the iteration process can be stopped, where n_i is the current generation number and n^* denotes the generation number when the best chromosome, among all generations, is first found. Then the best chromosome can be output as the optimal solution.

(9) Construct the regions for different material constituent compositions and material microstructures

With the optimal solution obtained, the types of material constituent compositions and material microstructures in all the regions of the component have been optimized.

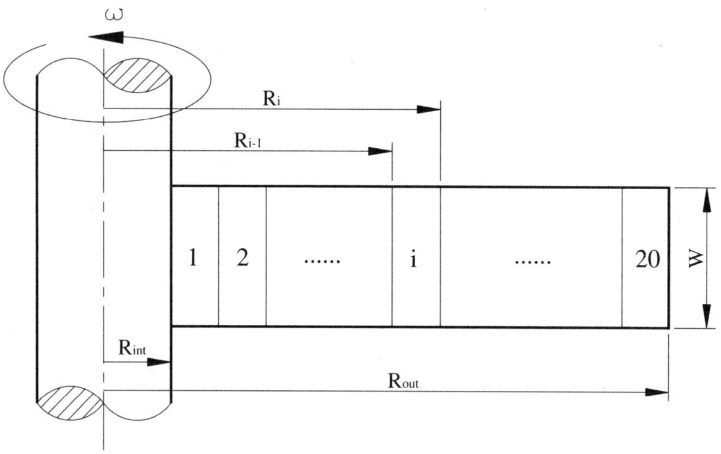

Figure 11. A flywheel and its material regions.

Based on the solution, the adjacent regions with similar material constituent compositions can be aggregated into a larger region, and those with similar material microstructures can also be combined into a larger region. Thus, two region sets are formed for material constituent compositions and material microstructures respectively.

2.6. An example of multi heterogeneous component design

Since the design procedure is justified by Axiomatic Design and all the techniques used are mature and justified already, a simple design example is introduced in this section for illustrating how to apply this method. As the example, a flywheel is now designed using the method introduced in this paper. This flywheel is not an ordinary one. It has many rigorous requirements or constraints and is used in a high-tech device. The constraints include very light weight, very high moment of inertia, disk-like shape, and other required working conditions (e.g., available space). If a homogeneous material or single heterogeneous material is used for it, this homogeneous material must have very large specific gravity to meet very high moment of inertia, which cannot satisfy the requirement of very light weight. Therefore, multi heterogeneous materials are needed for its design. These requirements or constraints can be divided into two types as introduced in Section 2.1. According to its first type of the component's performances (CA_1), the flywheel has been designed by geometric design as shown in Figure 11. Its shape is like a disk with a thickness W. Its outer radius is R_{out} and inner radius is R_{int}.

(1) Requirements for material design

Based on the geometric design, its second type of the component's performances (CA_2) should be further satisfied by material design according to Axiomatic Design (Eq. 1). Its CA_2 is to maximize the moment of inertia of flywheel (I). But it has to meet the constraints, including (a) Its mass must be smaller than a threshold, M_0; (b) The largest Von Mises stress in the flywheel must be smaller than a threshold, σ_0; and (c) Other constraints from manufacturability, material affinity between two adjacent regions, etc.

(2) Generate material regions

Based on the geometric design, its 3D variational geometric model can be built with the aids of current advanced CAD/CAE software. Then, the flywheel is divided into 20 (or even more) regions, as shown in Figure 11, each of which has a specified material constituent composition and a specified material microstructure. It does not mean final solution is 20 material regions with 20 different materials. After material design, the adjacent regions with the same or similar materials will be merged into a larger region, and the number of the sub-regions will become much less.

(3) Create optimization model

The optimization model for selecting the material in each region can be written as follows:

$$\text{Minimize: } U_0 = \frac{1}{I} = \frac{1}{\sum_{i=1}^{20} I_i} = \frac{1}{W\sum_{i=1}^{20} \frac{\pi\nu_i}{2g}\left(R_i^4 - R_{i-1}^4\right)} \tag{26}$$

$$\text{Subject to } M = W\sum_{i=1}^{20} \frac{\pi\nu_i}{g}\left(R_i^2 - R_{i-1}^2\right) \le M_0 \tag{27}$$

$$\sigma_{VM} \le \sigma_0 \tag{28}$$

where W is the width of the flywheel, ν_i is the specific gravity of material in the i-th region, g is acceleration of gravity, M is the mass of flywheel, and σ_{VM} is Von Mises stress in the flywheel.

(4) Sensitivity analysis of material properties

From Eq. (26), it can be known that the moment of inertia for the flywheel is only related to the specific gravities of materials (ν_i) among the properties of materials. Its sensitivity analysis is to evaluate the partial derivative of the moment of inertia of flywheel with respect to the specific gravities of material in each region. For the i-th region, its sensitivity can be obtained as follows:

$$S_i = \frac{\partial I}{\partial \nu_i} = \frac{W\pi}{2g}\left(R_i^4 - R_{i-1}^4\right) \qquad i = 1, 2, \ldots, 20 \tag{29}$$

(5) Search for the optimal material property vector of different regions of the flywheel

According to steepest descend method introduced above, optimization is implemented as follows:

(a) Start with an initial point V_1, which is $(v_1^{(1)}, v_2^{(1)}, \ldots, v_{20}^{(1)})^T$. Set the iteration number as $k = 1$.
(b) Find the search direction S_k using sensitivity analysis as introduced above.
(c) Determine the optimal step length h_k in the direction S_k and set

$$V_{k+1} = V_k + h_k S_k \tag{30}$$

(d) Test the new point, V_{k+1}, for optimality.

It is obvious, from Eq. (29), that the sensitivity of outside region is larger than that of inside region. After the specific gravities of materials in regions are replaced using Eq. (30), the new objective performance of the flywheel can be estimated by Eq. (26), the mass of flywheel (M^*) can be calculated by Eq. (27), and the largest Von Mises stress in each region can be obtained using finite element analysis. If $M^* > M_0$, the specific gravity vector will be modified using:

$$V_{k+1} = \frac{M_0}{M^*}(V_k + h_k S_k) \tag{31}$$

so that the total mass of flywheel can be kept as M_0. If $\sigma_{VM}^* > \sigma_0$, the optimization process is over. After the material specific gravity of each region in the component is determined as introduced above, the suitable material constituent composition and microstructure should be able to be selected for each region from the database of heterogeneous materials, and should meet the constraint specified in Eq. (27) and (28), i.e., the total mass of flywheel is smaller than or equal to the limit M_0 and the tensile strength of the material selected for the i-th region should be larger than the largest Von Mises stress in each region.

If the scheme of material design is better than the original one, set the new iteration number $k = k + 1$ and go to step (b). The above procedure from Step (b) will be repeated until the decrement of objective performance of the flywheel (Eq. 26) is smaller than a threshold. During the process, the specific gravity of material in outside region will be increased more and more, and those in inside regions decreased. The last material specific gravity vector of all the regions in the flywheel obtained is the optimal solution.

(6) Select material constituent composition and microstructure for each region

According to the optimized specific gravity vector, there are many suitable material constituent compositions and material microstructures for each region of the component. Among them, the most suitable one is selected with good material affinities for adjacent regions, the lowest material cost, and the lowest manufacturing cost using Genetic Algorithms introduced in Section 2.5.

3. CAD MODELING METHOD FOR THE COMPONENTS MADE OF MULTI HETEROGENEOUS MATERIALS

After design, the computer models for representing components made of multi heterogeneous materials need first to be built so that further analysis, optimization and manufacturing can be implemented based on the models.

Current modeling techniques can capture only the geometric information [15, 16]. Some researchers [23–28] are focusing on modeling heterogeneous objects by including the variation in constituent composition along with the geometry in the solid model for functional graded materials. But representing the microstructure of heterogeneous components is beyond their scope [23]. Since the microstructure size is very small, the model consisting of such microstructures has huge number of data to be stored. Even with the help of high-speed modern computers, the processing of the model is extremely difficult and needs extreme care and thoughts for I/O operations. This paper develops a modeling method, which can implemented by applying the functions of current CAD graphic software and build the model that includes all the material information (about periodic microstructures, constituent compositions, inclusions, and embedded parts) along with geometry information in current 3D solid modeling without compromising on the speed of the operations and reasonable utilization of computer resources. A special supporting component will be taken as a practical example to describe the modeling method for the component.

3.1. Analyses of the requirements for representing the components made of heterogeneous materials

The requirements for representing a component made of heterogeneous materials should be made clear first before developing a modeling method for multi heterogeneous components. Since heterogeneous materials cover composite materials, functionally graded materials, and heterogeneous materials with a periodic microstructure, the requirements for each of them are analyzed, respectively, as follows:

As introduced in Section 1, a composite material consists of one or more discontinuous phases distributed in one continuous phase as shown in Figure 1. The properties of composite materials result mainly from the material properties of both their matrix and inclusions and the geometrical feature and distribution of their inclusions. Thus, to describe a component made of a composite material, its CAD model will have to specify the geometric feature, material, and distribution of the inclusions and the matrix material as well as the geometric model of the material region in the component. The geometric feature is represented by a code name that can be used to retrieve the necessary information from a database for confecting the spraying material. The necessary information includes the type of inclusions, such as fibers, sheets or lump, and normal distribution parameters of their dominant dimensions.

Functionally graded materials are used to join two different materials without stress concentration at their interface. Actually, there are many material composition functions [5]. The designers can choose certain composition functions from them for their applications. For example, the following parabolic function is selected for material composite function of the metal/ceramic functionally graded material in the cylinder of vehicular engines or pressure vessels:

$$V_A = a_0 + a_1 x + a_2 x^2 \tag{32}$$

where V_A is the volume fraction of metal and x is the distance from one side. The coefficients of the parabolic function are optimized subject to criteria that the thermal flux across the material is minimized, and the thermal stresses are minimized and restricted below the yield stress of the material. In fact, many nature's organisms have had their functionally graded tissue, such as teeth, skins, bones, and bamboo. Their composition functions have been optimized by evolution based on nature's survival-of-the-fittest mechanism. After the determination of composition function, physical properties can also be estimated based on property estimation models [5]. Thus, in order to describe a component made of a functionally graded material, its CAD model will have to specify its material constituents and their composition functions as well as the geometric model of the material region in the component.

A heterogeneous material with a periodic microstructure is described by its base cells, which is the smallest repetitive unit of material and comprises of a material phase and a void phase, as shown in Figure 2. To describe a component made of a heterogeneous material with a periodic microstructure, its CAD model will have to specify its variable geometric model, material constituents and distribution function of the base cells as well as the geometric model of the material region in the component.

According to the previous analysis of the requirements for representing the components made of the three types of materials, it is obvious that the functional requirement (*FR*) of its CAD model can be decomposed into three sub-*FR*s: representing geometries of the material regions in the component (needed for all these materials), their material constituent compositions, and their material microstructures (including the geometric feature and distributions of inclusions for composite materials and the base cell for those with a periodic microstructure), which are noun phrases corresponding to "**what** we want to achieve" and can be written as:

FR_1 = Representing geometries of the material regions in the component
FR_2 = Representing material constituent compositions of the material regions in the component
FR_3 = Representing material microstructures of the material regions in the component

Thus, according to Axiomatic Design [11, 12], the CAD model should be decomposed into three sub-models to satisfy the three sub-*FR*s, respectively, as the design solutions (*DS*). These are stated starting with a verb corresponding to "**how** we achieve it" and can be written as:

DS_1 = Build their geometric models
DS_2 = Build their material constituent composition models
DS_3 = Build their material microstructure models

Therefore, the design equation for it can be obtained as follows:

$$\begin{Bmatrix} FR_1 \\ FR_2 \\ FR_3 \end{Bmatrix} = \begin{bmatrix} X & 0 & 0 \\ X & X & 0 \\ X & X & X \end{bmatrix} \begin{Bmatrix} DS_1 \\ DS_2 \\ DS_3 \end{Bmatrix} \quad (33)$$

From the equation obtained, it can be seen that the design matrix is a triangular matrix, which indicates that the design solution is a decoupled design and satisfies Independence Axiom [11, 12]. In other words, it is correct to decompose a CAD model of the multi heterogeneous component into the three types of sub-models without coupling for successful application since satisfying Independence Axiom can ensure the independence of these sub-models.

3.2. Unified CAD modeling for the component made of heterogeneous materials

According to the analysis in the previous section, CAD models for the components made of the three types of materials can be uniformly formed or integrated by the three types of sub-models. The first type of sub-model is a geometric model. A 3D solid model representing the geometry of a component can be made by using current CAD graphic software and is indicated by G. It can be divided into n portions or regions based on their material constituent compositions. Thus, the material constituent composition set can be indicated by:

$$C = \{C_i, i = 1, 2, \ldots, n\} \quad (34)$$

According to its material microstructures, the geometry model can also be divided into m parts or regions if there are m different microstructures. The material microstructure set can be written as:

$$S = \{S_j, j = 1, 2, \ldots, m\} \quad (35)$$

Thus, the material region set (M) of the component can be obtained by solving Cartesian product of C and S as:

$$M = C \times S = \{M_{ij} \mid i \in (1, 2, 3 \ldots, n), j \in (1, 2, \ldots, m)\} \quad (36)$$

For example, there are six material constituent composition regions ($n = 6$) and four material microstructure regions ($m = 4$) in the component G as shown in Figure 12. Solving its Cartesian product of C and S can obtain fourteen material regions, each of

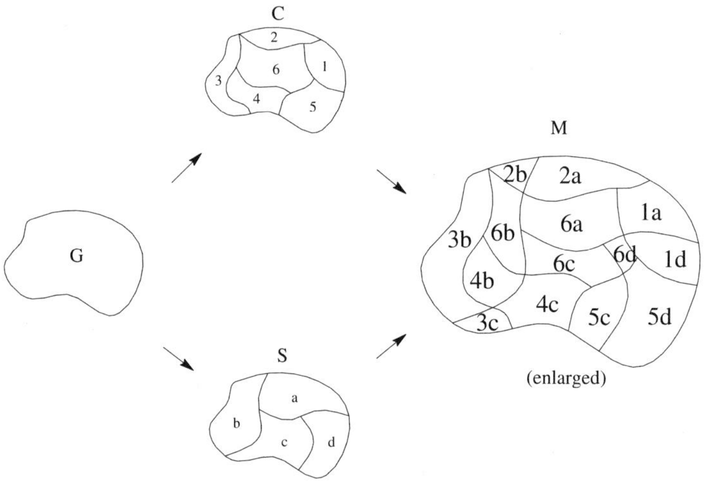

Figure 12. Material regions for the components made of heterogeneous materials.

which has a specified material constituent composition and a specified microstructure. The first Arabic figure of the symbol of each region is the code name of material constituent composition region, and the second English letter is the code name of material microstructure region. Region 6*a*, for instance, indicates that its material constituent composition in this region is determined by that in Region 6 of material constituent composition set and its material microstructure is specified by that in Region *a* of material microstructure set.

The last two sub-models are material constituent composition model, and material microstructure model, which cannot be represented by 3D solid model and have to be in other forms. In fact, a model is an approximation of the component or object along one or more dimensions of interest, and can be any entity that exhibits some aspect of the component that is required for the purposes concerned [29]. Therefore, a model can be in many different forms, such as a physical model, a wire-wrapped circuit board, a system of equations, frames and slots (i.e. schema [30]), 3D solid models, or their combinations. We use a *schema* to represent the structural knowledge or information for each of the last two sub-models since the schema is easy to be used to establish the linkage among graphic library, database and application software, which is prerequisite for modeling the components with several sub-models. Each *schema* consists of several *frames*. Each *frame* represents a type of inclusion or periodic microstructure cell and consists of several *slots*. Each *slot* contains a type of information to describe the frame in more detail, such as the type of the local coordinate system of a material region, the location and orientation of the local coordinate system in the global coordinate system, the type of spraying material, the inserting array for each type of periodic microstructure cell, the composition function of each material constituent, or the code name of the variable geometrical model of a periodic microstructure cell.

3.3. Material constituent composition models

Each region in material constituent composition set has a specified material constituent composition. The volume fraction of the h-th material constituent at the position (x, y, z) in Cartesian coordinate system, for example, can be represented as:

$$V_h = f_h(x, y, z) \tag{37}$$

This material composition function along with primary material combinations and intended applications can be obtained from many literatures [5], and organized into a database for applications. Designers may select suitable material composition functions from it for their applications according to the functional requirements of a component.

Based on schema theory [30], frame and slots can be used to organize the knowledge for modeling. The model for the i-th material constituent composition region is then designed as the following typical schema with one frame:

$$
\begin{aligned}
C_i = \{ & \text{Coordinate system type: Cartesian, cylindrical, or spherical coordinate system} \\
& \text{Origin of coordinate system: } Xc_i,\ Yc_i,\ Zc_i \\
& \text{Orientation of coordinate system: } \alpha c_i,\ \beta c_i,\ \gamma c_i \\
& \text{Number of material types: } Nc_i \\
& \text{Material types: } A_1,\ A_2,\ \ldots,\ A_{Nc_i} \\
& \text{Material constituent composition function: } \left[V_{hCi} = f_{hCi}(x, y, z), \right. \\
& \left. h = 1, 2, \ldots, N_{Ci} \,\middle|\, \sum_{h=1}^{Nc_i} V_{hCi} = 1,\ (x, y, z) \in C_i \right] \\
\} &
\end{aligned}
\tag{38}
$$

The first slot is the local coordinate system type of the i-th material region, which may be Cartesian, cylindrical, or spherical coordinate system. The second and the third slots are the origin and the orientation of the local coordinate system, respectively, which are based on global coordinate system. The fourth slot is the number of material types in the material region. The fifth slot is the material types used in the material region, which are represented by their code names. All the information about each type of material can be retrieved from a material database according to its code name. The sixth slot is the material constituent composition function set, which includes the composition function of each material constituent in the region that is the function of the position (x, y, z) in Cartesian coordinate system, for example. In each position, the sum of their volume fractions should be equal to one or 100%.

3.4. Material microstructure models

The material microstructure model (S) covers those for composite materials (R), heterogeneous materials with a periodic microstructure (P) and the materials without inclusions and periodic microstructures (O), i.e.,

$$S = [S_j, j = 1, 2, \ldots, m \mid m = (u + v + w), S_i \in (R + P + O)] \tag{39}$$

where $R = [R_a, a = 1, 2, \ldots, u]$, $P = [P_b, b = 1, 2, \ldots, v]$, and $O = [O_d, d = 1, 2, \ldots, w]$. Since there is no spraying or insertion operation in the region without inclusion and periodic microstructure, there is no need to build a material microstructure model for the region, i.e., $O = [O_d = \text{"nil"}, d = 1, 2, \ldots, w]$.

3.4.1. Material microstructure models for composite materials (R)

As mentioned previously, composite material consists of matrix and inclusions. The latter may have various shapes, sizes, and distributions. Their shapes and sizes are varied randomly, and their distributing densities in the matrix may be variable or not variable. Since the components are considered to be made by layered manufacturing technology in this paper, the inclusions are sprayed onto the layer where the matrix material is being spread. Using the schema theory, the model for the a-th material microstructure region can be designed as follows:

R_a = {Coordinate system type: Cartesian, cylindrical, or spherical coordinate system
Origin of coordinate system: X_{Ra}, Y_{Ra}, Z_{Ra}
Orientation of coordinate system: α_{Ra}, β_{Ra}, γ_{Ra}
Number of spaying operations: N_{Ra}
Spraying operation 1:
Spraying operation 2:
......
Spraying operation N_{Ra}:
} (40)

The first three slots are the same as those in Formula (38). The fourth slot is different from that in Formula (38) and is the number of spraying operations (N_{Ra}), below which N_{Ra} sub-frames are listed. Each sub-frame describes one type of spraying operation and consists of two slots for the detail of its operation. The sub-frame for the first spraying operation, for example, can be written as:

Spraying operation 1:
Spraying material: Code name of material 1
Spraying function: $V_{Ra1} = [f_{Ra1}(x, y, z) | (x, y, z) \in R_a]$

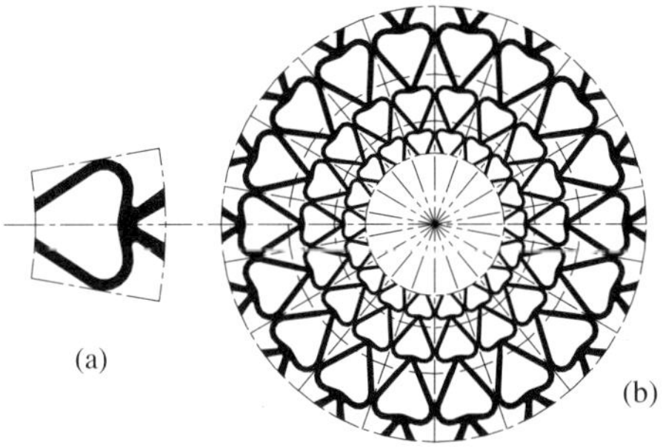

Figure 13. Periodic microstructures in cylindrical coordinate system.

The first slot in the sub-frame is the code name of material type. All the information about the inclusion (e.g., its material type, shape, and average size) can be retrieved from a material database according to its code name. The second slot in the sub-frame is the spraying volume fraction of inclusion and a function of the spraying position (x, y, z) in Cartesian coordinate system, for example. In each position, the sum of volume fractions of all the inclusions and matrix should be equal to one, which will be ensured in a main model introduced in Section 3.5.

3.4.2. Material microstructure models for heterogeneous materials with a periodic microstructure (P)

As introduced previously, a heterogeneous material with a periodic microstructure is described by its base cell, which is the smallest repetitive unit of material and comprises of a material phase and a void phase. The base cells are arranged into a rectangular array (Figure 3(b)), cylindrical array or spherical array. Figure 13(b), for example, shows a cross section of the base cells shown in Figure 13(a) in a cylindrical array, and also represents the cross section passing the center in a spherical array.

The model for the b-th material microstructure region with a heterogeneous material with a periodic microstructure can be expressed by a schema like Formula (41).

$P_b = \{$Coordinate system type: Cartesian, cylindrical, or spherical coordinate system

Origin of coordinate system: X_{Pb}, Y_{Pb}, Z_{Pb}

Orientation of coordinate system: α_{Pb}, β_{Pb}, γ_{Pb}

Number of insertion operations: N_{Pb}

Insertion operation 1:

Insertion operation 2:

......

Insertion operation N_{Pb}:

$\}$ (41)

The first three slots are the same as those in Formula (40). The fourth slot is different and the number of insertion operations. If the base cell consists of only one type of material, the number of insertion operation is 1 and there is only one sub-frame below the fourth slot, which includes six slots. Taking the base cells (in the Cartesian coordinate system) shown in Figure 3(b) as an example, its sub-frame can be expressed as follows:

Insertion operation 1:
  Insertion: Code name of base cell
  Insertion material: Nil
  Inserting position function: $(x, y, z) = [(x_1(t_1), y_1(t_2), z_1(t_3))|(t_1, t_2, t_3) \in \text{"Integer"}, (x, y, z) \in P_b]$
  Dimension: $F_{D1}(x, y, z)$
  Orientation: $F_{\theta 1}(x, y, z)$
  Type of RBO: Matrix dominant complex_union

The first slot in the sub-frame is the pattern of base cell, which can be retrieved from a variable microstructure graphics library according to the code name of its pattern. The second slot is the material of base cell. When the heterogeneous material with a periodic microstructure consists of only one type of material, its material is matrix material, which has been determined by material constituent composition model already. Thus, this slot can be filled by "Nil". The third slot is the inserting positions of base cells, which should be at the points in an array of local coordinate system and within its material microstructure region. For example, if Cartesian coordinate system is applied, its array can be determined, as shown in Figure 14, by:

$$\begin{aligned} x &= \{b_x t_1 + c_x, t_1 = 1, 2, \ldots\} = \{x_1, x_2, \ldots\} \\ y &= \{b_y t_2 + c_y, t_2 = 1, 2, \ldots\} = \{y_1, y_2, \ldots\} \\ z &= \{b_z t_3 + c_z, t_3 = 1, 2, \ldots\} = \{z_1, z_2, \ldots\} \end{aligned} \tag{42}$$

where b_x, b_y, b_z, c_x, c_y and c_z are constants. The fourth slot is the dimension of base cell, which is determined by a special function set, $F_{D1}(x, y, z)$, which is a vector including all the parameters of 3D parametric model of the base cell while x, y, z are the coordinates of inserting points of base cells. In Cartesian coordination system, the "Dimension" for all the base cells shown in Figure 3(b) are the same, i.e., Dimension: "constant". But, if cylindrical or spherical coordination system is used as shown in Figure 13, the dimensions vectors of all the base cells in the same circle are the same and those in different circles are the linear functions of their radial position coordinates. The fifth slot is the orientation of base cell, which is also determined by a special function set, $F_{\theta 1}(x, y, z)$, which is a vector including three axial angles of base cell while x, y, z, are the coordinates of inserting points of base cells. In Cartesian

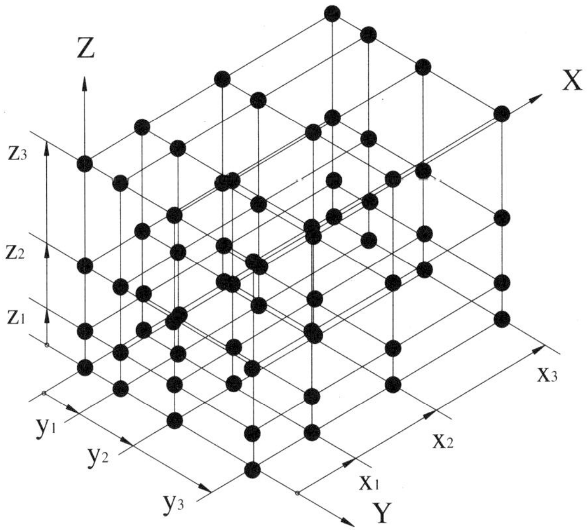

Figure 14. Inserting positions.

coordination system, the orientation vectors for all the base cells shown in Figure 3(b) are the same, i.e., Orientation: "constant". But, if cylindrical or spherical coordination system is used as shown in Figure 13, the orientation vectors of base cells are the normal vectors of their inserting points. Thus, the orientation vector of all the base cells in the same radial are the same. The sixth slot is the type of Reasoning Boolean Operations (RBO) [31, 32]. The RBO is different from the conventional Boolean Operation [15, 16]. The latter deals with only geometry, but the former deals with both geometry and material information. Unlike conventional Boolean Operations, the RBO needs to be executed according to the dominant material information, which is defined either matrix dominant or inclusion dominant union, subtract, and intersect according to the design intent. Here, three types of RBO will be used and are illustrated as follows:

- **Matrix dominant subtraction**
  In Figure 15, let the constituent compositions of matrix material A, inclusion material B and inclusion material C be C_A, M_B and M_C respectively. Matrix dominant subtraction is to excavate matrix material at the inserting position according to the shape of inclusion to obtain a gaseous inclusion or void. This operation can be expressed as:

$$A(C_A) - B(M_B) \tag{43}$$

and the result is shown in Figure 15(a).

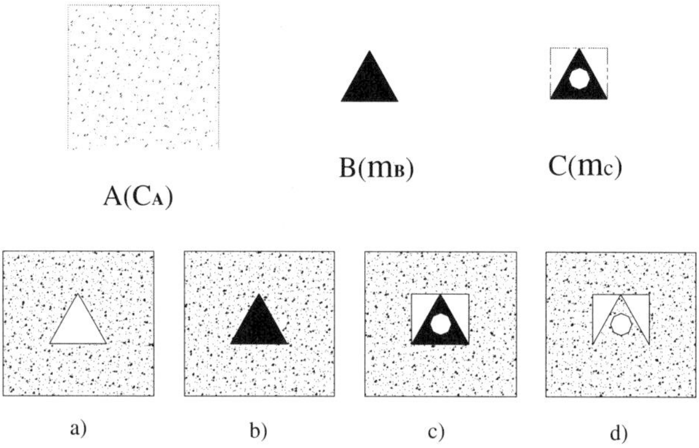

Figure 15. Reasoning Boolean Operations.

- **Inclusion dominant complex_union**
  This operation is to excavate matrix material at the inserting position according to the shape of inclusion to obtain a void first and then insert the inclusion in it. When inclusion B is applied, the operation can be expressed as:

$$\{A(C_A) - B(M_B)\} + \{B(M_B) \cap A(C_A)\} \quad (44)$$

  and the result is shown in Figure 15(b). If inclusion C is applied, its result can be shown in Figure 15(c).
- **Matrix dominant complex_union**
  This operation is to excavate matrix material at the inserting position according to the shape of inclusion to obtain a gaseous inclusion first, then insert the inclusion in it, and replace the inclusion material with the matrix material. If inclusion C is applied, the operation can be expressed as:

$$\{A(C_A) - C(M_C)\} + \{A(C_A) \cap C(M_C)\} \quad (45)$$

  and the result is shown as Figure 15(d).

When the heterogeneous material with a periodic microstructure (e.g., that shown in Figure 16 [8]) consists of several types of materials, such as three types of materials as shown in Figure 17, its basic cell can be decomposed into three sub-cells. Its model is the same as Formula (41). The number of insertion operations should be 3, below which there are three sub-frames. Each sub-frame represents a sub-cell insertion and also has six slots. The material of sub-cell with the largest volume or functionally graded material in a cell is defined as matrix material. For the basic cell in Figure 17, sub-cell 1 has the largest volume, and its material is taken as matrix material and is determined by its material constituent composition model. Thus, its insertion material is still "Nil" and its type of RBO is still matrix dominant complex_union. But, in each

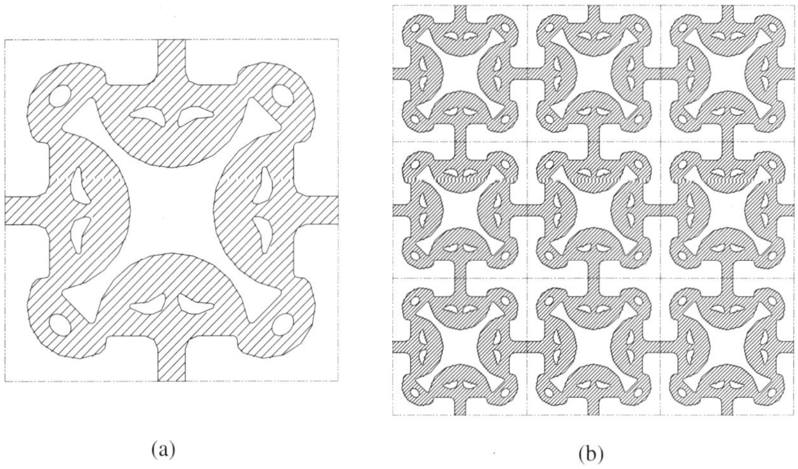

Figure 16. An example of the microstructures with a single material.

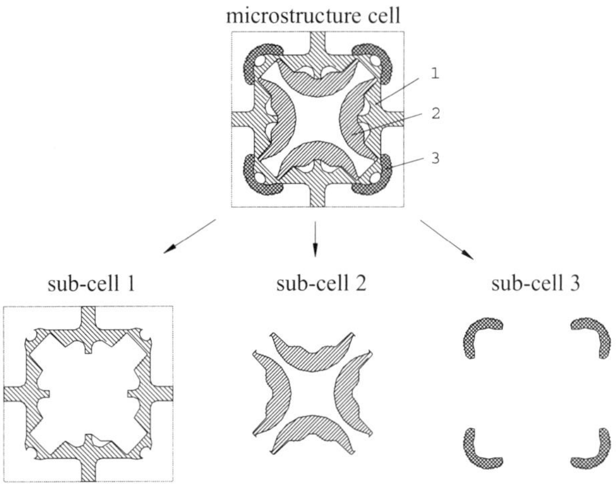

Figure 17. An example of the microstructures with three material constituents.

of the next two sub-frames for other two sub-cells, "code name of its material" should be specified for the insertion material in the second slot and the "inclusion dominant complex_union" should be filled for the type of RBO in the sixth slot.

3.5. Main model for integrating the two types of sub-models

After the sub-models have been made in the form of schema for material constituent composition and material microstructure in each region, a main model can be built to integrate these sub-models for application. The main model can be written as:

$$
\begin{aligned}
Q_G = \{ & \text{Material constituent composition model:} C = \{C_i, i = 1, 2, \ldots, n\} \\
& \text{Material microstructure model:} S = \{S_j, j = 1, 2, \ldots, m | m = (u + v + w), \\
& \qquad\qquad S_j \in (R + P + O)\} \\
& \text{Composite material model:} R = \{R_a, a = 1, 2, \ldots, u\} \\
& \text{Periodic microstructure model:} P = \{P_b, b = 1, 2, \ldots, v\} \\
& \text{Model for those without microstructures:} O = \{O_d = \text{"nil"}, d = 1, 2, \ldots, w\} \\
& \text{Material region: } M = C \times S = \{M_{ij} | i \in (1, 2, \ldots, n), j \in (1, 2, \ldots, m)\} \\
& \text{Number of material regions: } N_M \\
& \text{Materials region 1:} \\
& \text{Material region 2:} \\
& \ldots\ldots \\
& \text{Material region } N_M: \\
\} &
\end{aligned} \tag{46}
$$

The first five slots in Q_G are used to describe sub-models of the component. The sixth slot is material region set. The seventh slot is the number of material regions, below which there are N_M sub-frames for the details of the N_M material regions. In the sub-frame of each material region, the first two slots are the identification codes (IDs) of material constituent composition model and material microstructure model respectively. If the material microstructure is composite material, the third slot must be added to specify the volume fraction of its matrix material since the sum of volume fractions of all the inclusions and matrix in each position should be equal to one as mentioned previously. If material region 1 is a composite material region, for instance, its sub-frame can be written as:

Materials region 1:
ID of material constituent composition model: $[C1, C1 \in C]$
ID of material microstructure model: $[S1, S1 \in S]$
Volume fraction of matrix: $V_{hC1} = V_{hC1}(1 - \sum_{N=1}^{N_{R1}} V_{R1N}), h = 1, 2, \ldots, N_{C1}$

where $C1$ is not C_1 and is one region in C, $S1$ is also not S_1 and is one region in S, and the like.

3.6. An example of modeling

Figure 18 shows a special support component. Its right end is required to provide high abrasion resistant capacity, and its lengthwise thermal deformation should be close to zero. In order to meet these requirements, a kind of material (m_1) with good strength is employed for the left end part, another kind of material (m_2) with a special microstructure (M_2) and very small thermal expansion coefficient is used for the intermediate body, and a kind of composite material (material m_3 as matrix material and m_4 as inclusions) with high abrasion resistant capacity is applied for its

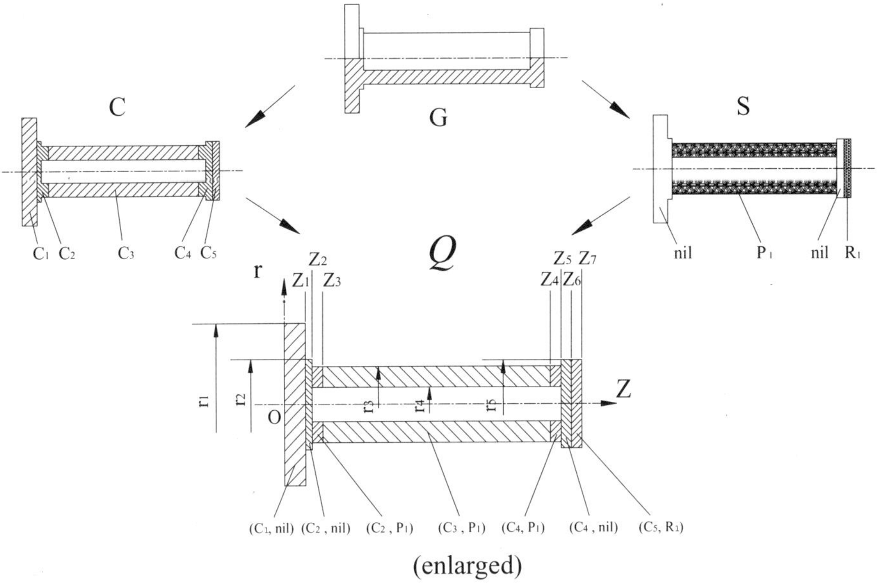

Figure 18. An example of CAD modeling for a component.

right end part. To prevent high stresses and crack at the interface between two kinds of materials, functionally graded materials are applied both between m_1 and m_2 and between m_2 and m_3. Therefore, this component can be divided into five material constituent composition regions and four material microstructure regions.

Its CAD model can be built by integrating the following sub-models:

(1) 3D solid models of the component

According to Eqs. (34) and (35), its material constituent composition set and material microstructure set are indicated as follows:

$$C = \{C_1, C_2, C_3, C_4, C_5\} \tag{47}$$

$$R = \{R_1\} \tag{48}$$

$$P = \{P_1\} \tag{49}$$

$$O = \{O_1, O_2\} = \{\text{nil, nil}\} \tag{50}$$

$$S = \{S_j, j = 1, 2, 3, 4 | S_j \in (R + P + O)\} = \{\text{nil}, P_1, \text{nil}, R_1\} \tag{51}$$

The material regions of the component can be obtained by solving Cartesian product of C and S as:

$$\begin{aligned} Q = M = C \times S &= \{M_{11}, M_{21}, M_{22}, M_{32}, M_{42}, M_{43}, M_{54}\} \\ &= \{(C_1, \text{nil}), (C_2, \text{nil}), (C_2, P_1), (C_3, P_1), (C_4, P_1), (C_4, \text{nil}), (C_5, R_1)\} \end{aligned} \tag{52}$$

Thus, the B-rep scheme [15, 16] can be used to represent the shape of the whole component and all the borders between different material regions in the component.

(2) Its material constituent composition model C
Since there are five material constituent composition regions, its five models can be built according to the schema shown in Formula (38), where all the attributes for the slots of each model are listed in Table 3.

(3) Its composite material model R
It has only one composite material region and its model can be written as follows:

R_1 = {Coordinate system type: cylindrical coordinate system
Origin of coordinate system: 0, 0, Z_6
Orientation of coordinate system: 0, 0, 0
Number of spraying operations: 1
Spraying operation 1:
Spraying material: m_4
Spraying function: $V_{R11} = [f_{R11}(z) \mid 0 \leq z \leq (Z_7 - Z_6)]$
} (53)

(4) Its periodic microstructure model P
It has only one periodic microstructure region and its model can be obtained as:

P_1 = {Coordinate system type: cylindrical coordinate system
Origin of coordinate system: 0, 0, Z_2
Orientation of coordinate system: 0, 0, 0
Number of insertion operations: 1
Insertion operation 1:
Insertion: Code name of basic-cell
Insertion material: Nil
Inserting position function: $(r, \theta, z) = [(k_{r1}t_1 + c_{r1}, k_{\theta 1}t_2 + c_{\theta 1}, k_{z1}t_3 + c_{z1}) \mid (t_1, t_2, t_3) \in$ "Integer", $r_4 \leq r \leq r_3, 0 \leq \theta \leq 2\pi, 0 \leq z \leq (Z_5 - Z_2)]$
Dimension: $k_{D1}r + c_{D1}$
Orientation: θ
Type of RBO: Matrix dominant complex_union
} (54)

Table 3 Attributes for each slot in material constituent composition models

Region No. of material constituent composition	Type of coordinate system	Origin of coordinate system	Orientation of coordinate system	Number of materials	Material type	Material composition function
1	Cylindrical coordinate system	0, 0, 0	0, 0, 0	1	m_1	even
2		$0, 0, Z_1$		2	m_1	$V_1 = 1 - z/(Z_3 - Z_1)$ $0 \leq z \leq (Z_3 - Z_1)$
					m_2	$V_2 = z/(Z_3 - Z_1)$ $0 \leq z \leq (Z_3 - Z_1)$
3		$0, 0, Z_3$		1	m_2	even
4		$0, 0, Z_4$		2	m_2	$V_2 = 1 - z/(Z_6 - Z_4)$ $0 \leq z \leq (Z_6 - Z_4)$
					m_3	$V_3 = z/(Z_6 - Z_4)$ $0 \leq z \leq (Z_6 - Z_4)$
5		$0, 0, Z_6$		1	m_3	even

Note: Where Z is the coordinate of the global coordinate system of the component and z is that of the local coordinate system of a material region.

4. FINITE ELEMENT ANALYSIS BASED ON THE MODEL

The CAD models of components made of multi heterogeneous materials is intended to be used not only for depositing the information from design procedure described in section 2 of this chapter but also for subsequent analysis, optimization, and layered manufacturing. This section illustrates its finite element analysis.

A component made of multi heterogeneous materials normally requires more nodes and finite elements to model and describe completely the response of the whole structure since it possesses a non-homogeneous character at a microscopic scale. It is possible that the number of order of its final stiffness matrix will be very large. Its stiffness matrix and equations for solution will possibly exceed the memory capacity of the computer. A procedure to overcome this problem is to separate the whole structure into smaller units called substructures [33, 34], which are analyzed separately to obtain the relationship between forces and displacements, for instance, at the common interfaces or boundaries. These boudary variables are then determined and are used to obtain the unknowns within each substructure. In this case, each material region of its material set can be considered as a substructure. Therefore, its finite element analysis can be implemented according to the following procedure:

(1) Create and discretize the component into finite elements based on material regions of its material set
The material constituent composition and the material microstructure have been clarified in each region. The number of finite elements to be constructed depends on the precision of analysis and the non-homogeneous degree of its materials. The higher the precision of analysis and/or the non-homogeneous degree of materials is, the more finite elements will be required.
(2) Build the stiffness matrix for the boundary of each material region
In each finite element constructed, there are very small changes in material constituent composition if functionally graded material is used in it, and the distribution of inclusions is even when composite or heterogeneous material with a periodic microstructure is used in it. The stiffness matrix for each finite element can be obtained by using the theory of homogenization [6–10], which has been developed since the 1970s and can be used as an alternative approach to find the effective properties of the equivalent homogenized material. From a mathematical point of view, the theory of homogenization is a limit theory which uses the asymptotic expansion and assumption of periodicity to substitute the differential equations with rapidly oscillating coefficients, with differential equations whose coefficients are constant or slowly varying in such a way that the solutions are close to the initial equations [35]. After the finite elements in a material region are assembled to represent the entire region, an equilibrium equation can be obtained as follows:

$$\{F^{(r)}\} = [K^{(r)}]\,\{\delta^{(r)}\} \tag{55}$$

where $\{F^{(r)}\}$ is the load vector, $\{\delta^{(r)}\}$ is the displacement vector, and $[K^{(r)}]$ is the global stiffness matrix of the r-th material region in its material set. For the r-th material region, there are two types of nodes: those on its boundary and those inside it; and the stiffness matrix, the displacement vector and the load vector can be partitioned corresponding to boundary and internal degrees of freedom, $\{\delta_b^{(r)}\}$ and $\{\delta_i^{(r)}\}$, respectively. Its equilibium equation can thus be rewritten as:

$$\begin{bmatrix} F_b^{(r)} \\ F_i^{(r)} \end{bmatrix} = \begin{bmatrix} K_{bb}^{(r)} & K_{bi}^{(r)} \\ K_{ib}^{(r)} & K_{ii}^{(r)} \end{bmatrix} \begin{Bmatrix} \delta_b^{(r)} \\ \delta_i^{(r)} \end{Bmatrix} \tag{56}$$

where $F_b^{(r)}$ and $\delta_b^{(r)}$ are load and displacement vectors of nodes on its boundary respectively; and $F_i^{(r)}$ and $\delta_i^{(r)}$ are load and displacement vectors of nodes inside the region respectively. Then, the stiffness matrix of its boundary can be obtained as follows [33]:

$$\left[K_b^{(r)}\right] = \left[K_{bb}^{(r)}\right] - \left[K_{bi}^{(r)}\right]\left[K_{ii}^{(r)}\right]^{-1}\left[K_{ib}^{(r)}\right] \tag{57}$$

(3) Build the global stiffness matrix $[K_b]$ for the boundaries of all the regions in the component

The above analysis will be carried out for all the material regions in its material set and the stiffness matrix for each region will be obtained. Then, treating each region as an element, the global structure stiffness matrix can be formed by the usual assembly procedure by direct stiffness method as:

$$[K_b] = \sum_{r=1}^{L}\left[K_b^{(r)}\right] \tag{58}$$

where L is the number of material regions in its material set.

(4) Generate load vector for nodes on the boundaries of all the regions in the component

First, the loads on nodes inside each region are converted to the loads on nodes on the boundary of each region using:

$$\left\{R_b^{(r)}\right\} = \left[K_{bi}^{(r)}\right]\left[K_{ii}^{(r)}\right]^{-1}\left\{F_i^{(r)}\right\} \tag{59}$$

and then the load vector for the nodes on the boundaries of all the regions in the component can be obtained using:

$$\{S_b\} = \{F_b\} - \sum_{r=1}^{L}\left\{R_b^{(r)}\right\} \tag{60}$$

Here, the physical interpretations of $\{R_b^{(r)}\}$ is the force required to be applied at the region boundaries to keep the boundary displacements equal to zero, i.e., for fixing the boundaries.

(5) Calculate displacement vector for the boundaries of all the regions in the component
After the stiffness matrix and load vector for the boundaries of all the regions in the component are obtained in step 3 and 4 respectively, the displacement vector can be calculated according to the equilibium equation as:

$$\{\delta_b\} = [K_b]^{-1}\{S_b\} \tag{61}$$

so that the displacement for the boundaries of each region, $\{\delta_b^{(r)}\}$, can be obtained.

(6) Determine the displacement vector for the nodes inside each material region
According to Eq. (19), the displacement vector can be determined by [22]:

$$\left\{\delta_i^{(r)}\right\} = \left[K_{ii}^{(r)}\right]^{-1}\left\{F_i^{(r)}\right\} - \left[K_{ii}^{(r)}\right]^{-1}\left[K_{ib}^{(r)}\right]\left\{\delta_b^{(r)}\right\} \tag{62}$$

(7) Analyzing the stress for the component
Up to now, all the displacement for nodes both inside and on the boundary of each region have been obtained. Thus, the stresses can be calculated following the usual finite element procedure [33, 34].

5. SUMMARY

With rapid developments of high-tech in various fields, there appear more critical requirements for special functions of components/products, which cannot be satisfied by using conventional homogeneous materials. The attention has focused on heterogeneous materials, including composite materials, functionally graded materials, or heterogeneous materials with a periodic microstructure. The design method for conventional components made of homogeneous material or single heterogeneous material is always to choose a kind of material first, and then design component's configuration and check whether the component can satisfy the functional requirements. For the components made of multiple heterogeneous materials, however, their design process has to be reversed, i.e., from functional requirements in high-tech application to a component's configuration to material properties and to microstructures and/or constituent compositions. The design procedure goes though (1) design component's configuration according to the first type of performance requirement (CA_1), using conventional CAD technology; (2) determine material properties in different portions or regions of the component according to the second type of performance requirements, using Sensitivity Analysis and Steepest Descend Method; (3) Select optimal material constituent compositions and microstructures for different portions of the component to satisfy material property requirements and various constraints from material affinity, manufacturability, etc., supported by a related heterogeneous materials database, using Genetic Algorithms; and (4) optimize the parameters of configuration based on the material selection using Finite Element Analysis. The first and the fourth phases belong to geometric design that is well developed. The second and the third phases concentrate on material design, which is introduced in more detail in this chapter. With the design method, all the information (about both configuration and material) needed for creating a CAD model of the component made of multi heterogeneous materials can be obtained. Since this method and subsequent CAD modeling both must be implemented in computers by using the functions of current CAD/CAE software, the method is also a computer-aided design method.

After geometric and material design, a CAD model for representing the component made of multi heterogeneous materials need to be built so that further analysis, optimization and manufacturing can be implemented based on the models. The CAD modeling method for the component made of multi heterogeneous materials divides a component into many material regions (M_{ij}), based on two region sets (C and S), each of which has a specified material constituent composition and a specified microstructure. For each region, its CAD model consists of three sub-models: geometric model, material constituent composition model, and material microstructure model. The first sub-model is 3D solid model, and the last two sub-models are in the form of schema. The CAD model for a component made of multi heterogeneous materials is formed by integrating the three sub-models for each material region. This method can be implemented by employing the functions of current CAD graphic software and build a model that includes all the material information (about periodic microstructures, constituent composition, and inclusions) along with the geometry information in current 3D solid modeling without the problem arising from too much data. Such a CAD modeling system has also been developed and applied.

The CAD models of components made of multi heterogeneous materials is intended to be used not only for depositing the information from design procedure described in section 2 of this chapter but also for subsequent analysis, optimization, and layered manufacturing. A component made of multi heterogeneous materials normally requires more nodes and finite elements to model and describe completely the response of the whole structure since it possesses a non-homogeneous character at a microscopic scale. It is possible that the number of order of its final stiffness matrix will be very large. Its stiffness matrix and equations for solution will possibly exceed the memory capacity of the computer, and solution efficiency will be very poor. A procedure to overcome this problem is to separate the whole structure into smaller units called substructures (in this case, each material region of its material set can be considered as a substructure), which are analyzed separately to obtain the relationship between forces and displacements, for instance, at the common interfaces or boundaries. These boudary variables are then determined and are used to obtain the unknowns within each substructure. Therefore, its finite element analysis can be simplified and implemented based on its CAD model

ACKNOWLEDGEMENTS

The reported research is supported by Competitive Earmarked Research Grant of Hong Kong Research Grants Council (RGC) under project code: HKU 7062/00E. The financial contribution is gratefully acknowledged. This chapter is further written based on the authors' two journal papers: Computer-Aided Design, Vol.35, 2003, pp. 453–466, "Computer–aided design method for the components made of heterogeneous materials" and "CAD modeling for the components made of multi heterogeneous materials and smart materials" with permission from Elsevier.

REFERENCES

[1] Berthelot, J. M. Composite materials: mechanical behavior and structural analysis. New York: Springer-Verlag, 1999.

[2] Chawla, K. K. Composite materials: science and engineering. New York: Springer-Verlag New York, Inc., 1998.

[3] Barbero, E. J. Introduction to composite materials design. Ann Arbor, MI: Taylor & Fancis, 1998.

[4] Miyamoto, Y. et al. Functionally Graded Materials: Design, Processing and Applications. Boston: Kluwer Academic Publishers, 1999.

[5] Bhashyam S, Shin, K. H., and Dutta, D. An integrated CAD system for design of hetergeneous objects. Rapid Prototyping Journal, 2000; 6: 119–135.

[6] Larson, U. D., Sigmund, O., and Bouwstra, S. Design and fabrication of compliant micromechanisms and structures with negative Poisson's ratio, Journal of Microelectromechanical Systems, 1997; 6: 99–106.

[7] Silva, E. C. N., Fonseca, J. S. O., and Kikuchi, N. Optimal design of piezoelectric microstructure. Computational Mechanics, 1997; 19: 397–410.

[8] Sigmund, O. and Torquato, S. Design of materials with extreme thermal expansion using a three-phase topology optimization method. J. Mech. Phys. Solids, 1997; 45(6): 1037–1067.

[9] Bendsoe, M. P. Optimization of structure topology, shape, and material. Berlin: Springer-Verlag, 1995.

[10] Hassani, B., and Hinton, E. Homogrnization and structural topology optimization: theory, practice and software. New York: Springer-Verlag, 1999.

[11] Suh, N. P. The Principle of Design. New York: Oxford University Press, Inc., 1990.

[12] Suh, N. P. Axiomatic Design: Advances and Applications. New York: Oxford University Press, Inc., 2001.

[13] Rao, S. S. Engineering Optimization: Theory and Practice. New York: John Wiley & Sons, Inc., 1996.

[14] Chen, K. Z., Identifying the relationships among design methods: key to successful application and development of design methods, Journal of Engineering Design, 1999; 10: 125–141.

[15] Lee, K. Principle of CAD/CAM/CAE System. Reading: Addison-Wesley Longman, Inc., 1999.

[16] McMahon, C. and Browne, J. CADCAM: Principles, Practice and Manufacturing Management. Reading: Addison-Wesley Longman Inc., 1998.

[17] Prinja, N. K. Use of Finite Element Analysis in the Design Process. Glasgow: NAFEMS, 2000.

[18] Bakshi, P. and Pandey, P. C. Semi-analytical sensitivity using hybrid finite elements. Computer and Structures, 2000; 77: 201–213.

[19] Gen, M. and Cheng, R. Genetic Algorithms & Engineering Design. New York: John Wiley & Sons, Inc., 1997.

[20] Chen, K. Z., Zhang, X. W., Ou, Z. Y., and Feng, X. A. Recognition of digital curves scanned from paper drawings using Genetic Algorithms. Pattern Recognition, 2003; 36(1): 123–130.

[21] Milne-Thomson, L. M. The Calculus of Finite Differences. New York: Chelsea Pub. Co., 1981.

[22] Blaha, M. R. A. Manager's Guide to Database Technology: Building and Purchasing Better Applications. Prentice Hall, 2001.

[23] Kumar, V. and Dutta, D. An approach to modeling & representation of heterogeneous objects. Journal of Mechanical Design, 1998; 120: 659–667.

[24] Kumar, V., Burns, D., Dutta, D., and Hoffmann, C. A framework for object modeling. Computer-Aided Design, 1999; 31: 541–556.

[25] Jackson, T. R., Liu, H., Patrikalakis, N. M., Sachs, E. M., and Cima, M. J. Modeling and designing functionally graded material components for fabrication with local composition control. Materials and Design, 1999; 20(2/3): 63–75.

[26] Siu, Y. K. and Tan, S. T. Source-based heterogeneous solid modeling. Computer- Aided Design, 2002; 34(1): 41–55.

[27] Siu, Y. K., and Tan, S. T. Modeling the material grading and structures of heterogeneous objects for layered manufacturing. Computer-Aided Design, 2002; 34(10): 705–716.

[28] Morvan, S. and Fadel, G. M. MMA-Rep, A V-Representation for Multi-material Object. Software Solutions for Rapid Prototyping, PEP Press, UK, 2002.
[29] Ulrich, K. T. and Eppinger S. D. Product design and development, Boston: McGraw-Hill Company, Inc., 2002.
[30] Jonassen, D. H., Beissner, K., and Yacci, M. Structural knowledge: techniques for representing, conveying, and acquiring structural knowledge. Hillsdale, New Jersey: Lawrence Erlbaum Associates, Inc., 1993.
[31] Sun, W., Lin, F., and Hu, X. Computer-aided design and modeling of composite unit cells. Composite Science and Technology, 2001; 61: 289–299.
[32] Sun, W., and Hu, X. Reasoning Boolean operation based modeling for heterogeneous objects. Computer-Aided Design, 2002; 34: 481–488.
[33] Krishnamoorthy, C. S. Finite element analysis: theory and programming. New Delhi: Tata McGraw-Hill Publishing Company Limited, 1994.
[34] Logan, D. L. A first course in the finite element method using Algor. Boston: PWS Publishing Company, 1997.
[35] Oleinik, O. A. On homogenization problems. Trends and Application of Pure Mathematics. Berlin: Springer, 1984.

QUALITY AND COST OF DATA WAREHOUSE VIEWS[1]

ANDREAS KOELLER[2], ELKE A. RUNDENSTEINER, AMY LEE[3], AND ANISOARA NICA[4]

1. INTRODUCTION

Query rewriting has been used as a query optimization technique for several decades to reduce the computational cost of a query. Traditional problems in query rewriting include in particular query optimization [28, 60, 6] and rewriting queries using views [40, 7]. Most of these works deal with the problem of maintaining the *exact original* interface (schema) and extent of a given query while optimizing performance.

They are thus based on the restricting assumption that the rewritten query must be *equivalent* to the initially given query. Recently, query rewriting with *relaxed semantics* has been proposed as a means of retaining the validity of a data warehouse (i.e., materialized queries) in situations where *equivalent* rewritings may not exist—yet alternate but *not necessarily equivalent* query rewritings may still be preferable to users over not receiving any answers at all [34, 43, 53].

Other scenarios that also motivate a relaxation of the "exact query" assumption include loosely-specified query paradigms [44], relaxed restrictions on WHERE-clauses to generate approximate result sets [8], vaguely specified queries in semistructured

[1]This work was in part supported by several NSF grants, namely, the NSF NYI grant #IRI 9796264, NSF CISE Instrumentation Grant #IRIS 9729878, and the NSF grant #IIS 9988776.

[2]This work was performed while Andreas Koeller was a Research Assistant at Worcester Polytechnic Institute.

[3]This work was performed while Amy Lee was a Research Assistant at Worcester Polytechnic Institute and a Ph.d. student at the University of Michigan, Ann Arbor.

[4]This work was performed while Anisoara Nica was a Ph.d. student at the University of Michigan, Ann Arbor.

environments that need to be refined during query evaluation, as well as market-oriented environments in which very similar (but not equal) results in answering a query can lead to dramatically different query computation costs. Some more recent work in XML also addresses the approximate query answering problem, for example the approxQL project [55] or the XXL project. [59]

Generating non-equivalent query results raises a new problem in the context of query rewriting. Since results returned for a given query may now be quite distinct, it leads to the problem of having to *compare* "incomparable" query results, or rewritings, for a given query. As one would expect, the number of non-equivalent query rewritings is much larger than the number of equivalent query rewritings in general. Given that the search space is now even larger than for the equivalent query rewriting problem, an automated means of comparison of various rewritings is needed.

In this chapter, we report the development of such a measurement model for non-equivalent rewritings. While, as illustrated above, the problem arises in many different environments in which queries are used, for the purpose of this work we focus our attention on E-SQL [53] as the relaxed query model and on the issue of view maintenance in data warehouses as motivation for establishing the model.

In this work, we introduce the two dimensions of *information preservation* (quality) and *view maintenance performance* (cost) of query rewritings as two key components of the proposed model. The paper addresses the need for measuring the divergence between queries in a quantifiable manner by proposing measures for the interface and extent *divergence* of the query results, referred to as the *quality* of the rewriting. Given that the independent dimensions of quality and cost cannot be easily evaluated and compared against each other, we analyze the semantics of these dimensions and propose a model of assigning numerical values and trade-off parameters in order to achieve a quantifiable overall evaluation for query results. The resulting model, which we call *Quality-Cost-Model (QC-Model)*, combines these two dimensions into a single measure. We address several core issues of the problem including the definition of a *distance* between view extents (called here "degree of divergence") and several properties of the cost model, which we adapted from the literature on incremental view maintenance cost. [6, 65]

We describe the comprehensive test bed we have developed for the purpose of experimentation and demonstration (built as part of the EVE-System demonstrated at ACM SIGMOD 1999 [52]), which also incorporates the QC-model as presented in this current paper. We report upon an experimental study we have conducted. Our experiments assess the trade-offs among the different factors of the quality and cost measures, characterizing correlations and independence among them. We also study the effect of different parameters of the view rewritings on the *QC-Model*, such as number of ISs over which the view is defined, the distribution of relations over a fixed number of ISs, and so on. Using our experimental setup, we have evaluated the accuracy of our proposed view overlap estimation for the quality portion of the QC-Model. The experiments indeed show a strong correlation between estimated and actual view extent overlaps. Similarly, we have also conducted a number of experiments designed to assess the predictability of the proposed QC-Model in terms of its cost measure in estimating the actual view maintenance cost. The experiments show a strong correlation between the predicted and actual incremental view maintenance cost, and thus support the utility of our proposed QC-model.

In summary, this work makes the following contributions: First, it identifies the problem of trade-offs of quality against cost for non-equivalent query rewritings and the need for a model for assessing these measures. Second, we introduce the measure of *quality* for a query, and establish techniques for determining the quality measure for a given query based on empirically supported findings. Third, we establish an integrated measure for both quality and cost, based on an existing cost model for distributed view maintenance. [65] The resulting Quality-and-Cost(QC)-model that we propose assigns numerical values to approximate query rewritings. Fourth, we have developed a fully distributed data warehouse maintenance system for demonstrative and experimental purposes. [52, 15] Our prototype not only includes view synchronization algorithms [43, 29, 45, 63] and algorithms for incremental view maintenance [4, 62, 22], but it also utilizes the QC-model as criteria for selecting a good view rewriting among the ones generated by the view synchronizer. Fifth, we perform an analytical evaluation on the properties of our model, characterizing trends, correlations and independence among the different QC-Model factors. Sixth, we use our software for an experimental evaluation demonstrating the utility and soundness of the QC-Model by using statistical methods and measuring correlation between predicted and measured QC-Values. While we have developed the QC-Model in the context of data warehousing [53], it is also applicable to other areas of query reformulation, as mentioned above.

The remainder of this chapter is organized as follows: Section 2 introduces background concepts necessary for the development of the QC-Model, whereas Sections 3 and 4 present a detailed analytic model of quality and cost trade-offs, respectively. Section 5 describes our prototype implementation. Section 6.2 summarizes experimental results and Section 7 reviews related work, while Section 8 discusses our conclusions.

2. NON-EQUIVALENT QUERY REWRITINGS

The notion of relaxed queries has appeared in the past in several contexts, such as the EVE system [53, 11, 9] and, more recently, XML. [55, 58] The notion of a relaxed view definition is a generalization of the problem of traditional query rewriting, in which the execution plans or queries generated may be different syntactically, but will always be (semantically) equivalent to the original query, i.e., compute the same output relation.

On the other hand, relaxed queries may compute a different extent and even a different view interface (schema) than the original query. Relaxed queries are useful in the context of *approximate rewritings* of views in the presence of partly redundant information sources. A typical case would be a view definition using information from an information source *R* which becomes unavailable at some point in time. The view may then be rewritten to replace the missing information with information from another information source R', as long as R and R' are known to contain the same, or similar, data.

Clearly, such a system would not have to nor should be restricted to produce *equivalent* query rewritings. Rather, in order to achieve meaningful yet relaxed query rewritings, we propose that it would be useful to specify user preferences as to which elements of a query (attributes, selection conditions, relations) may be replaced and/or removed from the query without sacrificing the usefulness of the view to its users.

Two factors guide the rewriting process: the degree of redundancy in the information space and the degree of relaxation allowed as expressed by user preferences about flexibility in the query definition. Depending on those factors, the rewriting process may yield a large and possibly exponentially (over the size of the information space) growing number of legal rewritings for an affected query.

Under the assumption of non-equivalent query rewriting, each new query could be specified on disparate base relations with different cardinalities at different sites, hence return a different view interface a view extent, or even both. This leads to the necessity to *compare* such *non-equivalent* queries in order to find a rewriting that *best* matches the view user's needs. The goal of this paper is thus to develop a "desirability" model for query rewritings.

Towards this end, we will introduce the two concepts of *quality* and *cost* of a query rewriting as two key measures for establishing such a comparison. The first measure is the degree of divergence of quality (i.e., information preservation) between two queries (cf. Section 3). The second measure represents the long term maintenance cost associated with a view, which for example occurs in a data warehousing context, where the cost to maintain a view significantly influences the usefulness of the view to the user (cf. Section 4). Other costs could of course be incorporated for the later measure depending on the purpose of the overall measurement model.

3. EFFICIENCY MODEL: QUALITY OF A QUERY REWRITING

3.1. Information preservation in rewritings

The information, i.e., quality, returned by a query is of great importance to its users. The information returned in the (relational) result of a query can be determined in terms of two aspects, namely the query interface (i.e., the set of attributes in the SELECT clause of the query definition) and the query extent (data). When a relation or attribute that is used by a view definition V becomes unavailable, the view V would be rewritten, making use of redundant information in the underlying information space and of user preferences regarding the "rewritability" of the view.

Ideally we would like to replace V by a rewriting V_i such that V_i is "equivalent" to V in terms of both quality aspects, although some information may be taken from other information sources. When V_i is not equivalent to V, we say that V_i *diverges* from V. Ranking rewritings which preserve V to different degrees is not trivial. This can best be demonstrated by an example.

Name	Address	City	Phone
Smith	1st St.	Somerville	617-123-4567
Baker	2nd Ave.	Boston	617-321-6547
Davis	Blue St.	Boston	617-987-6543

(a) Original Extent of V (Base Table **Customer**)

Name	Address
Baker	2nd Ave.
Davis	Blue St.

(b) Rewriting V_1 (Base Table **BackBay**)

Name	City	Phone
Smith	Somerville	617-123-4567
Baker	Boston	617-321-6547
Davis	Boston	617-987-6543
Adam	Worcester	508-123-4567
Jones	Worcester	508-321-6547

(c) Rewriting V_2 (Base Table **MABranch**)

Figure 1. Different amounts of information are preserved in rewritings.

Example 1.
Let the view V over the database in Fig. 1 be defined as follows:

```
CREATE VIEW V AS
SELECT      Name, Address, City, Phone
FROM        Customer                          (1)
WHERE       CustomerSince < 1996
```

Assume the relation **Customer** *is deleted from its site. Two possible rewritings, by replacing* **Customer** *with* **BackBay** *and* **MABranch**, *respectively, are:*

```
CREATE VIEW V1 AS
SELECT      Name, Address
FROM        BackBay                           (2)
WHERE       CustomerSince < 1996
```

```
CREATE VIEW V2 AS
SELECT      Name, City, Phone
FROM        MABranch                          (3)
WHERE       CustomerSince < 1996
```

From the viewpoint of the query interface, V_1 and V_2 are able to preserve a different subset of attributes of the original interface, **Name** *and* **Address** *by V_1 and* **Name**, **City**, *and* **Phone** *by V_2. From the viewpoint of the query extent, by considering the common set of attributes between the original query and a query rewriting, V_1 is able to preserve two out of three tuples of the original query without introducing any extra tuples (i.e., precise but not total recall), while V_2 is able to preserve the original query with two surplus tuples (i.e., total recall but not precise).*

Obviously, we need a mechanism to decide which rewriting is closer to the original and thus the best choice for a replacement for V and thus superior to others. Therefore, our system must trade-off the pros and cons between the query interface and query extent preservation (and also between the two dimensions of the query extent: precision and recall) in order to rank these potential rewritings of V so that the "best" solution with regard to that ranking can be selected.

3.2. Information preservation on the view interface

In this section, we propose a method to measure the preservation of the interface (schema) of a view in its non-equivalent rewritings. The basic principle is to assign *user preferences* to attributes in the view schema. There are two fundamental dimensions in which such user preferences can be expressed: dispensability and replaceability.

3.2.1. Dispensable and replacable attributes

For each attribute in the view schema, we assign two Boolean parameters: *attribute replaceable (AR)* and *attribute dispensable (AD)*.

Definition 1 (Replacement) *Consider a view V whose schema contains an attribute $V.A$ originating from a base table R. Additionally, consider a relation R' that contains data* related *to R, in the sense that both relations contain information about the same real-world objects, and some of their respective attributes contain the same data about those objects. Let V' be a non-equivalent rewriting of view V.*

Then, attribute $V'.A$ is a replacement *for attribute $V.A$ if (1) it originates from table R', which must be a superset, subset, or equivalent to R and (2) $V'.A$ stores the same data about the same objects as $V.A$.*

The authors of this paper have explored ways to express the concept of the "same data" in attributes as well as the overlap of base table extents. [53, 33]

Definition 2 (Attribute replaceable (AR)) *An attribute A in a view schema V is considered* replaceable *if the view user regards a view rewriting V' containing a replacement for A as useful.*

Definition 3 (Attribute dispensable (AD)) *An attribute A in a view schema V is considered* dispensable *if the view user regards a view rewriting V' that does not contain A as useful.*

There are four possible combinations of these attribute parameters:

- AR=true/AD=true: attribute can be replaced or deleted in any rewriting. The semantics of this case are quite clear—a user would specify such semantics if the attribute is not very important for her.
- AR=true/AD=false: attribute can be replaced but not deleted. These parameters would apply for an attribute whose data might be supplied from a different source but which always needs to be supplied in some way.
- AR=false/AD=true: attribute can be deleted but not replaced. This case justifies a closer look. The concept of "replaceability" expresses a user's preferences with regard

to the *trustworthiness* of an attribute. Declaring an attribute replaceable means that the user trusts other data sources to provide reliable information about that attribute. On the other hand, by declaring an attribute non-replaceable, a user declares that s/he will not trust the data in the attribute if it is not supplied by the original data source. Therefore, a user might allow that an attribute A can be deleted (if it is dropped from its original data source) but cannot be replaced from other data sources "offering" this information. The issue here is one of trust in the reliability of information provided by alternative sources.

- AR=false/AD=false: attribute cannot be deleted or replaced. These semantics would be specified for essential attributes in a view whose only trusted source is the original one.

With our explanations above, it becomes clear that the two dimensions (or *preferences*) of replaceability and dispensability are orthogonal. Note that the dimension of "replaceability" (trustworthiness) could be expanded to allow for different quality levels depending on the source of the data. For example, a user of a travel data view might trust information supplied by a major travel agency, but not data originating from consolidators or small unknown data suppliers. Here, however, we restrict ourselves to a Boolean replaceability measure for simplicity.

The choice of essentially two classes of relaxation parameters (dispensability and replaceability) is an approach at trading off the complexity of the system (i.e., the expressiveness of the quality model) against the ease of use by a user (i.e., the simplicity in specifying such relaxed query semantics). Various extensions of this model, such as a replacement of the Boolean preference values by numeric "fuzzy" values (as done for WHERE-clauses only in CoBase) [8], are of course possible, but are beyond the scope of the current paper (nor, would we expect them to result in a significant change of the treatment of this current work).

After defining the semantics of all four combinations of the two preferences, we can now measure the *preservation* of a view interface in numeric terms. In order to achieve this, we observe that since the categories AD and AR are orthogonal, a user will generally have separate preferences on whether it is better to replace an attribute or to delete it, in the case both operations are allowed. Therefore, we simply assign numerical *weights* to an attribute for each of the four combinations of the AD and AR parameters. An attribute with a higher weight is then more "important" than an attribute with a lower weight and should have a higher chance to be preserved. However, we also observe that indispensable attributes (AD false) *must* be preserved in any view rewriting, thus forcing the weights for those cases to be infinite.

In summary, we have the situation depicted in the table in Fig. 2. The table expresses that a view rewriting is legal if it omits attributes in categories 1 or 2 (i.e., dispensable attributes) but that a user might have preferences between these two cases. As the ultimate goal of our preference model is the comparison of view rewritings, we will normalize all results and thus require ($0 \leq w_1, w_2 \leq 1$). Note that there are two choices on the relative values of w_1 and w_2:

Category (AD, AR)	Weight
C1: (true, true)	w_1
C2: (true, false)	w_2
C3: (false, true)	∞
C4: (false, false)	∞

Figure 2. Weights for the four classes of preserved attributes.

$w_1 \geq w_2$ This represents the fact that a user is in favor of preserving the replaceable attributes (i.e., attributes in category 1). A view having replaceable attributes may be evolved further as more schema changes occur as our experimental evaluation in Section 6.2 confirms, whereas having relatively many non-replaceable attributes (i.e., attributes in category 2) has a negative effect on the further ability of a view query to evolve. In other words, it is harder to find good legal rewritings for a view if its view elements are non-replaceable.

$w_1 < w_2$ This represents the case in which a user finds a non-replaceable attribute more worthy to be preserved in a view rewriting than a replaceable attribute. This would express a low confidence of a user in the reliability of alternative data sources, and would state that s/he prefers to lose access to some information over having unreliable information in the view.

3.3. Information preservation on view extent

We now introduce a notation for *common subset of attributes* and some set operators using the common-subset-of-attributes semantics. For this notation, we will use bag semantics, i.e., duplicates which may occur after projection of a relation to a subset of attributes are *not* removed.

Definition 4 Common Subset of Attributes of V with respect to V_i. *Let V and V_i be two relations, such that $Attr(V) \cap Attr(V_i) \neq \emptyset$. We use $V^{\pi(V_i)}$ to denote the projection of relation V on the common attributes of V and V_i. That is, $V^{\pi(V_i)} = \pi_{Attr(V) \cap Attr(V_i)} V$. Similarly, $V_i^{\pi(V)}$ is defined as $\pi_{Attr}(V) \cap Attr(V_i) V_\pi$.*

Besides considering the attributes preserved in the legal rewritings, the *sets of tuples* returned by the queries will also have an impact on the user's satisfaction with a view rewriting V_i. When the view interfaces of a legal rewriting V_i and the original view V are not the same, the extent preservation evaluation is done by comparing tuples on the common subset of attributes only. When the view interfaces of V_i and V are the same, the extent comparison is done as usual.

We can also define set (bag) intersection and difference under the implicit assumption of "common-subset-of-attributes".

Set Operator	Semantics
$V \cap_\pi V_i$	$\{z \mid \exists t \in V \wedge \exists t_i \in V_i,\ z = t[Attr(V) \cap Attr(V_i)] = t_i[Attr(V) \cap Attr(V_i)]\}$
$V \setminus_\pi V_i$	$\{z \mid \exists t \in V, z = t[Attr(V) \cap Attr(V_i)] \wedge \nexists t_i \in V_i,\ z = t_i[Attr(V) \cap Attr(V_i)]\}$

Figure 3. Set operators on the common subset of attributes of V and V_i.

3.4. Metric of quality: Degree of Divergence ($\mathcal{DD}$)

When choosing from among a number of rewritings, we would like to choose a legal rewriting such that the view or query extent V does not change. If it is not possible to find a rewriting that satisfies this condition, we choose a rewriting that produces a view extent as *close* as possible to the original one. Some rewritings may have a larger number of tuples in V preserved, but at the same time generate extra tuples that were not in V. On the other hand, some legal rewritings may preserve less tuples in V, but also generate less surplus tuples. In this section, we discuss how to generate a *good* rewriting according to the user's preference by making a choice which tries to generate a rewriting that preserves information to as large a degree as possible.

Below, we discuss how we quantify the quality of query rewritings in terms of the query interface and the query extent, individually, and how to unify these two measures into one single measure—the *Degree of Divergence ($\mathcal{DD}$)* of a rewriting V_i from the original query V.

3.4.1. *Degree of divergence on the query interface ($\mathcal{DD}_{attr}$ (V_i))*

Let $|A_i^1|$ be the number of dispensable attributes (AD $=$ true) in the query interface of V_i that are replaceable (AR $=$ true, category 1 in Fig. 2). Likewise, $|A_i^2|$ is the number of attributes in category 2. The query flexibility value of the query interface of V_i can then be defined as follows:

$$QF_{V_i} = \left|A_i^1\right| \cdot w_1 + \left|A_i^2\right| \cdot w_2 \tag{4}$$

with w_1, w_2 weights on the two measures as introduced in Section 3.2.1. As those weights are expressing a relative preference between the two attribute types, we require them to not both be 0 at the same time (i.e., $w_1, w_2 \geq 0$ and $w_1 + w_2 = 1$). The query flexibility value of the original view V is defined likewise and denoted by QF_V. The normalized degree of divergence of V_i from V in terms of the query interface, denoted by $DD_{attr}(V_i)$, can then be defined as:

$$DD_{attr}(V_i) = \begin{cases} 0 & \text{if } QF_V = 0 \\ \frac{QF_V - QF_{V_i}}{QF_V} & \text{otherwise} \end{cases}$$

This is a measure of *distance* of the interface of a rewriting from the original query interface. $QF_V = 0$ occurs if the attributes contained in the original query V are all indispensable. In this case, any legal rewriting V_i of V must preserve the entire view interface. That is to say, V_i can not diverge from V on the query interface, i.e., $DD_{attr}(V_i) = 0$. When there are dispensable attributes in V, and $QF_V \geq 0$, then $DD_{attr}(V_i)$ is computed as defined above. If V_i does not preserve any of the dispensable or replaceable attributes, then $QF_{V_i} = 0$ and $DD_{attr}(V_i) = 1$. In terms of the query interface, V_i is preferred to V_j if $DD_{attr}(V_i) < DD_{attr}(V_j)$.

Example 2. *Let us look at the query and rewritings defined in Example 1. In that example,* $Attr(V) = \{$**Name, Address, City, Phone**$\}$, $A^1 = \{$**Address, City, Phone**$\}$, *and* $A^2 = \emptyset$ *(since* **Name** *is indispensable). Therefore,* $QF_V = 3 \cdot w_1$. *The rewriting* V_1 *preserves the attribute* **Address** *(besides attribute* **Name**). *Therefore,* $QF_{V_1} = 1 \cdot w_1$. *On the other hand, the rewriting* V_2 *preserves two of the dispensable attributes* **City** *and* **Phone**. *Therefore,* $QF_{V_2} = 2 \cdot w_1$. *Thus,* V_2 *is preferred to* V_1 *as indicated by* $DD_{attr}(V_2) < DD_{attr}(V_1)$.

3.4.2. Degree of divergence on the query extent ($\mathcal{DD}_{ext}(V_i)$)

The divergence of a legal rewriting V_i from V is computed in two dimensions:

D1. The (relative) number of tuples in the original V that are not preserved in the new V_i, denoted by

$$DD_{ext\_D1}(V_i) = 1 - \frac{|V_i \cap_\pi V|}{|V^{\pi(V_i)}|} \tag{5}$$

D2. The (relative) number of tuples in the new view V_i that are not in the original view V, denoted by

$$DD_{ext\_D2}(V_i) = \frac{|V_i \setminus_\pi V|}{\left|V_i^{\pi(V)}\right|} = \frac{\left|V_i^{\pi(V)}\right| - |V \cap_\pi V_i|}{\left|V_i^{\pi(V)}\right|} = 1 - \frac{|V \cap_\pi V_i|}{\left|V_i^{\pi(V)}\right|} \tag{6}$$

We express the number of tuples that are *not preserved* (Case **D1**) as a ratio to the size of the original view extent $|V^{\pi(V_i)}|$, whereas the number of extra tuples coming into the new view (Case **D2**) is seen in relation to the size of the *new* view extent $|V_i^{\pi(V)}|$. That means, we see the loss of tuples (imperfect *recall* in information theoretical terms) as occuring in the old view, whereas the negative effect of additional "wrong" tuples (imperfect *precision*) are seen in relation to the new view.

The total extent divergence of V_i from V is the weighed sum of $DD_{ext\_D1}(V_i)$ and $DD_{ext\_D2}(V_i)$, denoted by $DD_{ext}(V_i)$, and defined as follows:

$$\begin{aligned} DD_{ext}(V_i) &= \varrho_1 \cdot DD_{ext\_D1}(V_i) + \varrho_2 \cdot DD_{ext\_D2}(V_i) \\ &= 1 - \frac{\left(\varrho_1 \left|V_i^{\pi(V)}\right| + \varrho_2 \left|V^{\pi(V_i)}\right|\right) \cdot |V_i \cap_\pi V|}{|V^{\pi(V_i)}|\left|V_i^{\pi(V)}\right|} \end{aligned} \tag{7}$$

where ϱ_1 and ϱ_2 are the trade-off parameters between $DD_{ext\_D1}(V_i)$ and $DD_{ext\_D2}(V_i)$ ($\varrho_1,\ \varrho_2 \geq 0$ and $\varrho_1 + \varrho_2 = 1$).

Again, the view definer is given an opportunity to set the trade-off parameters, with the default setting being $(\varrho_1, \varrho_2) = (0.5, 0.5)$. Those default setting reflect an assumption that recall and precision of a rewriting are of equal importance for end-users.

Note that in this section, we do not discuss how to obtain accurate estimates for the input parameters of the formulae above. Estimating such parameters is application-dependent and a variety of techniques are available to help with the task (notably sampling-based techniques to estimate sizes of arbitrary queries such as [23, 25, 16, 47]).

3.4.3. Total degree of divergence

With the findings of this section, we now define the total degree of divergence of V_i from V as:

$$DD(V_i) = \varrho_{attr} \cdot DD_{attr}(V_i) + \varrho_{ext} \cdot DD_{ext}(V_i),\ \ where\ \varrho_{attr},\ \varrho_{ext} \geq 0,\ \varrho_{attr} + \varrho_{ext} = 1. \quad (8)$$

ϱ_{attr} and ϱ_{ext} are parameters assigned by the view user. They represent user preferences for view interface over view extent.

4. EFFICIENCY MODEL: VIEW MAINTENANCE COST OF A LEGAL REWRITING

In this section, we now discuss the measure of *view maintenance cost* as a method for ranking view rewritings.

4.1. View maintenance basics

For most applications, data updates such as inserts or deletes of tuples to/from the base relations take place more frequently than schema changes in the information space. Therefore, we choose to rank the legal rewritings by their *long term* view maintenance costs[5]. A legal rewriting is considered to be *preferred* if its expected view maintenance costs are low compared to other legal rewritings. We further assume that a conventional incremental view maintenance algorithm similar to the one specified in [65] is used to bring the view extent up-to-date right after the information source data is updated. Adopting their approach, we introduce three major cost factors (for a single data content update) for a particular legal rewriting: the number of messages exchanged, the number of bytes transferred, and the I/O cost at the local ISs.

Our cost model works well for such view maintenance environments and is therefore explained here. Other cost models are conceivable for other purposes, as long as the return a single numeric cost value for a given query.

[5]The cost for recomputing the original view extent after a view re-definition is a one-time cost. Thus we do not rank the legal rewriting on this one-time view update cost.

4.2. Cost factor based on number of messages exchanged (CF_M)

The number of messages exchanged between the information space and the view site for a single base data update, denoted as CF_M, is in the range $[0, 2m]$ (with m denoting the number of information sources involved in the view). To be more specific:

$$CF_M = \begin{cases} 0 & \text{if } m = 1 \text{ and } n_1 = 0 \\ 2 & \text{if } m = 1 \text{ and } n_1 > 0 \\ 2 \cdot (m-1) & \text{if } m > 1 \text{ and } n_1 = 0 \\ 2 \cdot m & \text{otherwise} \end{cases}$$

with n_1 the number of relations in the update-generating IS *besides* the relation where the update occured. The best case $CF_M = 0$ occurs when there is only one relation referred to in the view V or when V is self-maintainable as discussed by Gupta and others. [20] Self-maintainability is out of the scope of this paper, so we do not discuss it any further. Note that when there is only one relation in IS_1 referred to in V ($n_1 = 0$), then no query needs to be sent to IS_1.

4.3. Cost factor based on bytes of data transferred (CF_T)

Considering an information space consisting of n relations $R_1, \ldots, R_n$ in m information sources $IS_1, \ldots, IS_m$, it is possible to estimate the number of bytes transferred in the entire system during the incremental maintenance of the view after an update. Such a computation will generally assume that one inserted/deleted tuple is sent from an information source IS_1 to the view site, which is the initial delta relation. Then this delta relation is sent down to the information source IS_1 to join with other relations in IS_1 referred to in the view query, and the resulting new delta relation is sent back to the view site. The same process iterates through all the information sources referred to in the view to build up the delta relation that contains the tuples affected by the data update. This is the conventional incremental view maintenance approach. [65]

Depending on the distribution of values in the join attributes of each underlying relation, estimates of the number of bytes transferred can be computed by statistical methods, possibly involving sampling [23, 25, 16, 47] or using traditional database statistics such as join selectivities, relation sizes, and duplicate counts. [13] View maintenance algorithms that deal with concurrent updates [4] or use parallel algorithms [64] will require a more careful estimation of the amount of data transfer.

4.4. Cost factor based on I/O ($CF_{I/O}$)

We use the total number of estimated input/output operations (block accesses) performed by local ISs in order to process incremental view maintenance for each legal rewriting as a criterion to rank the legal rewritings. Let $CF_{I/O}(IS_i)$ be the number of estimated I/Os at the information source IS_i. $CF_{I/O}(IS_i)$ is the sum of the I/Os of the relations that reside at source IS_i, i.e., incorporating the I/O-costs of all relations at IS_i. Then the total number of I/Os, denoted as $CF_{I/O}$, is the sum of the I/Os at all m sources, i.e.,

$$CF_{I/O} = \sum_{i=1}^{m} CF_{I/O}(IS_i) \tag{9}$$

Algorithms to estimate the number of blocks accessed in order to retrieve a tuple from a database are given in the literature, dating back to Yao. [61]

4.5. Total view maintenance cost for a single data update

The total view maintenance cost of a view V with respect to a single data update can now be defined as:

$$Cost\,(V) = CF_M \cdot cost_M + CF_T \cdot cost_T + CF_{I/O} \cdot cost_{I/O} \tag{10}$$

where $cost_M$, $cost_T$, and $cost_{I/O}$ are the unit prices for sending a message, transferring a data block, and performing a disk I/O, respectively.

We can now compute the total view maintenance costs, $\mathrm{COST}(V_i)$, for the updates within a certain time unit. In order to normalize the cost for our model, we find the highest and lowest costs, respectively, from all view rewritings generated, and normalize the cost for each rewriting over the range given by the maximum and minimum.

If we assume that there are k legal rewritings for an affected view, the total cost of legal rewriting V_i can be normalized as follows:

$$COST^*(V_i) = \frac{COST(V_i) - \min\limits_{1\le j\le k}(COST(V_j))}{\max\limits_{1\le j\le k}(COST(V_j)) - \min\limits_{1\le j\le k}(COST(V_j))} \tag{11}$$

This gives us a view maintenance cost between 0 and 1 that we can trade off against the view quality (Section 3). The rewriting with cost 0 is the best (lowest maintenance cost), and the rewriting with cost 1 is the worst in our model.

4.6. Overall efficiency of a legal rewriting

The *overall efficiency* of a legal rewriting can now be computed as:

$$QC(V_i) = 1 - (\varrho_{quality} \cdot \mathcal{DD}(V_i) + \varrho_{cost} \cdot Cost(V_i)) \tag{12}$$

with $\varrho_{quality}, \varrho_{cost} \ge 0$ and $\varrho_{quality} + \varrho_{cost} = 1$. With both quality and cost normalized, this number will be between 0 and 1. If $\varrho_{quality} > 0 \land \varrho_{cost} > 0$, an efficiency of 0 means a legal rewriting that preserves the least amount of information among all rewritings at the highest cost. Likewise, an efficiency of 1 would identify a "perfect" legal rewriting preserving the complete view interface and all tuples at the lowest possible cost.

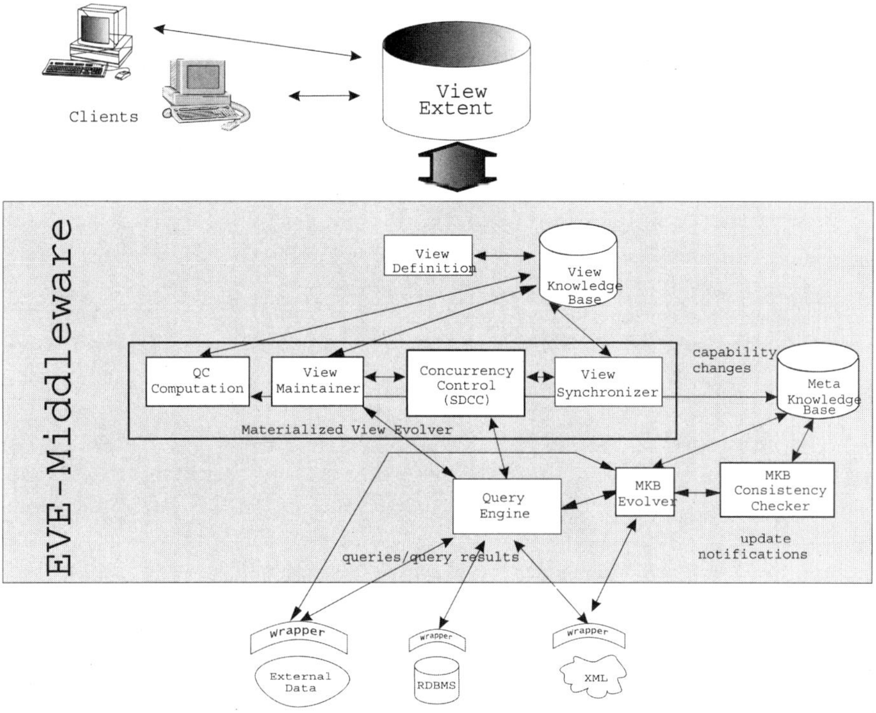

Figure 4. The framework of the evolvable view environment (EVE).

5. REVIEW OF THE EVE PROJECT

Our quality-and-cost model can be used for a variety of enviroments in which multiple, non-equivalent, queries are generated. However, it was developed in the context of the context of the *Evolvable View Environment* (EVE) [53, 54], which we will now briefly review as an example for an application of our proposed model. This example will show how the QC-model can be integrated with a query rewriting system and how the features of the model complement the system under consideration.

As mentioned earlier, views over distributed information sources are affected by capability changes of such sources. Our EVE-system provides a solution for the problem of views becoming undefined after such meta data changes (Figure 4). Major concepts of this architecture [53] are the registration of information sources and the storage of meta knowledge in a Meta Knowledge Base (MKB) which allows for a certain degree of cooperation between sources and middleware in EVE, the storage of view definitions in a View Knowledge Base (Section 5.1), and the application of View Synchronization Algorithms (Section 2). We give a very brief overview over the functions of those modules:

- **Meta Knowledge Base (MKB)**
  Meta information about participating ISs is stored in the MKB. The MKB consists primarily of information about semantic interrelationships observed between different ISs registered in the system. The data in the MKB is either entered manually, or the MKB can be filled partly or fully with the results of a meta-data discovery process (e.g., [30]).
- **View Knowledge Base**
  The view knowledge base stores information about views defined over the ISs by different users. These views are augmented with a user preference model about view evolution (cf. Section 5.1 for Evolvable SQL, below),
- **QC-Computation**
  This module computes the QC-Value, described in this paper, for newly rewritten views. This value is then used by the View Synchronizer to select the view rewriting to be used.
- **View Maintainer**
  This module is responsible for traditional incremental view maintenance after data updates in the sources. In EVE , we have implemented SWEEP [4] for this purpose.
- **Concurrency Control (SDCC)**
  This module handles the complex concurrency issues that occur in an environment that has to deal with both data and schema updates. [63]
- **View Synchronizer**
  When underlying ISs change their *schema* (not just their *data*), existing *view queries* have to be adapted in order to keep providing information to their users. This goal is accomplished in EVE by *synchronizing* views with the schema changes of underlying ISs. [43, 45]
- **MKB Evolver/Consistency Checker** These modules update the Meta Knowledge Base according to the schema changes occuring in the underlying information sources.
- **Wrappers** connect information sources with the data warehouse, by translating information-source specific query mechanisms and data models into the relation query model assumed for the system.

5.1. A relaxed SQL query model—E-SQL

We now introduce the E-SQL query language (or Evolvable-SQL), which is our approach towards relaxed query semantics and implements and extends the semantics of attribute replaceability and dispensability, introduce earlier (Sec. 3.2). E-SQL is an extension of SQL that has been designed to allow for the specification of relaxed query semantics by users. We take the stand that it is most appropriate for the view definers themselves to specify the relaxed semantics at the time of query specification, as they are the ones that know the criticality and dispensability of the different components of their query.

The main idea of E-SQL is to allow a user to specify as part of a query definition what information is indispensable, what information is replaceable by similar information

Table 1 Relaxation parameters (preferences) of the E-SQL query language

Relaxation parameter		Domain	Default
Attribute-	dispensable ($\mathcal{A}D$)	*true/false* (dispensable/indispensable)	false
	replaceable ($\mathcal{A}R$)	*true/false* (replaceable/non-replaceable)	false
Condition-	dispensable ($\mathcal{C}D$)	*true/false* (dispensable/indispensable)	false
	replaceable ($\mathcal{C}R$)	*true/false* (replaceable/non-replaceable)	false
Relation-	dispensable ($\mathcal{R}D$)	*true/false* (dispensable/indispensable)	false
	replaceable ($\mathcal{R}R$)	*true/false* (replaceable/non-replaceable)	false
View-	extent ($\mathcal{V}E$)	$\approx$: no restriction on the new extent $\equiv$: new extent is equal to old extent $\supseteq$: new extent is superset of old extent $\subseteq$: new extent is subset of old extent	$\equiv$

from other ISs, and what relationship between original and new query result is desired, if obtaining the original query result becomes impossible in the changed information space.

Relaxation parameters (*preferences*) are associated with the different components of a query, such as the attributes in the SELECT clause, the conditions in the WHERE clause, and so on. Table 1 lists the seven types of relaxation parameters used in E-SQL.

It has three columns: column one gives the parameter name and the abbreviation for each parameter, column two the possible values each parameter can take on plus the associated semantics, and column three the default value. When the parameter setting is omitted from an E-SQL query, then the default value is assumed (column 3 of Table 1). This means that a conventional SQL query (without explicitly specified preferences) has well-defined semantics in our model, i.e., anything the user specified in the original query must be preserved exactly as originally defined in order for the query to be well-defined. Our extended query semantics are thus well-grounded and compatible with regular (non-relaxed) SQL semantics.

We now use an E-SQL example query (Equation 13) to demonstrate the usage of the relaxation parameters, while for a full description the reader is referred to [53].

```
CREATE VIEW  Asia-Customer (VE = "⊇") AS
SELECT       C.Name,
             C.Address,
             C.Phone (AD = true, AR = true)
FROM         Customer C,                                  (13)
             FlightRes F (RR = true)
WHERE        (C.Name = F.PName) AND
             (F.Dest = 'Asia') (CD = true)
```

The semantics of this query are as follows. Any query rewriting is acceptable as long as the new view extent is a superset of the old one (expressed by $\mathcal{V}E$ = "$\supseteq$"); the attribute **Phone** is dispensable and can also be replaced from another source (expressed by $\mathcal{A}D = true$, $\mathcal{A}R = true$); the relation **FlightRes** (but not **Customer**) can be replaced with another relation ($\mathcal{RR} = true$); and the user will still have use for the view even if the second WHERE condition cannot be kept valid ($\mathcal{CD} = true$).

Furthermore, there are some dependencies between different settings for the relaxation parameters. For example, it is meaningless for a relation to be marked dispensable if one of its attributes is indispensable. Therefore the parameter settings ($\mathcal{AD} = false, \mathcal{RD} = false$) and ($\mathcal{AD} = false, \mathcal{RD} = true$) for a particular attribute are equivalent. We have developed a theory of *strongest E-SQL queries* [42], which describes equivalence classes of relaxation parameter settings based on their semantics.

6. IMPLEMENTATION AND EVALUATION

6.1. Implementation of the EVE System

In the context of the EVE-project [45, 51, 43, 53, 34], we have implemented an experimental data warehouse maintenance system that is able to maintain a data warehouse over distributed sources handling both schema and data changes of ISs. The system is capable of breaking down queries and reassembling results from distributed ISs, incremental view maintenance using a simple multisource view maintenance algorithm, performing data warehouse evolution according to a view synchronization algorithm [45], computing QC-Values for the rewriting solutions for a given view and schema change as defined in the current paper and thus supporting the user in selecting a rewriting for a view. The QC value is computed as described in Sections 3 and 4, with the cost part computed according to the view synchronization algorithm used. Details on this method are given in the experiment in Section 6.2.3. The entire system is written in Java and uses a Swing (JFC) user interface. Connections to the databases are realized in JDBC with appropriate drivers, which gives us the flexibility to incorporate any relational DBMS available on the network. We have tested and run the system on different combinations of Oracle Server 8.0 and MS Access. The system has been tested on both Windows NT/2000 and Linux.

Figure 5 shows an example screenshot of the running EVE-System. An IS provider has just deleted a table and the system has generated four different view rewritings defined over the new information space that could replace the old view. Each view has a QC-Value assigned to it (see the left side of Figure 5), and the user can browse the composition of that QC-Value from the factors introduced earlier (see the right side of Figure 5), and then decide which view rewriting should be used. Based on our model, the rewriting with the highest QC-Value is the one 'closest' to intent and extent of the original view.

The results of this paper have been incorporated into our EVE system which had previously simply picked the first legal view rewriting it discovered and not necessarily the best one. As illustrated in Figure 5, the current system presents a number of choices for a view rewriting to the user, sorted by their numerical QC-Value. The user can then select the exact rewriting for each view, based on the QC-Value and its composition from quality and cost factors (see Figure 5). The implementation of the EVE system is

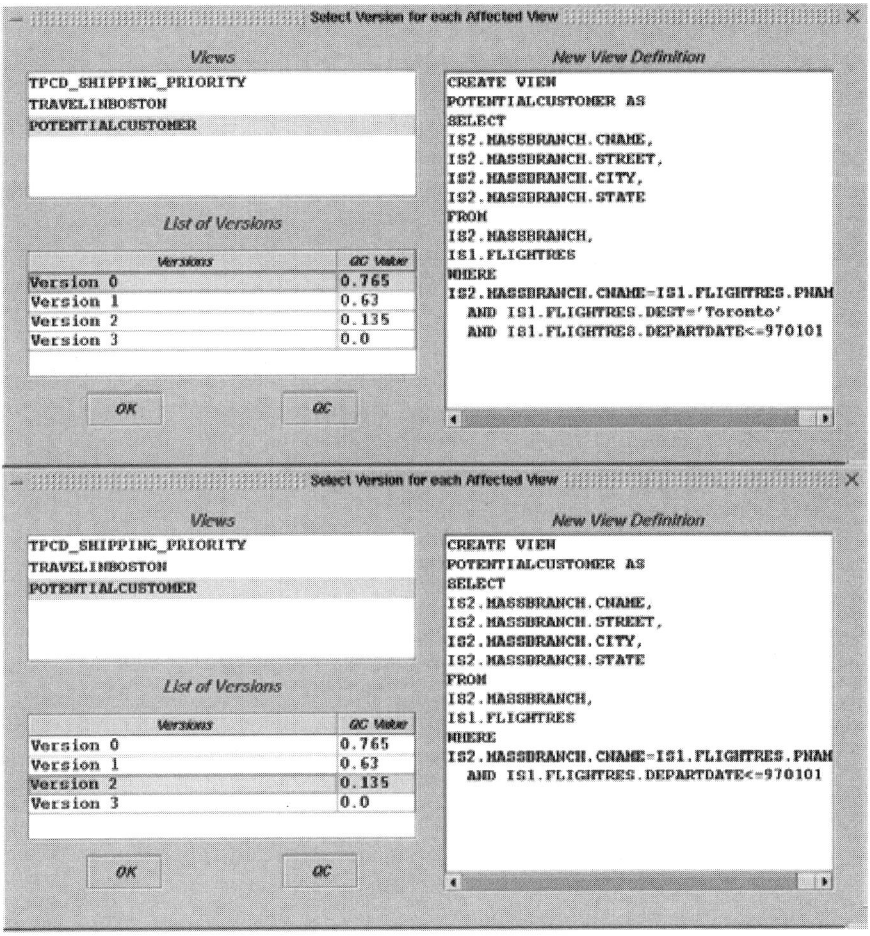

Figure 5. Different rewritings for a view and their respective QC-values.

fully functional, and has been demonstrated at the IBM technology showcase during the CASCON '98 conference [34] as well as at SIGMOD '99. [52]

6.2. Evaluation and discussion

We now set out to verify the validity of our proposed *QC-Model* and gain an understanding of the interplay between quality and maintenance costs through a number of experiments. Using the prototype implementation described earlier, we conducted experiments to evaluate the QC-Model. The experimental system holding the data warehouse was a Pentium 233 PC with 64 MB RAM running Windows NT 4.0 and

Java (JDK 1.1.6). As DBMSs, we used instances of Oracle 8.0 on separate Windows NT PCs as server for each IS. We use tables without indexes for predictable assessment of I/O-operations. Where large amounts of data were needed for an experiment, we used synthetic data generated by the TPC/D benchmark data generator. These experiments were conducted in the context of our EVE system, i.e., the rewritings of a view were being generated by our synchronization algorithm. [34, 43]

In Section 6.2.1, we discuss the influence of certain parameters of the query and information space on the overall QC-Value. In Section 6.2.2, we assess how the cardinalities of base relations may influence both the quality and the cost of a view rewriting. In the experiment in Section 6.2.3, we show actual performance measures using the Java-based implementation of the system described in Section 6.1, to calibrate the trade-off coefficients to associate with the different components of the QC-model. These empirically determined coefficients are then verified to result in accurate predications of the QC-model with the actually measured maintenance costs, for out testing environment. This also has resulted in a methodology that can be used to find cost factors that help to predict actual query execution time if the QC-model is used in a different system.

6.2.1. Influence of relation distribution on view maintenance cost

In this section, we study the relationships between the number and distribution of ISs involved in a view and the incremental view maintenance cost.

We first assess the effects of a variation of the number of ISs involved in a view, while fixing all other parameter settings, such as the selectivity and the join selectivity. The purpose is to find a heuristic for a view synchronization algorithm to choose between otherwise similar views (that is, in particular, views with the same number of base *relations*) if the main difference between views is the number of information sources on which it is based.

We look at the three cost factors introduced in Section 4. We observe that:

1. the number of messages exchanged between data warehouse and base relations (CF_M) grows proportionally with the number of ISs,
2. the number of bytes transferred between the warehouse and sources (CF_T) grows with the number of information sources. This is due to the fact that a view based on fewer information sources can accomplish part of its joins inside information sources (Fig. 6).
3. the number of I/O-operations ($CF_{I/O}$), which refers to the *total* number of such operations across all base relations, remains roughly the same, since we assume access to the same base relations which are simply stored in distinct information sources with similar system parameters.

That is, the view maintenance cost of a single data update tends to be higher for views with many information sources, allowing us to use this fact for a heuristic to guide a view rewriting algorithm. Secondly, we study the effect on the relation

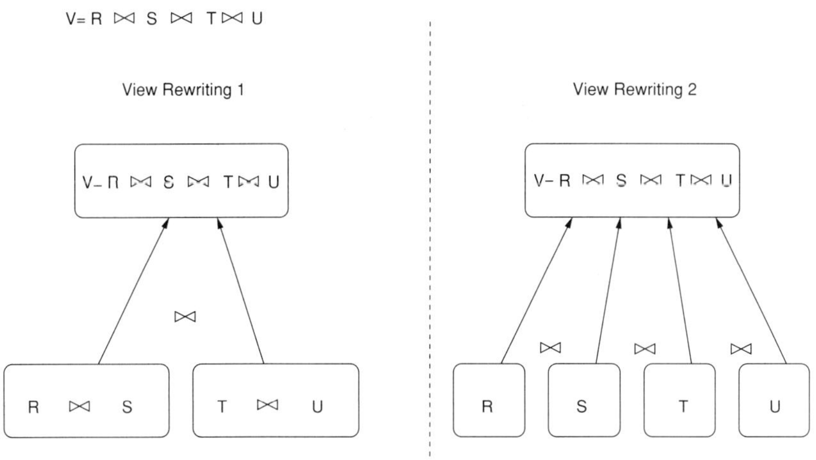

Figure 6. Effect of base relation distribution on view maintenance cost.

distribution among information sources. That is, we want to assess whether in terms of view maintenance cost, it is beneficial for a view to have its base relations distributed evenly across information sources, or whether it is better to have most of its relations in one information source and only a few relations in others. Of course, this situation is of interest only for views base on many relations (at least 6 . . . 7). Figure 7 shows results for the number of bytes transferred (CF_T) for a number of representative cases. The other two factors (CF_M and $CF_{I/O}$) are not affected. The charts show the number of transferred bytes for a particular view maintenance operation, where we varied the distribution of relations among information sources. The view has 6 relations, which are distributed among 2, 3, or 4 information sources. For example, the leftmost bar in the figure (marked $(1, 5)$) shows the number of bytes transferred for a particular update for our view, where the view is defined on a single relation in one information source, plus 5 relations in one other information source. We repeated the experiment for different average join selectivities (js).

From Fig. 7, we observe that there is no correlation between the relation distribution and the view maintenance cost. That is, a heuristic that would choose a particular relation distribution from among otherwise similar view rewritings would not be helpful in our environment.

6.2.2. Effect of relation cardinality on QC-value

In this experiment, we study the relationship between the cardinalities of the substituted relations and the *overall efficiency* of the legal rewritings. We conduct this experiment by varying the cardinalities of the substituted relation while keeping all other parameter

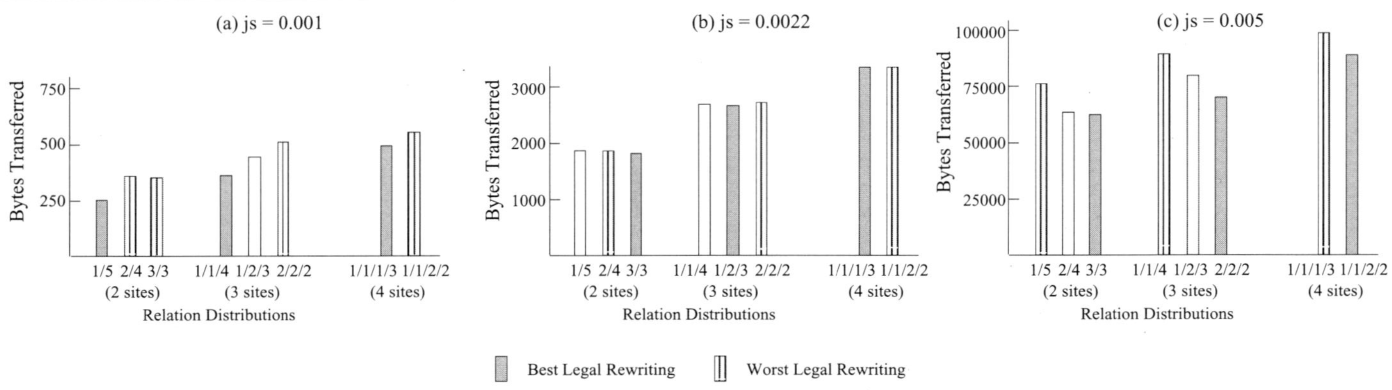

Figure 7. The relationships between relation distribution and view maintenance cost.

Table 2 Cardinalities of *Lineitem*, $Lineitem_1, \ldots, Lineitem_5$

Site name	Relation name	Cardinality
IS_1	*Lineitem (Orderkey, ...)*	4016
IS_2	$Lineitem_1$ *(Orderkey, ...)*	2008
IS_3	$Lineitem_2$ *(Orderkey, ...)*	3012
IS_4	$Lineitem_3$ *(Orderkey, ...)*	4016
IS_5	$Lineitem_4$ *(Orderkey, ...)*	5020
IS_6	$Lineitem_5$ *(Orderkey, ...)*	6032

settings the same. Let us assume a view V is defined as follows (this is a view defined over the TPC-D schema):

```
CREATE VIEW V (VE = '≈') AS
SELECT      ..., Lineitem. Orderkey (AR = true) ...
FROM        Order, Customer, Lineitem (RR = true)                        (14)
WHERE       Lineitem. Orderkey = Order. Orderkey (CR = true) AND ...
```

Let us assume that relation *Lineitem* is deleted by its information provider, and that there are five relations $Lineitem_1, \ldots, Lineitem_5$ in the information space that are identified by the view synchronizer to be appropriate substitutes for *Lineitem*. Five new views, $V_1 \ldots V_5$, can be defined that are formed by replacing relation *Lineitem* with the respective relation $Lineitem_n$. The cardinalities of *Lineitem* and the substitute relations for our experiment are summarized in Table 2.

We further assume that the following inter-relationships among these relations hold true: Relation $Lineitem_1$ is contained in relation $Lineitem_2$, denoted by a $\mathcal{CC}$ constraint: $\mathcal{CC}_{Lineitem_1, Lineitem_2} = (Lineitem_1 \subseteq Lineitem_2)$, $Lineitem_2$ in turn is contained in $Lineitem_3$, $Lineitem_3$ is equivalent to the deleted relation *Lineitem*, $Lineitem_3$ is contained in $Lineitem_4$, and $Lineitem_4$ contained in $Lineitem_5$ (i.e., $Lineitem_1 \subseteq Lineitem_2 \subseteq Lineitem_3 = Lineitem \subseteq Lineitem_4 \subseteq Lineitem_5$). Therefore, replacing *Lineitem* with $Lineitem_i$, for $1 \leq i \leq 5$, we get five alternate yet legal rewritings with different view extents and view maintenance costs[6]. Setting the system parameters to $w_1 = 0.7$, $w_2 = 0.3$, $\varrho_{D1} = 0.5$, $\varrho_{D2} = 0.5$, $\varrho_{attr} = 0.7$, $\varrho_{ext} = 0.3$, $cost_M = 0.521 \frac{s}{\text{message}}$, $cost_T = 0.000623 \frac{s}{\text{byte}}$, $cost_{I/O} = 0.00196 \frac{s}{\text{I/O-operation}}$, $\varrho_{quality} = 0.9$, and $\varrho_{cost} = 0.1$, we get the metrics of quality and cost that are summarized in Table 3 (see also Case 1 in Figure 8). The above coefficients are empirically validated using experiments that are described in Sec. 6.2.3. The other two cases in Figure 8 are obtained with ($\varrho_{quality} = 0.75$, $\varrho_{cost} = 0.25$) and ($\varrho_{quality} = 0.5$, $\varrho_{cost} = 0.5$), respectively.

In Section 3 we postulated that the degree of divergence $DD(i)$ for a view rewriting V_i will be large for a relation whose size is very different from the size of the original relation, and vice versa. The cost of a legal rewriting will be larger, all other factors equal, with a growing size of the replaced relation(s). Trading off these two factors

[6]Note that we assume that $\mathcal{V}E$ = '≈' for this view is given in Equation 14.

Table 3 Ranking of legal rewritings for experiment 6.2.2. (Detailed data for Case 1; $\varrho_{quality} = 0.9$)

Rewriting	DD_{attr}	DD_{ext}	DD	Cost (Normalized Cost)	$QC(V_i)$	Rating
V_1	0	0.25	0.075	39.5 (0)	0.9325	3
V_2	0	0.13	0.0375	45.1 (0.17)	0.9496	2
V_3	0	0.00	0.00	50.7 (0.33)	0.9667	1
V_4	0	0.10	0.027	56.3 (0.5)	0.9230	4
V_5	0	0.25	0.075	73.2 (1)	0.8325	5

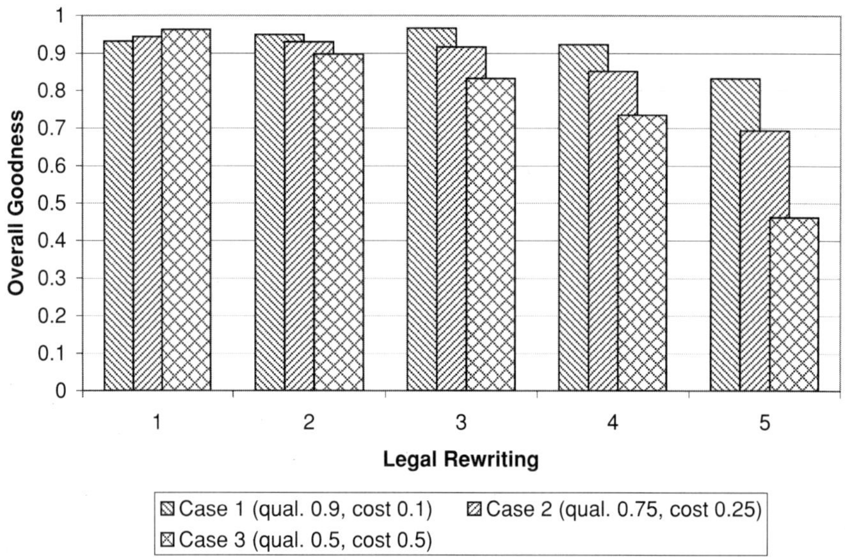

Figure 8. Results of assessing legal rewritings for experiment 6.2.2.

against each other will therefore lead to different results depending on how the trade-off parameters are set. Our experiment validates these findings.

For example, when the parameters are set to ($\varrho_{quality} = 0.9$, $\varrho_{cost} = 0.1$, Case 1), the QC-Model chose legal rewriting V_3 over the other four legal rewritings. Here, we give a high priority to the quality of the rewriting, which is best when the replacing relation comes as close as possible to the original relation, which is the case in legal rewriting V_3. The graph depicted in Figure 8 shows that the overall efficiency increases from legal rewriting V_1 until V_3 (because the size of the replacing relation approaches the size of the original relation), then becomes worse as the difference between the relation sizes grows bigger.

However, in Case 3, with ($\varrho_{quality} = 0.5$, $\varrho_{cost} = 0.5$), the cost has a larger impact on the overall efficiency of the legal rewriting. Since the cost is continuously increasing as the replacing relations get bigger (i.e., from legal rewriting V_1 to V_5), the overall efficiency of the rewritings decreases, so rewriting V_1 (with the smallest replacing relation) is chosen by our view synchronizer. Even in Case 2, the influence of the cost on the total result is large enough for V_1 to be selected as best legal rewriting.

Two observations we made from Figure 8 are:

- If we focus our attention on the legal rewritings V_3, V_4, and V_5 (labeled 3, 4, and 5 in Figure 8, rows 3 to 5 in Table 3), we can see that these rewritings are obtained by substituting the deleted relation *Lineitem* by a *superset* relation. Among these three legal rewritings, V_3 is always ranked highest among the three in various parameter settings. This is because the degrees of divergence (fourth column in Table 3, labeled *DD*) as well as the view maintenance costs (fifth column, labeled Cost) go up when the cardinalities of the replaced relations go up. For these cases, the trade-off parameters have no influence on what rewriting is selected to be best. A consequence is that if we have only superset replacements at our disposal, the replacement that is closest to the original in terms of the relation size is also the smallest replacement and will always rank best among legal rewritings.
- If we focus on the legal rewritings V_1, V_2, and V_3 (labeled 1, 2, and 3 in Figure 8, rows 1 to 3 in Table 3), these rewritings are obtained by replacing the deleted relation *Lineitem* with a *subset* relation. The degrees of divergence of the rewritings go down as the sizes of the replacement relations go up (column four in the table), but the view maintenance cost of the legal rewritings increases with the cardinality of the substituted relations (column five). Therefore, the overall efficiency of these rewritings depends on the trade-off parameters. For Case 1, V_3 is the best among the three. For Cases 2 and 3, i.e, when the view maintenance costs have a higher weight, then V_1 is ranked higher by the efficiency model.

6.2.3. *Experiments on accuracy of cost model prediction*

EXPERIMENTAL DESIGN. We conducted a series of experiments that support the soundness and correctness of the cost part of our QC-Model, namely, to determine how well the estimation that our cost model gives predicts the actual cost of maintenance after data updates.

An important result of this experimental study is that it yields a method to empirically compute the unit costs $cost_M$, $cost_T$, and $cost_{I/O}$ (Equation 12), which will be described in this section. For different setups, these parameters will be different but generally constant for a given data warehouse implementation. Thus, for other implementations using this cost model one could use our proposed suite of experiments to calibrate these factors.

While the cost part of QC incorporates aspects such as data transported, I/O-cost at the ISs, etc., for these experiments, we measure cost as the (real) time it takes our data warehouse to update its extent after a data update in an underlying IS. Using a fixed view and IS schema, we conducted the following experiments:

1. Inserting tuples into different sized base relations with a constant join selectivity, i.e., with a constant number of tuples joining with the update tuples. The purpose of this experiment was to assess the impact of I/O-cost ($CF_{I/O}$) on the QC-Value computation while keeping the other two cost factors constant.

CF_M	CF_T	$CF_{I/O}$	t_{upd} (sec)
40	6750	2130	24.5
40	6750	4260	33.2
40	6750	6430	37.9
40	6750	8580	43.0
40	6750	10760	47.0
40	6750	15940	52.1
40	6750	21170	65.5

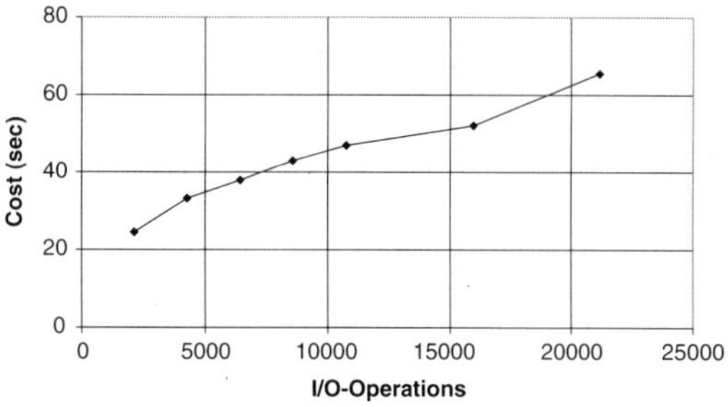

Figure 9. Execution times for updates on different-sized, constant-selectivity ISs.

2. Inserting tuples into a base relation whose join selectivity changes with its size. This leads to changes of I/O-costs *and* network costs ($CF_{I/O}$ and CF_T). The influence of the I/O-costs can be eliminated from the results by using the findings from the previous experiment, thus allowing us to isolate CF_T.
3. Inserting different sized sets of random tuples into the same information space (i.e., resetting base tables after each experiment). This leads to a changing number of messages, since some updates will lead to non-empty join results while others will not join with any tuple in the base relations of the view. Together with the findings from the previous two experiments, the influence of the number of messages on view maintenance cost can be assessed.

Under the assumption that the three cost factors are *orthogonal* (i.e., linearly independent from one another), we expect to have linear correlation between the (analytically obtained) cost factor and the (measured) view maintenance time for each of the three experiments. Using linear regression, we can then deduce the actual values for CF_M (in messages per second), CF_T (in bytes per second) and $CF_{I/O}$ (in IO-operations per second). If all three experiments in fact do show linear correlation, we conclude that the three-factor cost model is sound and the three base factors do not significantly influence each other.

INFLUENCE OF I/O-COST. First, we keep the number of messages and the number of bytes transferred constant and focus on changing I/O-costs. The values in Figure 9 (columns 1–3) were obtained using formulas that accurately describe the view maintenance algorithm used in this implementation, whereas the execution time (column 4) was measured using PC system time.

Leaving CF_M and CF_T constant, we can now compare how well our cost model predicts the actual execution cost using the I/O-cost as main cost factor (columns 3 and 4 in Figure 9). Executing a linear regression on data pairs in those two columns and computing the slope of the regression function yields $cost_{I/O} = 1.96 \cdot 10^{-3} \frac{\text{sec}}{\text{I/O-operation}}$. The correlation coefficient r for an assumed linear correlation is 0.98. We will now assume that the influence of the I/O-cost on the total cost that we found is independent

CF_M	CF_T	$CF_{I/O}$	t_{upd} (sec)	t_{adj} (sec)
40	6750	2130	25.5	21.3
40	9620	4090	33.3	25.3
40	12490	6050	38.0	26.2
40	15360	8010	41.6	25.9
40	18230	9970	45.5	26.0
40	26840	15850	65.6	34.6
40	32580	19770	77.2	38.5

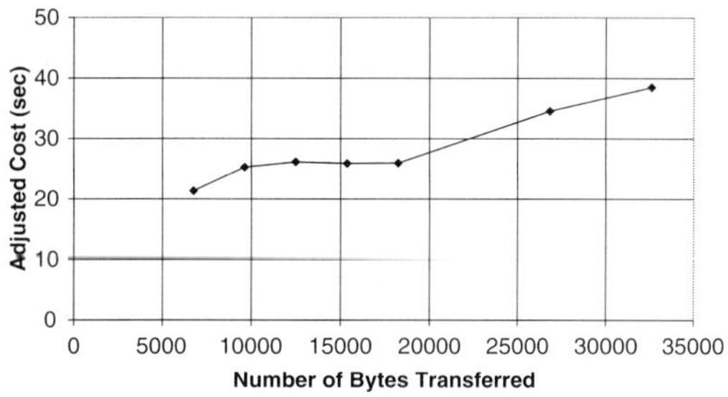

Figure 10. Execution times for updates on ISs with varying selectivity.

from the other two cost factors so we can use $cost_{I/O}$ to eliminate the influence of I/O-cost in later experiments. The high correlation in this data set suggests a strong linear correlation between I/O-costs and actual execution cost when the other two measures are held constant. This also means that there are no other important influences on the execution cost besides the three factors evaluated here.

INFLUENCE OF THE NUMBER OF BYTES TRANSFERRED (NETWORK COST). Next, we evaluate the influence of the amount of data transferred on the view maintenance cost in a similar fashion by running a second experiment. In order to compute the adjusted execution time in Figure 10, we multiply the number of I/Os with the value for $cost_{I/O}$ obtained above and subtract this time from the measured execution time ($t_{adj} = t_{upd} - CF_{I/O} \cdot cost_{I/O}$). We expect a linear correlation between columns 2 and 5 in Figure 10, meaning a linear dependency of number of bytes transferred and execution cost when eliminating the other two cost factors.

Assuming correlation between CF_T and the adjusted query execution time T_{adj}, linear regression yields a unit cost for the *Number of Bytes Transferred* of $cost_T = 6.23 \cdot 10^{-4} \frac{sec}{byte}$. The correlation coefficient is 0.97, which suggests a strong linear correlation.

INFLUENCE OF THE NUMBER OF MESSAGES. For Figure 11, we eliminate both network and I/O-cost in the way described above to determine the unit cost for messages: $t_{adj} = t_{upd} - CF_{I/O} \cdot cost_{I/O} - CF_T \cdot cost_M$. The last line in this table represents a set of updates that did not join with any tuples in the underlying relations. Thus, the I/O-cost is 0.

Eliminating the other two cost factors, we postulate linear correlation between CF_M and the adjusted time. Regression yields $cost_M = 0.53 \frac{sec}{message}$ with a correlation coefficient of 0.91. This again suggests a strong correlation between the *Number of Messages* and the total cost when the other two factors are eliminated. We find a remaining constant overhead time for our system of about 4.7 sec which cannot be accounted for using the three cost factors. This time is assumed to be constant for any incremental update, a finding which is supported by our experiments.

CF_M	CF_T	$CF_{I/O}$	t_{upd} (sec)	t_{adj} (sec)
16	791	5207	21.2	10.3
32	1541	9441	39.9	19.6
40	1711	6693	47.5	32.8
48	2007	10585	50.1	28.0
48	2209	11729	56.4	31.7
64	3123	19855	74.1	33.2
64	1056	0	40.3	39.3

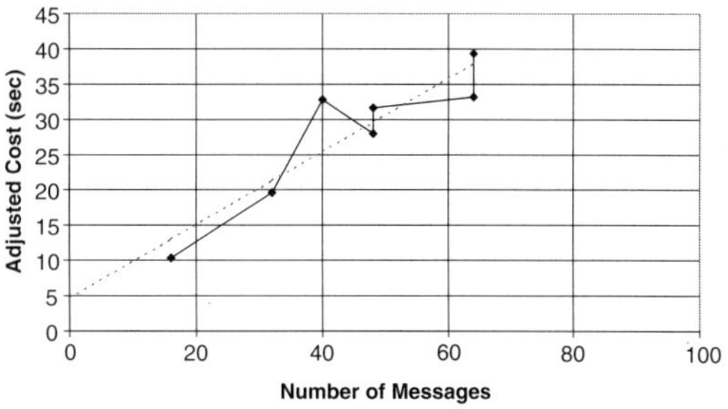

Figure 11. Execution times for varying number of messages.

CONCLUSIONS BASED ON EXPERIMENTAL ANALYSIS. The high correlation factors suggest that there is a correlation between our cost factors and the actual view maintenance cost. Through evaluating cost factors separately, we have found a linear dependency between the three cost factors and the actual measured execution time. We also found *unit costs* that we can use to predict the actual view maintenance cost for a given view in our system. Using these unit costs, we can now evaluate if our cost model correctly predicts the execution time (cost) for incremental view maintenance for a given view. For this, we use diverse views generated over the same base schema but in different information spaces and compute a predicted execution time by multiplying the respective values of CF_M, CF_T, and $CF_{I/O}$ with the unit costs found in the previous experiments.

Graphing computed and measured execution times and comparing them with the ideal line of Measured Cost = Predicted Cost, we obtain Figure 12.

The figure shows the correlation between predicted and measured view maintenance costs for a number of diverse views over different information spaces. The line labeled "Ideal" is the optimum, indicating a perfect prediction of view maintenance cost for our system. We can see that our cost model predicts the actual measured cost very well. The correlation coefficent between the predicted and measured cost is 0.96, the standard error for the computation of the predicted value is 4.48.

NON-UNIFORM DISTRIBUTION OF TEST DATA. The previous experiment was carried out using data from the TPC/D benchmark test, whose data are largely uniform. It is interesting to discuss how our cost model performs under non-uniform data sets.

The precision of the cost model on non-uniform data is affected by how precisely the factors CF_T, CF_M, and $CF_{I/O}$ can be estimated under different distributions of the base data. The number of messages CF_M will not be affected by data distribution. However, non-uniform data will not have a constant join selectivity and the accuracy of the prediction of I/O-cost will decrease also. So the overall accuracy of the cost model will depend on the relative errors of the base factors CF_T and $CF_{I/O}$. It is clear that a small deviation from the uniform distribution in the base data will have a smaller effect on the cost model accuracy than larger deviations.

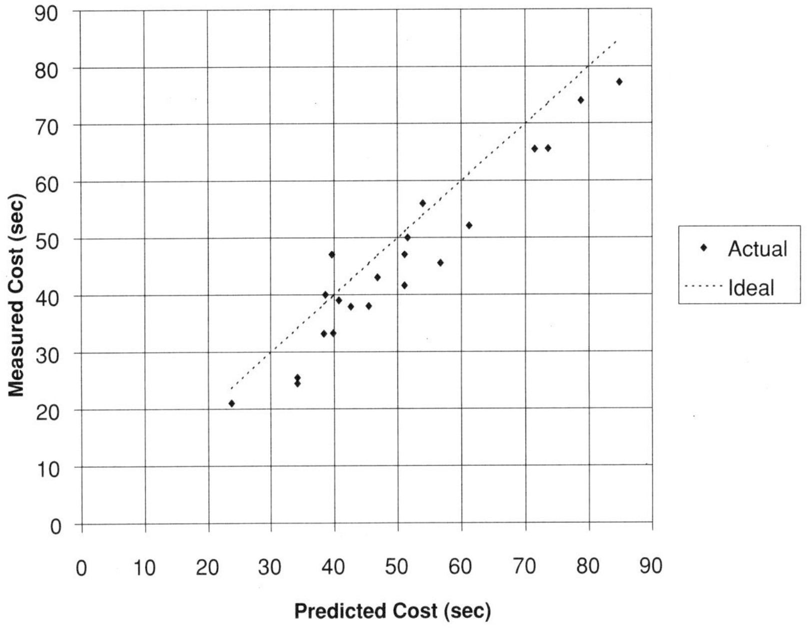

Figure 12. Correlation between predicted and actual view maintenance cost.

In some experiments that we ran in this context, we established that the base data distribution does have an effect on the accuracy of the cost model. If no distribution function for the base data is available, the prediction of I/O-cost and number of bytes transferred could have a large relative error. This would make the predictions of the cost model less reliable. However, small deviations in the base data distribution do not lead to significant reductions in prediction accuracy. If reliable measures for CF_T and $CF_{I/O}$ are available (e.g., through a precise estimation of join sizes, even in non-uniform data), our cost model will perform better as well. In addition, the field of estimating join sizes from simple system parameters [46, 24] or by sampling [25, 16, 27] is a very active research area and good solutions are available in the literature.

7. RELATED WORK

Materialized views over distributed information sources have been explored for a number of years. First work focused on questions of materialized view maintenance under data updates in the sources [22, 48, 4]. More recently, questions of optimizing view queries given varying parameters or capabilities of underlying sources have also been explored. Generally, work in this area assumes that the rewritten view query computes a view extent *equivalent* to the original one.

Prominent approaches that deal with equivalent query rewriting include work by Selinger et al. [56] with a recent optimization by Kossmann and Stocker [31], Jarke et al. [28], van den Berg et al. [60], Du et al. [10], or Levy et al. [36]. Also important is the Volcano Query Optimizer Generator by Graefe et al. [19, 18]

Some work has been done on rewriting queries using materialized views [37, 49, 40, 57, 50]. This work is relevant to ours, although it generally deals with rewriting queries into *equivalent ones* using underlying views.

Work on rewriting queries using views [35, 38] is used in subsequent work by Levy et al. which is closely related to our EVE project in terms of its goal of supporting views over dynamic environments, but not the approach taken. Levy introduced the notion of the *world-view* as a global, fixed domain model of a certain part of the world on which both information providers and consumers must define views. [39] This work is in some sense an approach inverse to the EVE-approach. [53] Where Levy et al. describe information sources in terms of a world model, we incrementally establish our world model in terms of the available sources. Levy's model provides a solution to a subset of problems that we also solve. It is nevertheless necessary to establish a world model before any source can provide information—a very complicated and often impossible task. Also, the concepts of quality and/or cost are no explored in the context of that work.

In an earlier paper [34], we introduce the overall EVE solution framework, in particular the concept of associating evolution preferences with view specifications and we introduce several algorithms that achieve view synchronization under deletions of underlying information. [43, 45, 29] All these algorithms generate large numbers of alternative legal rewritings, thus raising the need for an efficiency model. This current paper addresses this need by establishing a model for systematically ranking otherwise incomparable solutions for view synchronization.

Arens et al. [5] and the SoftBot project [14] provide similar approaches as Levy which solve similar problems. Although addressing different issues, SIMS' process of finding relevant information sources for a query raises some of the same problems as finding the right substitution for an affected view component in EVE. The SoftBot project has a very different approach to query processing as they assume that the system has to discover the "links" among data sources that are described by action schemas and that is does not use a cost model. While related to our view synchronization algorithm CVS [43], the SoftBot planning process also relies on discovering connections among information sources when very different source description languages are used. Neither SIMS nor SoftBot address the problem of evolution under capability changes of participating external information sources. All these projects do not discuss the problem of comparing non-equivalent rewritings of queries, but rather find some solution to a query without being able to evaluate the query result. Another relevant approach similar to Levy's is the Infomaster information integration project by Genesereth et al. [17] which tries to find the largest subset of data that can be provided for a certain query. This project is based partly on work done by Abiteboul, Duschka et al. [12, 2] on answering recursive queries using views.

CoBase by Chu et al. [8] relates to our work in that they also use the notion of relaxation of the *query extent*, similar to our E-SQL approach. [53] Chu established an SQL extension called CSQL (cooperative SQL) which relaxes the strictness of

SQL-*where*-conditions, i.e., it relaxes restrictions on the extent, but not the interface of a view query, whereas E-SQL allows for both. Given explicitly available knowledge about an application's domain, queries can be relaxed in a stepwise manner by altering local WHERE-conditions of a query until it returns approximate results to a user. Chu's work differs from ours in that it is limited to relaxing the values of local conditions in queries, whereas we handle relaxation of all elements in a Project-Select-Join-SQL-query. In contrast to CSQL, in which a manually established order of relaxation of conditions is needed to compare two rewriting possibilities, we have also defined a comprehensive model of quality and cost to automatically assess the desirability of a query rewriting [32, 33] (of which our algorithms would normally generate several) in order to help a view synchronization algorithm to find trade-offs among query rewritings.

Important work on integrating heterogeneous sources in one view using a common semistructured data model (OEM) has been done in the TSIMMIS-project [26, 41] and in a similar form by Abiteboul and others. [1] Incremental maintenance of views over such semistructured sources has also been considered, e.g., by Abiteboul. [3]

For the problem of *incremental view maintenance*, a concept which we use in our performance studies, earlier work has been done by several other projects in the literature. [21] Blakeley et al. [6] are concerned with a centralized environment only. Also, they have looked at incremental view maintenance assuming non-concurrent updates (updates are sufficiently spaced to not interfere with each other, each update reaches the data warehouse before the next update is executed at any of the base relations).

Lately, work on concurrent updates has been done. Based on the concept of updates interfering with each other due to long transmission times between base relations and the data warehouse, these works attack increasingly complex scenarios of handling concurrent updates by collecting update information in queues and handling them in batches. Zhuge et al. [65] introduce the ECA algorithm for incremental view maintenance and report on findings on the cost of their algorithm, but in a different environment from ours (a single information source is assumed). A second paper by the same authors ("Strobe" [66]) extends their findings towards multi-source information spaces, but does not incorporate any performance model or cost studies. Agrawal et al. [4] propose the SWEEP-algorithm, which can ensure consistency of the data warehouse in a larger number of cases compared to the Strobe family of algorithms. Finally, Zhuge et al. [65] contains a performance study. However, their work is limited to a comparison between traditional view recomputation and incremental view maintenance algorithms, and does not address the issue of view rewritings nor compares quality and cost between different rewritings for a query.

Preliminary results of this work have been published at the IDC'99 conference [33] and in a one-page poster summary in ICDE'99 [32]. This previous conference paper identified the problem of non-equivalent rewritings and presented a preliminary discussion on the idea of the QC-value. It does however not cover the implementation of the system, does not discuss the importance of workload models for the QC-Value, and omits a number of details that are necessary to fully evaluate the approach.

Furthermore, it does not give an in-depth evaluation of the approach—which is the core contribution of this current work.

8. CONCLUSION

View synchronization refers to the new and important problem of how to maintain views in dynamic distributed information systems. [53] These issues become important as more and more diverse and autonomous database systems are incorporated into large data warehouses. Local meta data updates at information sources participating in a data warehouse will generally cause a view in the warehouse to become invalid. This problem has been addressed by our previous work on the EVE-project. [34, 43, 29]

In this work, we now focussed on performance issues raised by view synchronization. Since view evolution under schema changes of underlying data sources will generate a large number of possible *rewritings* for an original view query, it is necessary to compare these rewritings and identify the *best* solution to maintaining a view. A novel measure of *efficiency* is introduced in this paper that explores the two dimensions of *quality* and *cost* and leads to the definition of the QC-Model. This model can be used to establish a ranking among alternate legal query rewritings for an affected view definition. It turns out that a ranking is possible among seemingly incomparable solutions using the QC-Model we developed, and that it is feasible to introduce *parameters* to trade off quality against cost (and also sub-dimensions of either against each other). While we have used a simple cost model in this paper and have not dealt with query optimization, alternative cost models can be incorporated as well, as long as they can correctly predict the incremental view maintenance cost of an arbitrary query under some workload model of updates. A combination of a query optimizer (producing equivalent rewritings) with our approach could for example lead to a system that could find view rewritings that show low divergence (i.e., are very similar to the original view) at a much lower execution cost.

We have conducted experiments that analyze the properties of our model, such as correlations between certain parameters. Also, we have run performance measurements and conducted a statistical analysis of the trade-off parameters in the cost model. A high correlation between computed view maintenance cost and actual cost (execution time) was found. The results of this work are being used in the EVE-System in an evaluation module for the view rewritings generated by our view synchronization algorithms.

Future work includes a deeper study as to how possible extensions of the model affect the quality dimension of our work, more sophisticated solutions for the cost part of the model (for instance, taking connection cost of information sources into account), and the support of other types of information sources (e.g., semistructured ISs through wrappers).

ACKNOWLEDGMENTS

This work was supported in part by several grants from NSF, namely, the NSF NYI grant #IRI 97-96264, the NSF CISE Instrumentation grant #IRIS 97–29878, and the NSF grant #IIS 97–32897. Dr. Rundensteiner would like to thank our industrial sponsors, in particular, IBM for the IBM partnership award and for the IBM corporate fellowship for one of her graduate students.

The authors would also like to thank students at the Database Systems Research Group at WPI for their interactions and feedback on this research. In particular, we are grateful to Yong Li and Xin Zhang for implementing several of the EVE components, including the MKB, the VKB, and the view synchronization algorithms.

REFERENCES

[1] S. Abiteboul, R. Goldman, J. McHugh, V. Vassalos, and Y. Zhuge. Views for semistructured data. In *Workshop on Management of Semistructured Data*, Tucson, Arizona, 1997.
[2] Serge Abiteboul and Oliver M. Duschka. Complexity of answering queries using materialized views. In ACM, editor, *Proceedings of ACM Symposium on Principles of Database Systems*, pages 254–263, New York, NY 10036, USA, 1998. ACM Press.
[3] Serge Abiteboul, Jason McHugh, Michael Rys, Vasilis Vassalos, and Janet L. Wiener. Incremental maintenance for materialized views over semistructured data. In *Proc. 24th Int. Conf. Very Large Data Bases, VLDB*, pages 38–49, 1998.
[4] D. Agrawal, A. El Abbadi, A. Singh, and T. Yurek. Efficient View Maintenance at Data Warehouses. In *Proceedings of SIGMOD*, pages 417–427, 1997.
[5] Y. Arens, C. A. Knoblock, and W.-M. Shen. Query Reformulation for Dynamic Information Integration. *Journal of Intelligent Information Systems*, 6 (2/3):99–130, 1996.
[6] J. A. Blakeley, P.-E. Larson, and F. W. Tompa. Efficiently Updating Materialized Views. *Proceedings of SIGMOD*, pages 61–71, 1986.
[7] S. Chaudhuri, R. Krishnamurthy, and S. Potamianos. Optimizing Query with Materialized Views. In *Proceedings of IEEE International Conference on Data Engineering*, 1995.
[8] W. W. Chu, M. A. Merzbacher, and L. Berkovich. The Design and Implementation of CoBase. *SIGMOD Record*, 22(2):517–522, June 1993.
[9] Wesley W. Chu, Hua Yang, Kuorong Chiang, Michael Minock, Gladys Chow, and Chris Larson. CoBase: A scalable and extensible cooperative information system. *Intelligent Information Systems (JIIS)*, 6(2/3):223–259, 1996.
[10] W. Du, R. Krishnamurthy, and M-C. Shan. Query Optimization in Heterogeneous DBMS. *International Conference on Very Large Data Bases*, pages 277–291, 1992.
[11] Oliver M. Duschka. *Query Planning and Optimization in Information Integration*. PhD thesis, Stanford University, Stanford, California, December 1997.
[12] Oliver M. Duschka and Michael R. Genesereth. Answering recursive queries using views. In ACM, editor, *Proceedings of ACM Symposium on Principles of Database Systems*, pages 109–116, New York, NY 10036, USA, 1997. ACM Press.
[13] R. Elmasri and S. B. Navathe. *Fundamentals of Database Systems*. The Benjamin/Cummings Publishing Company, Inc., 1994.
[14] Oren Etzioni and Daniel Weld. A Softbot-based interface to the Internet. *Communications of the ACM*, 37(7):72–76, July 1994.
[15] EVE Project Homepage: `http://davis.wpi.edu/dsrg/EVE`, 1998.
[16] Sumit Ganguly, Phillip B. Gibbons, Yossi Matias, and Avi Silberschatz. Bifocal sampling for skew-resistant join size estimation. *SIGMOD Record*, 25(2):271–281, June 1996.
[17] Michael R. Genesereth, Arthur M. Keller, and Oliver M. Duschka. Infomaster: An information integration system. *SIGMOD Record (ACM Special Interest Group on Management of Data)*, 26(2):539ff., 1997.
[18] G. Graefe, R. L. Cole, D. L. Davison, W. J. McKenna, and R. H. Wolniewicz. Extensible query optimization and parallel execution in volcano. In J. C. Freytag, G. Vossen and D. Maier, editor, *Query Processing for Advanced Database Applications*, page 305. Morgan Kaufmann, San Francisco, CA, 1994.
[19] Goetz Graefe and William J. McKenna. The volcano optimizer generator: Extensibility and efficient search. In *Proceedings of IEEE International Conference on Data Engineering*, pages 209–218. IEEE Computer Society, 1993.

[20] A. Gupta, H. V. Jagadish, and I. S. Mumick. Data Integration using Self-Maintainable Views. In *Proceedings of International Conference on Extending Database Technology (EDBT)*, pages 140–144, 1996.
[21] A. Gupta, I. S. Mumick, and V. S. Subrahmanian. Maintaining Views Incrementally. In *Proceedings of SIGMOD*, pages 157–166, 1993.
[22] A. Gupta and I. S. Mumick. Maintenance of Materialized Views: Problems, Techniques, and Applications. *IEEE Data Engineering Bulletin, Special Issue on Materialized Views and Warehousing*, 18(2):3–19, 1995.
[23] Peter J. Haas, Jeffrey F. Naughton, S. Seshadri, and Lynne Stokes. Sampling-based estimation of the number of distinct values of an attribute. In *International Conference on Very Large Data Bases*, pages 311–322, 1995.
[24] Peter J. Haas, Jeffrey F. Naughton, S. Seshadri, and Arun N. Swami. Fixed-precision estimation of join selectivity. In *Proceedings of ACM Symposium on Principles of Database Systems*, pages 190–201. ACM Press, May 1993.
[25] Peter J. Haas and A. N. Swami. Sampling-based selectivity estimation for joins using augmented frequent value statistics. In *Proceedings of IEEE International Conference on Data Engineering*, pages 522–531, 1995.
[26] J. Hammer, Héctor García-Molina, S. Nestorov, R. Yerneni, M. Breunig, and V. Vassalos. Template-Based Wrappers in the TSIMMIS System. In *Proceedings of SIGMOD*, pages 532–535, 1997.
[27] Wen-Chi Hou and Gultekin Özsoyoğlu. Statistical estimators for aggregate relational algebra queries. *ACM Transactions on Database Systems*, 16(4):600–654, December 1991.
[28] M. Jarke and J. Koch. Query Optimization in Database Systems. *ACM Computing Surveys*, pages 111–152, 1984.
[29] A. Koeller, E. A. Rundensteiner, and N. Hachem. Integrating the Rewriting and Ranking Phases of View Synchronization. In *Proceedings of the ACM First International Workshop on Data Warehousing and OLAP (DOLAP'98)*, pages 60–65, November 1998.
[30] Andreas Koeller and Elke A. Rundensteiner. Discovery of high-dimensional inclusion dependencies. Technical Report WPI-CS-TR-02-15, Worcester Polytechnic Institute, Dept. of Computer Science, 2002.
[31] Donald Kossmann and Konrad Stocker. Iterative dynamic programming: a new class of query optimization algorithms. *ACM Transactions on Database Systems*, 25(1):43–82, March 2000.
[32] A. J. Lee, A. Koeller, A. Nica, and E. A. Rundensteiner. Data Warehouse Evolution: Trade-offs between Quality and Cost of Query Rewritings. In *Proceedings of IEEE International Conference on Data Engineering*, Special Poster Session, page 255, March, Sydney, Australia 1999.
[33] A. J. Lee, A. Koeller, A. Nica, and E. A. Rundensteiner. Non-Equivalent Query Rewritings. In *Proceedings of the 9th International Databases Conference*, pages 248–262. City University of Hong Kong Press, Hong Kong, July 1999.
[34] A. J. Lee, A. Nica, and E. A. Rundensteiner. Keeping Virtual Information Resources Up and Running. In *Proceedings of IBM Centre for Advanced Studies Conference (CASCON'97), Best Paper Award*, pages 1–14, November 1997.
[35] A. Levy, I. S. Mumick, Y. Sagiv, and O. Shmueli. Equivalence, query reachability and satisfiability in datalog extensions. In *Proceedings of the Twelfth ACM SIGACT-SIGMOD-SIGART Symposium on Principles of Database Systems*, pages 109–122, Washington, DC, 25–28 May 1993.
[36] A. Y. Levy, Inderpal Singh Mumick, and Y. Sagiv. Query optimization by predicate move-around. In Jorgeesh Bocca, Matthias Jarke, and Carlo Zaniolo, editors, *International Conference on Very Large Data Bases*, pages 96–107, Los Altos, CA 94022, USA, 1994. Morgan Kaufmann Publishers.
[37] A. Y. Levy, A. Rajaraman, and J. D. Ullman. Answering queries using limited external processors. In *pods*, pages 227–237, Montreal, Canada, 3–5 June 1996.
[38] Alon Levy and Yehoshua Sagiv. Constraints and Redundancy in Datalog. In *Proceedings of the Eleventh ACM SIGACT-SIGMOD-SIGART Symposium on Principles of Database Systems, June 2–4, 1992, San Diego, CA*, pages 67–80, 1992.
[39] Alon Y. Levy, Divesh Srivastava, and Thomas Kirk. Data model and query evaluation in global information systems. *Journal of Intelligent Information Systems—Special Issue on Networked Information Discovery and Retrieval*, 5(2):121–143, 1995.
[40] A. Y. Levy, A. O. Mendelzon, and Y. Sagiv. Answering Queries Using Views. In *Proceedings of ACM Symposium on Principles of Database Systems*, pages 95–104, May 1995.
[41] C. Li, R. Yerneni, V. Vassalos, Héctor García-Molina, Y. Papakonstantinou, J. D. Ullman, and M. Valiveti. Capability Based Mediation in TSIMMIS. In *Proceedings of SIGMOD*, pages 564–566, 1998.

[42] A. Nica. *View Evolution Support for Information Integration Systems over Dynamic Distributed Information Spaces*. PhD thesis, University of Michigan in Ann Arbor, in progress 1999.
[43] A. Nica, A. J. Lee, and E. A. Rundensteiner. The CVS Algorithm for View Synchronization in Evolvable Large-Scale Information Systems. In *Proceedings of International Conference on Extending Database Technology (EDBT'98)*, pages 359–373, Valencia, Spain, March 1998.
[44] A. Nica and E. A. Rundensteiner. On Translating Loosely-Specified Queries into Executable Plans in Large-Scale Information Systems. In *Proceedings of Second IFCIS International Conference on Cooperative Information Systems CoopIS'97*, pages 213–222, June 1997.
[45] A. Nica and E. A. Rundensteiner. Using Containment Information for View Evolution in Dynamic Distributed Environments. In *Proceedings of International Workshop on Data Warehouse Design and OLAP Technology (DWDOT'98)*, Vienna, Austria, August 1998.
[46] Gregory Piatetsky-Shapiro and Charles Connell. Accurate estimation of the number of tuples satisfying a condition. *SIGMOD Record*, 14(2):256–276, 1984.
[47] Viswanath Poosala and Yannis E. Ioannidis. Selectivity estimation without the attribute value independence assumption. In *International Conference on Very Large Data Bases*, pages 486–495, 1997.
[48] D. Quass and J. Widom. On-Line Warehouse View Maintenance. In *Proceedings of SIGMOD*, pages 393–400, 1997.
[49] A. Rajaraman, Y. Sagiv, and J. D. Ullman. Answering Queries Using Templates With Binding Patterns. In *Proceedings of ACM Symposium on Principles of Database Systems*, pages 105–112, May 1995.
[50] A. Rajaraman and J. D. Ullman. Integrating Information by Outerjoins and Full Disjunctions. In *Proceedings of ACM Symposium on Principles of Database Systems*, pages 238–248, 1996.
[51] E. A. Rundensteiner, A. Koeller, A. Lee, Y. Li, A. Nica, and X. Zhang. Evolvable View Environment (EVE) Project: Synchronizing Views over Dynamic Distributed Information Sources. In *Demo Session Proceedings of International Conference on Extending Database Technology (EDBT'98)*, pages 41–42, Valencia, Spain, March 1998.
[52] E. A. Rundensteiner, A. Koeller, X. Zhang, A. Lee, A. Nica, A. VanWyk, and Y. Li. Evolvable View Environment. In *Proceedings of SIGMOD'99 Demo Session*, pages 553–555, May 1999.
[53] E. A. Rundensteiner, A. J. Lee, and A. Nica. On Preserving Views in Evolving Environments. In *Proceedings of 4th Int. Workshop on Knowledge Representation Meets Databases (KRDB'97): Intelligent Access to Heterogeneous Information*, pages 13.1–13.11, Athens, Greece, August 1997.
[54] Elke A. Rundensteiner, Andreas Koeller, and Xin Zhang. Maintaining Data Warehouses over Changing Information Sources. *Communications of the ACM*, pages 57–62, June 2000.
[55] Torsten Schlieder. Schema-driven evaluation of approximate tree-pattern queries. In *Proceedings of International Conference on Extending Database Technology (EDBT)*, volume LNCS 2287, pages 514–532. Springer, 2002.
[56] Patricia G. Selinger, Morton M. Astrahan, Donald D. Chamberlin, Raymond A. Lorie, and Thomas G. Price. Access path selection in a relational database management system. In *Proceedings of SIGMOD*, pages 23–34. ACM, 1979.
[57] D. Srivastava, S. Dar, H. V. Jagadish, and A.Y. Levy. Answering Queries with Aggregation Using Views. In *International Conference on Very Large Data Bases*, pages 318–329, 1996.
[58] Anja Theobald and Gerhard Weikum. Adding relevance to XML. *Lecture Notes in Computer Science*, 1997:105–??, 2001.
[59] Anja Theobald and Gerhard Weikum. The index-based XXL search engine for querying XML data with relevance ranking. In *Proceedings of International Conference on Extending Database Technology (EDBT)*, volume LNCS 2287, pages 477–495. Springer, 2002.
[60] C. A. van den Berg and M. L. Kersten. An Analysis of a Dynamic Query Optimization Schema for Different Data Distributions. In J. C. Freytag, D. Maier, and G. Vossen, editors, *Query Processing for Advanced Database Systems*, chapter 15, pages 449–473. Morgan Kaufmann Pub., 1994.
[61] S. B. Yao. An Attribute Based Model for Database Access Cost Analysis. *ACM Transactions on Database Systems (TODS)*, 2(1):45–67, March 1977.
[62] X. Zhang, L. Ding, and E. A. Rundensteiner. PSWEEP: Parallel View Maintenance Under Concurrent Data Updates of Distributed Sources. Technical Report WPI-CS-TR-99-14, Worcester Polytechnic Institute, Computer Science Department, May 1999.
[63] X. Zhang and E. A. Rundensteiner. The SDCC Framework for Integrating Existing Algorithms for Diverse Data Warehouse Maintenance Tasks. In *International Database Engineering and Application Symposium*, pages 206–214, Montreal, Canada, August, 1999.

[64] Xin Zhang, Elke A. Rundensteiner, and Lingli Ding. PVM: Parallel View Maintenance Under Concurrent Data Updates of Distributed Sources. In *Data Warehousing and Knowledge Discovery, Proceedings*, Munich, Germany, September 2001. 230–239.

[65] Y. Zhuge, Héctor García-Molina, J. Hammer, and J. Widom. View Maintenance in a Warehousing Environment. In *Proceedings of SIGMOD*, pages 316–327, May 1995.

[66] Y. Zhuge, Héctor García-Molina, and J. L. Wiener. The Strobe Algorithms for Multi-Source Warehouse Consistency. In *International Conference on Parallel and Distributed Information Systems*, pages 146–157, December 1996.

WEB DATA EXTRACTION TECHNIQUES AND APPLICATIONS USING THE EXTENSIBLE MARKUP LANGUAGE (XML)

JUSSI MYLLYMAKI AND JARED JACKSON

1. INTRODUCTION

The driving force behind the technology revolution has always been just one thing: information. Almost every invention related to the computer since the transistor has been made to aid in the transferring of a piece of information, or data, from one place to another. Despite the existence of a primitive form of what we now know of as the Internet, less than one generation ago digital information mostly needed to be carried around on magnetic devices such as tapes and disks. Fortunately, the prominent rise of the Internet and the World Wide Web in the mid-1990s removed the barrier that physical transportation of data placed on us.

Today, nearly every company, institution, or organization of note makes use of now ubiquitous Web technologies and avails all connected to the Internet of an abundance of information. Product catalogs, financial reports, service offerings, published information such as news reports, and more are stored on servers waiting to be queried by anyone from anywhere around the world. This wealth of information can be extraordinarily powerful for those who are able to filter through it and use it to their advantage.

The aim of this chapter is to introduce the key concepts behind how Web-based data is distributed and how this data can be collected in an efficient manner for future processing. First, a brief description of the relevant technologies that make up the Web will be given. This description will then be augmented with an examination of how data is delivered using Web technologies. With these concepts understood, we will illustrate how to use common tools of the Web in order to recreate the data sources used by those serving up the data we are interested in and store them in such a way that we can use the data for our own purposes.

The recreation of external data affords us the opportunity to work with the data in real time, cache it for later processing, and conduct analysis on data cumulated over time. These advantages show the rising importance of data extraction and the need for modern businesses to understand the technology.

2. WEB DATA EXTRACTION

2.1. Why Web data is important

Since Web-based data extraction is not an effortless process, we need to ask whether we gain anything by it in the first place. There are many sources of data, some easier to process than others. Print and voice sources are the most difficult to work with, but still are widely used. In complete contrast, some companies and organizations now offer direct connections to portions of their databases through Web Services [31] or other similar technologies. These technologies allow others to work directly with external data without involvement in the middle layer of Web data extraction. A major drawback to extracting information from print-based media is that it is quickly made obsolete, while the dynamic nature of the Web allows for continual updating of the desired data.

While there are no considerable drawbacks to using Web Services, they are unsurprisingly rare to find for accessing proprietary information. For instance, if some companies were to provide the information they make available via a Web-based catalog of products by exposing portions of their database directly, they may offer some of their competitors an easy to obtain advantage over them. For this reason key information is often only available through Web pages and not as Web Services.

Extracting information is not without challenge. On many sites, particular Web pages require some form of access control or authentication in order to view them, such as requiring a user to log on to the site with a site-determined username and password. The various challenges behind Web data extraction and their solutions will be covered later in this chapter.

So what value does all of this data bring to us? First there is a cost consideration, since many companies may charge large sums of money for services delivering data that is already available for free on their own Web site. Despite some technical challenges, there are many applications that can make valuable use of information. The possibilities are bound only by the creativity of the developer. Already applications exist for integrating information and presenting consolidated results, gaining competitive intelligence, managing supply chains, implementing competitive pricing and advertising, etc. New applications of this technology are being discovered and applied constantly.

2.2. Core technologies behind the World Wide Web

Before any Web-based data extraction can begin, a basic understanding of how the information flow of the Web works needs to be gained. The architecture of the Internet has many components. Web servers are machines connected to the Internet that accept

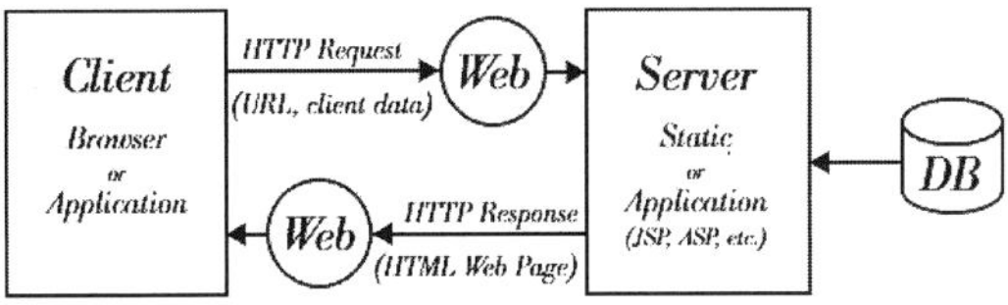

Figure 1. Interplay of Web Technologies: Web Client, Web Server, HTTP, HTML, Web Application, and Backend Database.

queries, or data requests, from other machines connected to the same network. The way in which the request to the Web server and its response are communicated on the Web is through a protocol called the Hyper Text Transport Protocol, or HTTP [11]. HTTP requests are sent from the requesting computer to the Web server and HTTP responses are returned with the data that has been requested. The most common scenario for this is when a computer user enters a Uniform Resource Locator (URL) into a Web browser and a Web page is returned, formatted by the browser, and presented visually to the user.

The most common response to a HTTP request is in the form of Hyper Text Markup Language, or HTML [10]. HTML is a text-based, human-readable way of formatting a document for presentation to a human reader. HTML works by placing tags around portions of the page's content to alter its presentation or add meta-data to the document. HTML is the pre-rendered form of Web pages, and is the primary source used in Web data extraction.

A similar technology, the eXtensible Markup Language, or XML [36], has gained prominence of late due to its common use in transferring Web data that is not necessarily rendered as a document within a Web browser (e.g. in Web Services). XML is similar to HTML in its structure, but instead of formatting data for presentation to a human reader, it formats the data to be easily processed by a computer. XML is text based and human readable, just like HTML, which makes it both easy to learn and use.

Web technologies are used to connect Web servers, HTTP, HTML, and XML together to deliver information from one source to another. Figure 1 demonstrates the inter-workings of these technologies. The request is sent via HTTP from a client machine to a Web server. The server processes that request and formats the resulting response in either HTML or XML and returns a response to the requesting client machine.

2.3. The challenges of web data extraction

The greatest challenge faced in extracting Web data comes from the loosely structured nature of the Web. During the browser wars of the mid-1990s the most popular Web browsers engaged in a pattern of becoming more and more tolerant of ill-formatted HTML pages. This had the positive effect of making pages otherwise unreadable available for browsing, however the long-term effect was that major errors in Web pages were never fixed and in fact were propagated and multiplied in future iterations on those pages. This is evidenced by Web pages whose source code is missing required tags or whose format and syntax are almost unreadable, even to a developer trained in Web page construction. Even the most widely used sites on the Internet today are often full of pages that do not conform properly to the published HTML standard.

A second challenge presents itself in the dynamic nature of the Web. Few pages of note on the Web are statically defined, meaning that a Web request simply looks up an HTML file on the Web server's file system and returns that file unaltered. Instead, Web servers often compose their responses from a variety of data sources, any of which could change at any time. The most common scenario for "interesting" Web data comes from a Web server communicating directly with a back-end database. Electronic commerce (E-commerce) Web sites are a good example of this scenario. Product information is stored and manipulated by the owning company on a central database, and when a Web browser requests the information, the server automatically retrieves the information from the database, allowing the data to be updated and presented accurately in real time.

This dynamic presentation of data does not mean that there is no underlying order to work with. If not the task of data extraction would be nearly impossible. The typical working of a Web server is to insert the variable data into the Web page response through the use of some sort of template. A template defines the unchanging portions of the Web page and provides the Web server with windows where it can put dynamic content. Examples of these template technologies include Sun's Java Server Pages (JSP) [16], Microsoft's Active Server Pages (ASP) [1], and the Extensible Style sheet Language (XSL) [40].

Like the Web pages themselves, these templates are susceptible to change over time as Web developers add or remove features on the page or even just update the page to change its look and feel. The last primary challenge then in extracting Web-based data is to make sure the solution is robust. This means that our extraction technique should not fail in light of minor changes from page to page or from iteration to iteration of the template.

While this may seem like a monumental task, there are good techniques that we will elaborate on that make this work less daunting. It is also important to note, that while small changes within the template are somewhat common, an empirical analysis of Web sites owned by corporations has shown that these templates rarely change in any large-scale fashion. Companies invest heavily in the development of their own look and feel and the costs of changing to a new template are so high that it is reasonable to rely on the continued use of particular templates on one Web site for several years.

Given these challenges, the goal of Web data extraction is in effect to impose order and strict structure on data that is at best semi-structured. This is often possible because the templates give us just enough common structure across similar pages in a site and over time that we can still identify the portions of the page we deem relevant.

The challenges illustrated above provide a preview of the considerations that have to go into the development of the technology for Web data extraction. These technical obstacles generally lie in the broad categories of design, change, and solution. We should now note that there are other challenges that present themselves in the accomplishment of this goal that are less technical in nature. In Section 3 we explore further these technical challenges and other problems that come up that are less related to the direct extraction of data, such as legal considerations. Of course, we will also examine the solutions that may be used in order to overcoming these problems.

2.4. Using XML technologies in web data extraction

Our technique for extracting data from a Web source is to transform the information given to us from the Web server into an XML document. It is certainly legitimate to ask why XML is used at all. Why not just use our transformation mechanism to store the extracted data directly into our own database since that is our ultimate goal?

While inserting data directly into a database is certainly possible, there are several advantages to using XML as a middle layer. One such advantage is that XML provides a method of imposing schemas on documents that is both easy to read and flexible. Since robustness is a key factor in the world of changing Web sources, extraction developers will need to be able to adapt their data models to the changing information at hand. This is a much more complicated task when dealing directly with database calls.

Adding to this advantage is the core integration that modern databases now have with XML. The most recent versions of all top-of-the-line databases have tightly integrated processes for importing and exporting data to and from XML documents. The integration tools offered by these databases will only improve in the near future. Thus we can leverage the ease of use and adaptability of XML without adding too much overhead to the entire process.

A second advantage to XML is its relation to existing Web sources. XML and HTML have much in common and mapping data from one to the other has become simple using XSL, another common Web technology. Also, as many Web sites begin adding Web Services support, the source of our data to extract will already be in XML, and we can use the same process to go from the XML given to our desired XML as we use to translate data from the HTML source to our XML result. This process has become a de facto standard in working XML and is easily integrated into most modern business systems.

With this overview of the technologies to be used in Web data extraction we need now to consider the business requirements and systems behind the technology. We discuss these in the next section.

3. FROM WEB TO SYSTEMS

3.1. Business requirements

While data extraction can be applied to any application domain that benefits from the public information available on the World Wide Web, it is particularly advantageous to companies that wish to incorporate external information and knowledge into their decision-making processes. For example, information on the pricing and features of competitive products on the market is a natural input to the pricing strategy of any company.

These modern business systems impose more stringent requirements on the data extraction process than would otherwise be the case. For instance, a university research team that wishes to retrieve news articles from the Web for research purposes might want to control the extraction process manually and use the file system as the repository for the resulting news article files. In contrast, the market analysis department of a company might want to run the same extraction process continuously and have the news articles flow into a business intelligence engine, which in turn triggers alerts to executives who are interested in certain topics appearing in the news. The company needs a continuous, reliable data extraction process that works silently in the background ("lights-off operation"), requires little manual effort, and provides powerful monitoring and administration tools.

E-commerce is a prime example of a business process that can both provide and utilize real-time product information. Suppose company A is interested in retrieving information from the E-commerce server of another company B which may be their supplier, vendor, competitor, or business partner. The anatomy of such an E-commerce server consists of three main components typically: a backend database where data is stored, an application server that contains programs for accessing the database, and a Web server that provides the visual interface to the system in the form of HTML pages.

The backend database may be tightly integrated into the business process of the company or it may just be extracted daily from some other database which the company does not want to make public. The application server runs the business logic, for example a shopping cart management and invoice processing. The Web server is configured with a set of HTML templates that convert data from the database into HTML pages.

3.2. Database-centric data extraction

A shallow data extraction process would attempt to use a Web crawler to find as many product pages on the E-commerce server as possible and extract the information contained on all of those pages. A deeper, more aggressive approach is to attempt to replicate the actual backend database of the target E-commerce server. In essence, the goal is to copy the remote database as completely as possible by accessing it through the Web server. The retrieved data is stored in a local database that is structured as identically as possible to the remote database but is initially empty. Appropriate data mappings between the remote and local database are required if the precise structure (database schema) of the remote database is not known. This will commonly be the case since not all aspects of the remote database are visible through the Web server. Database metadata such as consistency rules, constraints, and triggers are examples of items that are not visible through the Web server. While these metadata may be deducible from the data itself, the primary objective of a company in this situation is to get hold of the data itself and not the metadata.

This database-centric view suggests the following model for performing the data extraction. A crawler is used to periodically fetch pages from the target Web site and extract data as a set of well-structured XML documents. The XML data is converted to a set of insert and update operations on the local database. Performing those operations refreshes the local database so that it contains a replica of the remote database. The company can now execute sophisticated data analysis or decision support applications on the local database without requiring continuous access to the remote database.

3.3. Crawler-based data extraction

The basic mechanism for retrieving Web pages in a controlled, automated fashion is a well-understood topic. Search engines are a prime example of systems that involve fetching pages from Web sites. Some of the key parameters used to configure crawlers (also known as spiders and robots) are *seed URLs*, *crawling depth*, and *include/exclude rules*. The crawler starts by retrieving pages listed in its seed URL set. The seed URLs point to one or more pages on the target Web site one wishes to extract data from. On an E-commerce Web site, a likely seed URL would point to the root page of the product catalog section of the site.

In a corporate intranet, the seed URL set could include the home page URLs of different business units, organizational units, or geographic units. A corporation may have a well-connected intranet, in which case listing the top home page of the intranet as the seed URL is sufficient. In large corporate intranets, this is not likely to be sufficient and the root page of each disconnected sub-intranet needs to be listed individually.

Crawling depth specifies the number of hops a crawler will move away from a seed URL. A depth of 1 means that the crawler will fetch seed URLs and all pages they directly point to via hyperlinks. Increasing the depth to 2 extends the coverage of the crawl by also fetching pages pointed to by pages that are directly linked to the seed URLs. The crawling depth parameter has an exponential effect since every page contains links to many other pages. Since there may be many paths from a seed URL to a given page in the network, it is important to eliminate duplicates so that the same page (and all pages it points to and the pages they point to!) is not fetched multiple times.

The crawler can be configured to follow certain links and not others. A rule-based approach is a powerful method for achieving this. A rule specifies a URL pattern based on the protocol, hostname, and other parts of the URL syntax. An include rule says that any link that matches the pattern is followed. Conversely, an exclude rule tells the crawler not to follow a matching pattern. The rules are listed in some precedence order. For example, it might be necessary to say that pages at the Web site mycompany.com are to be crawled, except those that use any protocol other than HTTP, but FTP links to ftp.mycompany.com should still be crawled.

The concept of seed URLs, crawling depth, and include/exclude rules brings us to the notion of *crawling scope*. In Web data extraction, the goal of crawling is to fetch certain, interesting portions of a Web site or sites. The goal can be stated more formally as follows: retrieve pages that are of interest by starting at a convenient seed URL and following direct or indirect links to pages that contain interesting information. Retrieving any page that does not directly contribute to the goal is wasteful and

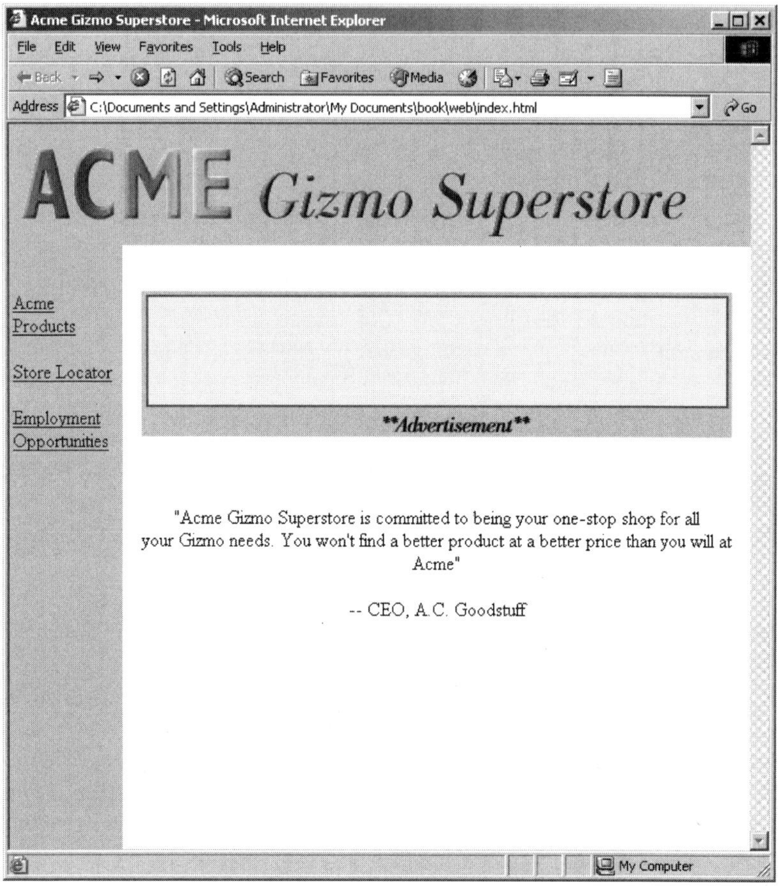

Figure 2. Home Page of the ACME Gizmo Superstore Web Site.

indeed counterproductive. Minimizing the number of unnecessarily fetched pages helps reduce the load on the crawler, and perhaps more importantly, on the network and target Web site. If the load placed on the target Web site is excessive, it is likely that the owner of the Web site notices the surge in traffic and asks the crawler to stop crawling that site.

Determining the optimal seed URL set, crawling depth, and include/exclude rules is a difficult problem in general but tractable in practice. One technique is to ask a human user to browse the target Web site and visit pages that contain interesting information. A tool can record the URL of pages visited, starting from the home page of the target Web site and traversing the navigational structure down to the pages one wishes to extract. If a sufficient number of pages are visited and recorded, one can apply data-mining techniques to discover common patterns.

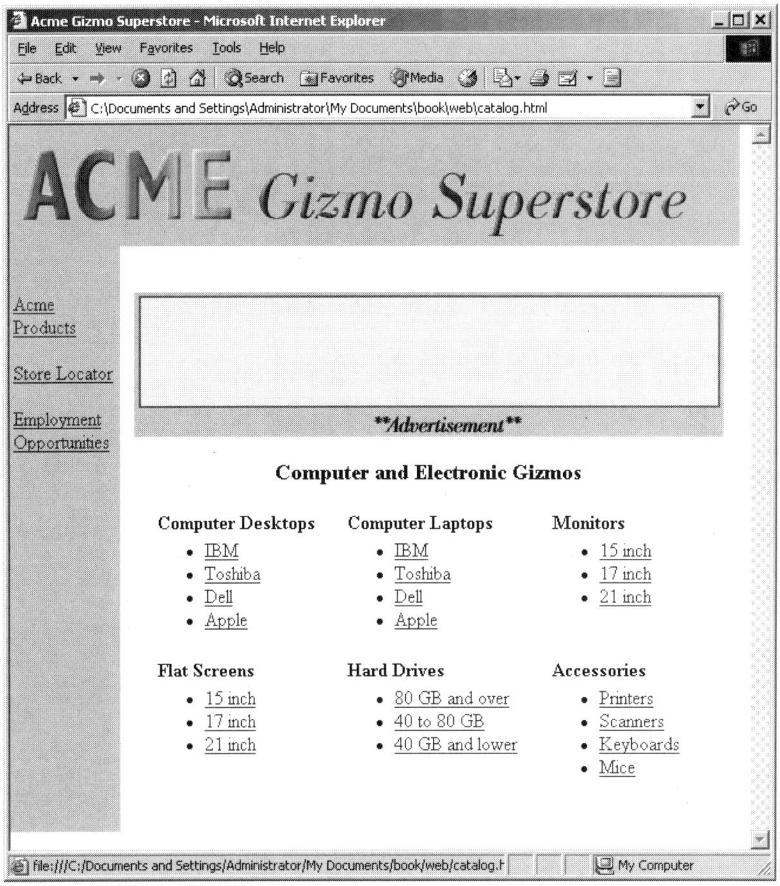

Figure 3. List of Categories and Subcategories on the ACME Gizmo Superstore Web Site.

To illustrate the process of determining proper crawler configuration parameters, consider an online shopping site called "ACME Gizmo Superstore." The home page of the company (Figure 2) provides links to many parts of the Web site, one of which is the product catalog link titled "Acme Products" (Figure 3). The product catalog page lists several product category-subcategory combinations such as "Hard Drives—40 to 80 GB" which in turn lists individual products (Figure 4). Additional product pages are shown in Figure 5.

By following the links as just described, it is possible to start at the home page and get to the product pages by following 2 links (crawling depth 2). However, since there are no direct links to product pages from the home page and from the home page one must go to the product catalog page, we consider the product catalog page to be a better starting point, or seed URL. It lets us reduce the crawling depth to 1, which

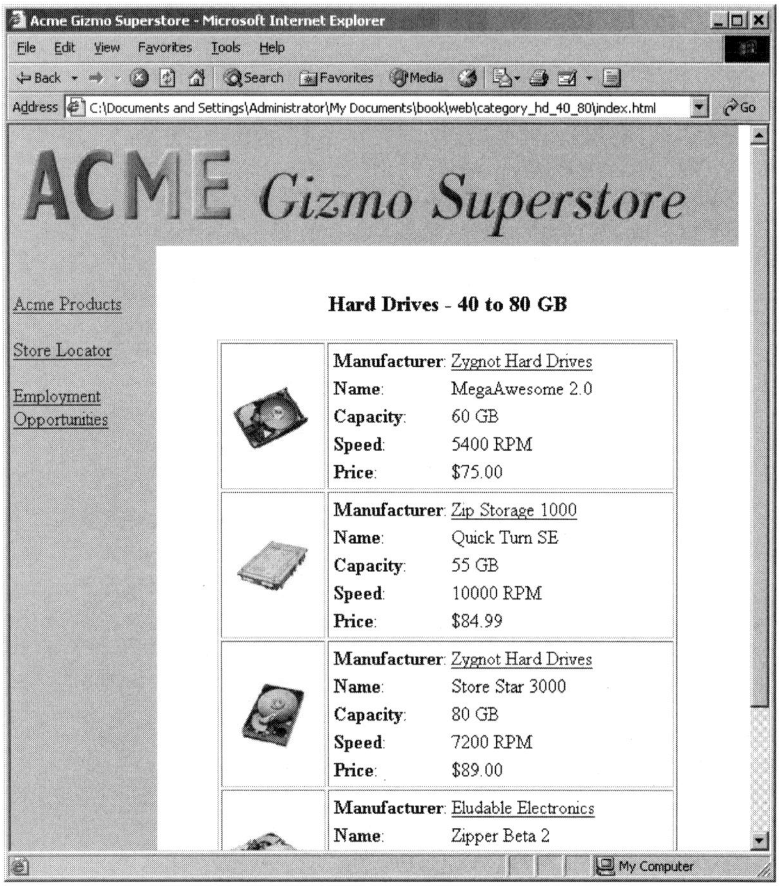

Figure 4. List of Products on the ACME Gizmo Superstore Web Site.

improves crawling efficiency and reduces the possibility that the crawler would wander around into parts of the Web site that it was not meant to go to.

An alternate configuration would be to list all product category pages as seed URLs (and reduce crawling depth to 0), but this would require us to maintain that list over time. For example, if a new category is added, the corresponding category page needs to be added to our list. Therefore, it is preferable to start from the product catalog page and just follow whatever categories the Web site happens to have at the time of crawling.

Next, we need to figure out the appropriate include/exclude rules. The seed URL is implicitly included in the include rule but we can still list it explicitly. The URL to product category pages appears to follow a common pattern "category_X_Y/index.html" where X denotes the category name and Y is a subcategory name. We add an include rule "category_*" where the asterisk matches any category and subcategory combination.

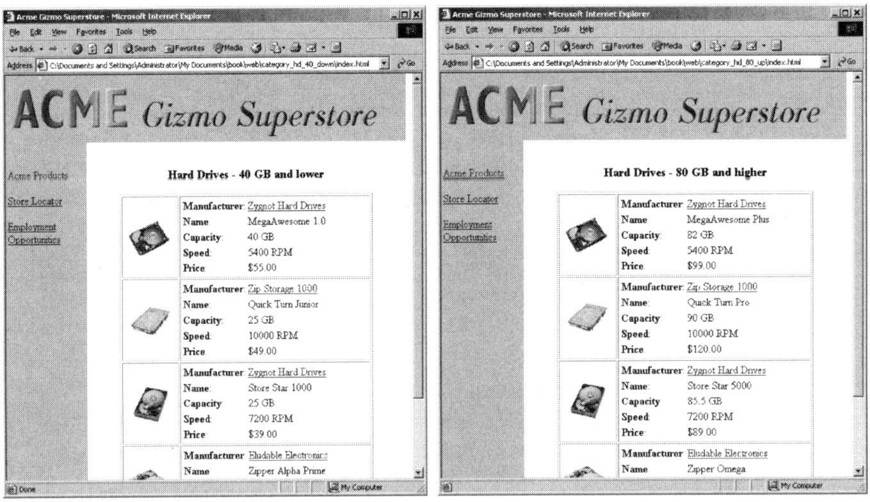

Figure 5. Additional Product Listing Pages from Acme Gizmo Superstore Web Site.

Suppose we do not want to crawl products in certain categories, for example those in the Accessories category. The exclude rule "category_Accessories*/index.html" tells the crawler not to follow links leading to the Accessories category. We can also tell the crawler not to follow links that use other protocols, such as HTTPS, FTP, or NNTP. Figure 6 shows the resulting crawling configuration expressed in the XML syntax adopted by the Grand Central Station crawler [32].

3.4. Challenges

Implicit in the processes described above is the assumption that data extraction is robust and trouble-free. However, as we have already highlighted earlier, detailed analysis of the steps involved in data extraction and their legal ramifications raise several challenges. These challenges may be broken into four main categories: legal, semantic, design, and change management.

Legal challenges. While information published on the World Wide Web is by and large public, the right of companies to automatically extract it and use it for their business advantage is debatable. Product information in particular has been aggressively protected by companies that own the data but want to publish it on the Web for human users to see. A case in point is the lawsuit filed by auction company eBay against "auction aggregator" company AuctionWatch.com in the late 1990's [6]. The lawsuit claimed that AuctionWatch.com was illegally retrieving auction data from the eBay Web site and republishing it on their own Web site. A casual user was not made aware of the fact that the data originated from eBay and furthermore was shielded from the advertising eBay wanted to display together with the auction information. The lawsuit was settled out of court.

```
<gcs-config>

  <group name="ACME Gizmo Superstore ">

    <crawler-config recursion-depth="1">

      <seed-list>
        <seed url="http://acmegizmo/catalog.html"/>
      </seed-list>

      <content-type-pattern-list>
        <url-name-pattern name="*"/>
      </content-type-pattern-list>

      <exclude-pattern-list>
        <url-obj-pattern file="/category_Accessories*"/>
        <url-obj-pattern protocol="https"/>
        <url-obj-pattern protocol="ftp"/>
        <url-obj-pattern protocol="nntp"/>
      </exclude-pattern-list>

      <include-pattern-list>
        <url-obj-pattern file="/catalog.html"/>
        <url-obj-pattern file="/category_*"/>
      </include-pattern-list>

    </crawler-config>

  </group>

</gcs-config>
```

Figure 6. Sample Crawler Configuration File Expressed Using an XML Syntax.

An additional challenge comes via a key technology that informs prospective users of Web data whether the data can be crawled and extracted automatically. This technology is known as the Robot Exclusion Standard (RES) [19] and manifests itself in the form of a "robots.txt" file placed on the Web site by the site owner. RES is a gentlemen's agreement that specifies which crawlers can access the Web site robotically and specifically which parts of the Web site are off-limits. The owner of an E-commerce server, for example, might want to tell crawlers that the product information section of the Web site cannot be crawled and extracted. In practice, however, our empirical studies have shown that the vast majority of Web sites do not take advantage of the RES standard to protect themselves and are therefore open to crawler access.

Semantic challenges. The desire to bring together datasets originating from different sources raises the likelihood of incompatible or conflicting schemas and vocabularies. The terms used by one source to describe the features of a product may be different from those used by another source, and the units of measure and product identification information (SKU numbers) may differ.

A related problem is to determine when two objects described by different sources really refer to the same object. For example, a product that is sold through different channels such as retail vendors, the OEM product market, or as part of a consulting services offering may have entirely different product model numbers depending on the channel used. Consequently, product data extracted from the Web sites of these channels is largely overlapping yet hard to integrate. Comparing the price of a product across different channels would require explicit knowledge of the mapping between product model numbers used by different channels, or some form of intelligence to analyze product descriptions and determine each product's "identity."

These semantic problems and requirements may lead to missing, conflicting, and redundant information if used without care. Referred to as *Information Integration*, the problem is widely recognized and has many research groups working on techniques and tools to solve it. One such project is the Clio project at IBM Almaden Research Center [26].

Design challenges. Web sites are increasingly using programming techniques that increase the level of interactivity of the site. In its simplest form, interaction means that a program script is embedded in the Web page to intercept a user's input to a form and validate it before submitting the form to the Web server. Validating the data before submission reduces data entry errors and increases the responsiveness of the Web application because validation is done locally in the user's browser.

While these design techniques increase the ease of use of the Web site, they also make it harder for crawlers to access the data. For instance, if accessing a product catalog on a Web site requires the user to submit a query as opposed to just following links (browsing), the problem arises that the crawler needs to know what to enter as the query. Similarly, program scripts may encode arbitrarily complex computations that affect the URL that is ultimately accessed. For crawlers not capable of dealing with forms, scripts, and other interactivity techniques, much of the Web is left inaccessible. This difficult-to-reach part of the Web is sometimes referred to as the "Deep Web."

More complex Web applications require the Web server to track the user's movements through the Web site. The concept of a session refers to a period of time during which the user enters the Web site, navigates the site and interacts with its forms and other information (e.g. shopping cart), and eventually leaves the site. Session management and tracking is usually done in one of two ways: using cookies or using variables embedded in the URL referring to the Web site. A session cookie contains a session identifier and associated host name and expiration time information [12]. Cookies are stored in the user's browser and returned to the Web server whenever the user accesses that site. Session information can be embedded into the URL of a Web site by using the Common Gateway Interface [4] mechanism. The URL lists one or more variable name-value pairs; the session identifier would be stored in one of the CGI variables.

The use of session identifiers on Web sites poses requirements on the crawler that are very similar to those posed by the interactivity features of the site. The notable difference is that session identifiers are usually assigned to the user only at the beginning of the session and only on certain "start pages" of the Web site. As a consequence, a user or crawler that starts navigating the Web site on any other page may receive an "invalid session" error message and be directed back to the start page. This means that a crawler needs to be configured in such a way that it starts from a start page and carefully retains the session information across page accesses, whether the information is stored in cookies or CGI variables.

Information that refers to a single "object" but is broken into multiple Web pages presents another design challenge for Web data extraction. Sometimes information is broken into multiple pages because it is too voluminous and simply would not fit on a single page or it would make it inconvenient for a user to browse it. A case in point are search engines that typically return the result set in chunks of 10 or 20 results per page. Another reason for broken-up Web pages is the desire to improve the visual design of a Web site. HTML frames provide a mechanism to design effective Web sites that are in many cases easier to navigate. However, the content of each frame is a separate Web page and involves a separate Web page access by a browser or crawler.

Merging pages that each individually contain part of the information relating to a single object suffers from the same semantic problem we discussed earlier. It is one of "object identity." Suppose one frame of a page contains the features of a product, while another frame contains the price of that product. Suppose further that the content of the two frames is retrieved at different times during the crawl, so there is no temporal association between them. What is now required is a process that attempts to merge the pieces of information contained in each frame in order to build object in whole. In an ideal case, the frame embeds an object identifier somewhere in its URL or HTML content and one simply extracts the identifier and does the merging of the pieces at the XML file level or perhaps in a database.

Change management. From a research point of view, perhaps the most challenging aspect of Web data extraction is ensuring the robustness of data extraction patterns. It is typically relatively easy to develop patterns that perform perfectly on a given set of input Web pages. It is much harder to choose patterns that work reliably with pages that have not been seen before and continue to work on pages in the future even if the structure of HTML pages or templates changes.

Empirical evidence suggests that the frequency of structural changes in Web sites is inversely proportional to the size of the organization operating it. The intuition behind this statement is that in large enterprises and other organizations decisions are not made by individual people but by committees, task forces, advisory teams, and so on. Changing the design of a Web site is a major decision, as it is affected by corporate design guidelines, consistency requirements with other mass media, adherence to prevailing design standards (e.g. Web content accessibility standards [34]), and national language support. A large number of people and organizational entities have to come to an agreement over major changes affecting a Web site.

In contrast, a Web site owned by a small company or an individual can be changed much more frequently. In fact, we have observed changes to some Web sites almost weekly, and typically these changes parallel the increasing sophistication level of the Web designer making those changes. We can almost imagine a Web designer reading an HTML programming manual, discovering a "cool new feature" and implementing it in the Web site that very moment!

3.5. Techniques for effective data extraction

We now discuss various techniques for dealing with the challenges presented earlier. The techniques and associated tools involved suggest a blueprint for constructing and deploying an actual Web data extraction system. The prototype system architecture described in the next section builds on the blueprint.

Much of the data processing described so far has focused on storing, retrieving and transforming XML documents. XML storage and querying are well-understood concepts and current or future releases of all major commercial database systems include some support for them, either natively or through a database system extension. It is important to note that XML transformation is really part of the broader concept of XML query, for which a new XQuery standard is emerging [37]. While real XML databases will be targeted to very large XML document collections with the corresponding efforts made in XML query optimization, smaller data extraction systems consisting of perhaps a few thousand documents may be achievable using a file system based storage scheme instead. In the latter case, XML query and transformation really just means running XSL stylesheets or XPath expressions [39] over a collection of XML files.

Before XSL stylesheets or XPath expressions can be invoked over an arbitrary HTML page, however, one needs to "normalize" the page to a well-formed XML format, namely XHTML [35]. As Web design tools become more XHTML-conformant, it is likely that a significant fraction of future Web content will already be XHTML. Today and perhaps a few years into the future, however, it is still the case that the vast majority of Web content is plain old HTML and badly broken too. Normalization tools, such as HTML Tidy [33] are therefore still very much required.

As noted before, extraction from XHTML boils down to executing XSL stylesheets or XPath expressions over it. An XSL processor such as Xalan is required to execute stylesheets and expressions, so the problem really becomes one of figuring out what those stylesheets and expressions should be. Many different approaches are possible—manual tools, automatic tools, user-assisted tools, machine learning tools, and others. We take a detailed look at this issue in Section 5.

Bypassing the various obstacles of a Web site in order to get access to the "Deep Web" is a tough problem in general but tractable in practice. Our earlier discussion highlighted the fact that the Robot Exclusion Standard is a gentleman's agreement and basically says that anyone who wants to stay on good terms with others (and avoid lawsuits) better adhere to the agreement. This "obstacle" can stop many data extraction tasks in their tracks and should be the very first thing one checks when contemplating crawling a prospective Web site.

Although cookies and session IDs were designed to improve the usability and interactivity of a Web site, nothing prevents the crawler from mimicking a Web browser and responding to the Web sites cookie requests just like a normal browser would do. Careful configuration of the crawler ensures that cookies and session IDs are picked up by visiting the home page or other "session initiation page" of the Web site before proceeding to the actual content one wants to extract.

The same principle applies to JavaScript. Ideally, the crawler should be able to execute scripts embedded in an HTML page much like a browser would do. Script engines are available in the market and the Open Source community, so plugging one into a crawler is certainly possible. Full-scale script execution may be an overkill, however, as most scripts merely improve the interactivity of the Web site (e.g. checking input parameters before forms are submitted) and don't really contribute to the data content of the site.

An exception to this rule are scripts that modify the HTML page at run time according to the browser used and those that compute URLs on the fly, telling the browser to go to an alternate location instead of the one indicated in a static hyperlink or form. The former exception occurs when a script outputs page content only when executed; if the script is not executed, part of the page is not accessible. The missing part may contain links and other content that are critical to the proper function of the crawler and/or data extractor.

The second exception is more common than the first. It is not unusual to see HTML forms where the URL to which the form is submitted is computed on the fly by a script. The script may choose the appropriate URL based on form input or it may add extra field values to the target URL. In either case, not knowing what link to follow is a major obstacle to the crawler.

In the toughest cases, if a script engine is not available, one may need to resort to manual "reverse engineering" of the script code and recoding it in some other language that the crawler does understand, for instance XSL. When the crawler sees a page which is known to contain one of the "tough" scripts, the crawler loads the corresponding XSL sheet and transforms the page into a new page where the script has seemingly been executed. Simple script actions like adding or removing field values from URLs on the page are easily done using XSL.

Some Web sites cannot be crawled without filling out HTML forms. Forms may be used to submit query terms to the backend database of the Web site or submit user information (e.g. login ID) when entering the Web site. Even if the data extractor or crawler can deduce from the form itself what data needs to be entered (e.g. that a field is a city name), the problem remains that the values entered are domain-specific and the extractor or crawler cannot possibly know what to enter on the form. It may be possible to build up domain knowledge by analyzing the content of the Web site [27]. In very targeted crawls, it may be permissible to manually control what is entered. For example, if the task is to crawl products made by a certain manufacturer, this is a clear hint that that a manufacturer name must be entered on corresponding forms on the target Web site. One way to embed hints into the crawling process is to code them as XSL transformations (as was done with scripts) which take an HTML form as an input and produce one or more filled-out forms or simple hyperlinks as the output. Filling out forms and translating them into simple hyperlinks is known as "hyperlink synthesis" [24].

Yet another source of domain knowledge are Web proxy logs common in most organizations. A proxy log contains actual forms and data values entered by users browsing Web sites and the data can be directly applied for automated crawling of those same sites.

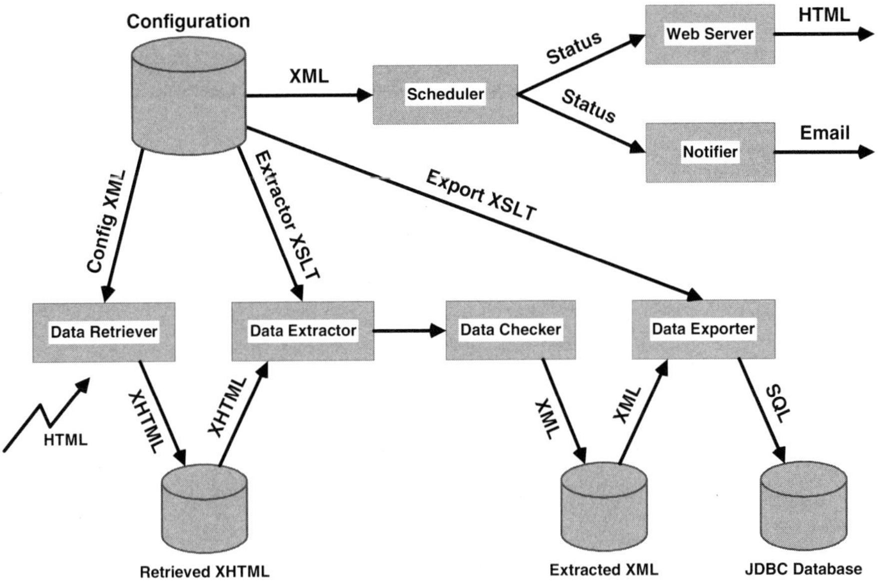

Figure 7. Outline of Data Extraction System Architecture.

4. OUTLINE OF A DATA EXTRACTION SYSTEM ARCHITECTURE

We now turn our attention to architectural issues in Web data extraction systems. We describe a sample architecture that suggests what components are required for effective data extraction and how those components interoperate. While particular systems may differ in terms of details, we believe that the discussion in this section will be helpful and provide a blueprint common to many such systems.

The architecture is based on ANDES, a research framework for reusable Web data extraction systems [24]. ANDES was inspired by previous work on Web query systems, e.g. TSIMMIS [9], STALKER [17], and Junglee [8], and has seen continuous use within IBM for a wide variety of data extraction tasks and application domains. Among the domains where ANDES has been applied are news articles, consumer product reviews and prices, real estate listings, computer products, and construction materials.

The architecture is composed of a set of Java and XML-based components that implement key features of data extraction systems. The components of the architecture are illustrated in Figure 7 and their tasks and relationships are summarized below.

Data Retriever gathers HTML pages from the Web using a crawler mechanism or some other method. Gathered pages are normalized into XHTML and forwarded to the Data Extractor component.

Data Extractor applies data extraction patterns encoded as XSL stylesheets to a set of XHTML documents. The output of the Extractor is a new set of XML documents which contain the extracted data. The XHTML documents are discarded and the XML documents are forwarded to the Data Checker component.

Data Checker inspects XML documents produced by the Extractor and ensures that the data contained in the XML documents is semantically and syntactically valid. Invalid documents could signify errors in the data extraction patterns and are marked for further inspection by the administrator. Valid documents are forwarded to the Data Exporter component.

Data Exporter converts valid XML documents to some output format, for example SQL statements for database update, spreadsheets for data dissemination, or HTML output for Web publishing. The system is configured to either keep the XML documents or discard them.

Administrative Interface is a Web-based management and monitoring tool for system administrators. Using the tool, the administrator can schedule new data extraction processes at specific times and days of the week and can inspect the progress of previously scheduled processes. Data that was extracted but marked as invalid can be browsed and acted upon.

Pattern Designer is a graphical tool for the analysis of target Web sites and their HTML pages. The output of the tool is a set of data extraction patterns specific for a given Web site.

We now describe each system component in more detail.

4.1. Data retriever

The Data Retriever is usually a crawler, such as the Grand Central Station (GCS) crawler developed at IBM Almaden Research Center [32]. An alternative Data Retriever is one that simply reads a list of URLs from a file and fetches each page on that list. This simple retriever works well for scenarios where the URLs are known in advance and they do not change over time. For instance, the home page of a target Web site does not move and could be extracted using the simple "URL Data Retriever."

The Data Retriever fetches HTML pages from the target Web sites and turns them into well-formed XML documents using a tool like HTML Tidy. The normalized XHTML pages are stored in a staging area as XML files where the Data Extractor can pick them up. Separating the Data Retriever and Extractor into two distinct phases is important because in certain situations the Data Retriever may run on an entirely different machine or network than the Extractor. Similarly, the use of the Pattern Designer and testing of the resulting extraction patterns is most conveniently done using locally cached files so there is no need to fetch target Web pages over and over again.

4.2. Data extractor

The Data Extractor reads the set of XHTML files retrieved by the Data Retriever and applies one or more XSL files on those input files [14][24]. The ultimate output of the Data Extractor is a set of domain-specific XML files, one per input XML file. XSL files can be stacked or pipelined. Stacking means that one XSL file "calls" another XSL file, as if it were a subroutine in a conventional programming language. This is done by having one XSL file import another XSL file and then invoking one of its templates.

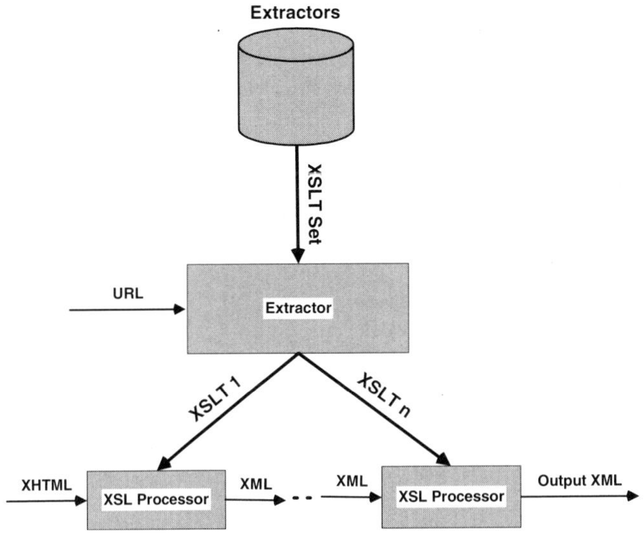

Figure 8. A Pipeline of XSL Stylesheets is Applied to an Input XHTML Page.

Pipelining XSL files is another powerful concept. Multiple XSL files are designed to operate as a sequence of transformations on the original input file (Figure 8). The output of the first XSL file is some intermediate XML format which is subsequently transformed by the second XSL file, and so on. The output of the last XSL file in the sequence is the final, domain-specific XML format.

Alternatively, each XSL in the pipeline can improve the quality of the domain data, without touching the structure of the XML per se. The first XSL can transform the input XML into the final syntax but not necessarily the final data content. Subsequent XSL files work on pieces of the content, removing redundant data or noise, normalizing the usage of whitespace or capitalization in the file, or performing a mapping from one vocabulary to another.

Consider a scenario where data is extracted from two E-commerce Web sites whose product catalogs contain identical products but use slightly different notations for product specifications. A first XSL file is designed for each Web site to perform basic extraction of relevant information from corresponding product pages and produce output whose structure conforms to some standard product markup language. The second XSL file for each Web site would work on the Manufacturer field of the markup and correct any misspellings or alternate spellings of manufacturer names. It could also normalize numerical values so that units of measure between the two sources match. A third XSL file is common to both sources. It removes redundant whitespace from every part of the XML document and inserts a standard header into the document. The output of this XSL file is the final output of the Data Extractor.

XPath expressions embedded in XSL files can be generated in one of several ways. The most straightforward way is to produce them manually using a Pattern Designer tool (discussed later). An alternative is to employ machine learning techniques and produce data extraction expressions automatically based on a sample set of pages. A hybrid, semi-automatic process is also possible. One could either use automatic tools to generate "rough" data extraction patterns and refine them using manual tools like the Pattern Designer. Or, one could use a manual tool to direct (or supervise) the learning process of the automated tool, ensuring that the right patterns are found and spurious extraction patterns are not generated.

4.3. Data checker

As Web sites change, the data extraction pattern encapsulated in an XSL stylesheet may fail to correctly extract data from the pages that changed. The Data Checker validates the quality of extracted data by inspecting the XML output of the Data Extractor, not the source XHTML files. This means that if a Web site changes but the XSL filter continues to correctly extract data from the changed pages, the new pages pass the data validation check and no alerts are generated.

Data validation is performed at several levels of abstraction. Syntactic checks are performed first: they verify that each XML element is present in the output and that values match their expected types (numeric vs. string). In the early days of XML, the prevailing method for syntax check was to rely on Document Type Definitions (DTDs). Those definitions did not provide sufficient means to check on numeric values, for example. Today, XML Schemas [38] are used and provide the necessary power to enforce these syntactic requirements. If a schema is defined for the XML output of the Data Extractor, then it is a relatively simple matter to "validate" the output against the corresponding schema. If validation fails, the document was not extracted successfully.

The syntactic check is followed by semantic checks which spot incorrect values. This is domain-specific but very powerful. For instance, if it is known that stock prices are usually less than $1000 (Berkshire-Hathaway shares being the notable exception), this can be described to the Data Checker which then separates the "bad" data from "good." The bad data is moved to a staging area and the administrator is asked to decide what to do with it.

The administrator can take one of four corrective actions using the Administrative Interface. The data can be accepted as-is or it can be treated as a one-time error (e.g. due to a network error) and discarded. The administrator can also manually correct the data if the data is mostly good but there are some invalid fields. Finally, if the data really is valid but did not pass the semantic checks, the administrator can modify the rules of the semantic check. For example, if the price of a hard disk drive was incorrectly flagged as invalid because it was below a previously set minimum (say, $30), the system can be told to adjust the boundary values to the new minimum.

4.4. Data exporter

The Data Extractor component transforms the extracted data into some export format. In many cases, the final destination of extracted data is a relational database, so the export format is a series of SQL statements which are then executed against the database. The SQL statements can either be INSERT statements (if the data is merely accumulated) or UPDATE statements (if new values replace old ones in the database).

In some domains it may be preferable to convert the data into a spreadsheet format such as Comma Separated Values (CSV) files or native spreadsheet format such as that used by Microsoft Excel. The spreadsheet files can then be disseminated via email or other mechanism without much trouble. Note that newer versions of Microsoft Excel support XML directly, so one approach is to convert the extracted XML data into the "spreadsheet XML" format expected by Excel. XML is also used natively by the spreadsheet component of the open-source OpenOffice suite (formerly StarOffice by Sun Microsystems).

An alternative method for inspection and dissemination of the data is to convert it back into HTML. However, this time the HTML format is quite different from the original HTML from which it was extracted. Whereas the original HTML format may have contained a large amount of extra "baggage" like advertising material, the new HTML format is lean and simple. The precise HTML format used is up to the system administrator.

The common aspect of all these conversions, and further proof of the significance of using XML as the intermediate format in data extraction, is that all conversions can be accomplished using XSL stylesheets, the same technology used for data extraction itself. Conversion of XML to SQL or CSV is no more difficult than the conversion to spreadsheet XML or HTML.

To support database updates natively, the Data Exporter attaches to a user-defined JDBC database using standard Java libraries. The access parameters of the database (its name and authentication parameters) are provided by the administrator in a configuration file. Once the Data Exporter has finished converting the extracted XML data into SQL, it executes the SQL statements without really needing to understand what those statements do. Again, the precise function of the statements is encoded in the XSL stylesheet and is up to the system administrator.

4.5. Scheduler

The Scheduler is responsible for activating the data extraction process at predetermined times and repeating the process periodically. The timing and frequency of activation is controlled by the system administrator using the Administrative Interface. The periodicity of data extraction depends largely on the frequency of data change, but also on domain-specific and corporate requirements. Data extraction is usually run during periods of low network activity, for instance at night. As discussed in Section 3, legal issues surrounding data extraction may have a strong influence on when and how data extraction is performed.

4.6. Administrative interface

The system needs a comprehensive, Web-based management interface that a system administrator can use for monitoring and controlling the system. Figure 9 shows an example of what the Administrative Interface might look like. The administrator

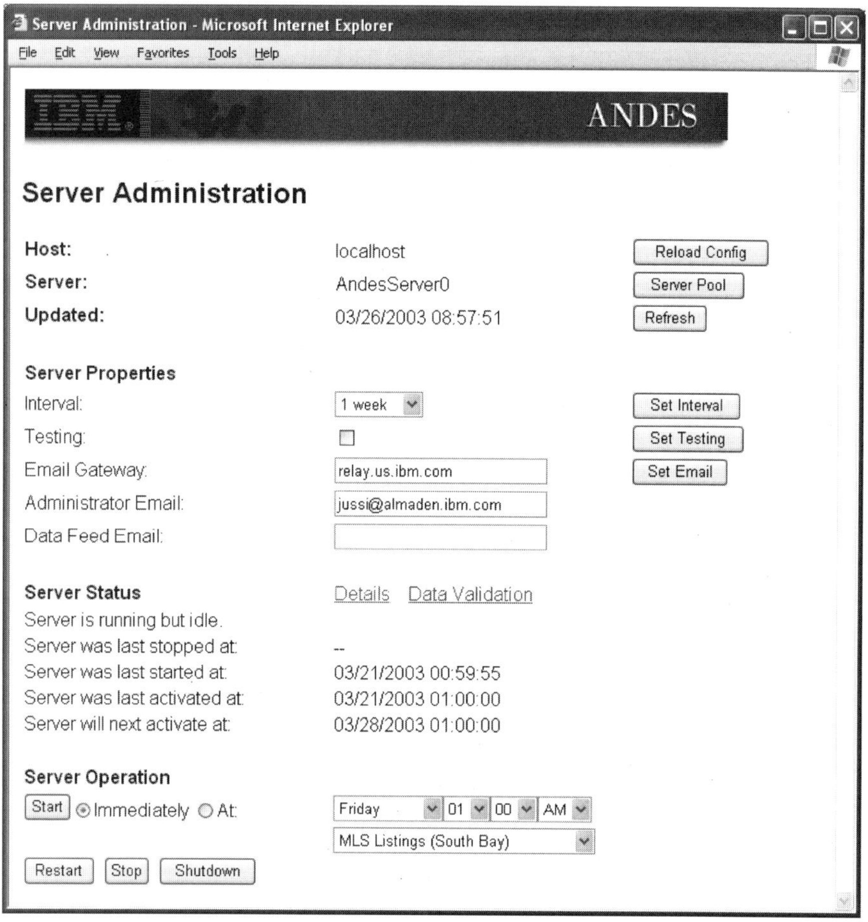

Figure 9. Screenshot of System Administrator's Console.

can start and stop crawler processes and see when the next crawl is scheduled to start. Clicking on the Details link displays a detailed view of the last crawl (Figure 10).

The statistics shown in Figure 10 tell the system administrator that over 10,000 pages (in this case, real estate listings) were successfully extracted from the Web and the total processing time was 6 hours. Dividing 10,000 pages by the total crawling time (4 hours) yields an average crawling rate of about one page per every 2 seconds. The crawler was configured to crawl the Web site very gently so as not to place too much load on the Web server. Once the pages have been retrieved from the Web site, they are processed locally. Total extraction and database processing time was 2 hours, or about one page per second. These numbers were gathered on a low-cost,

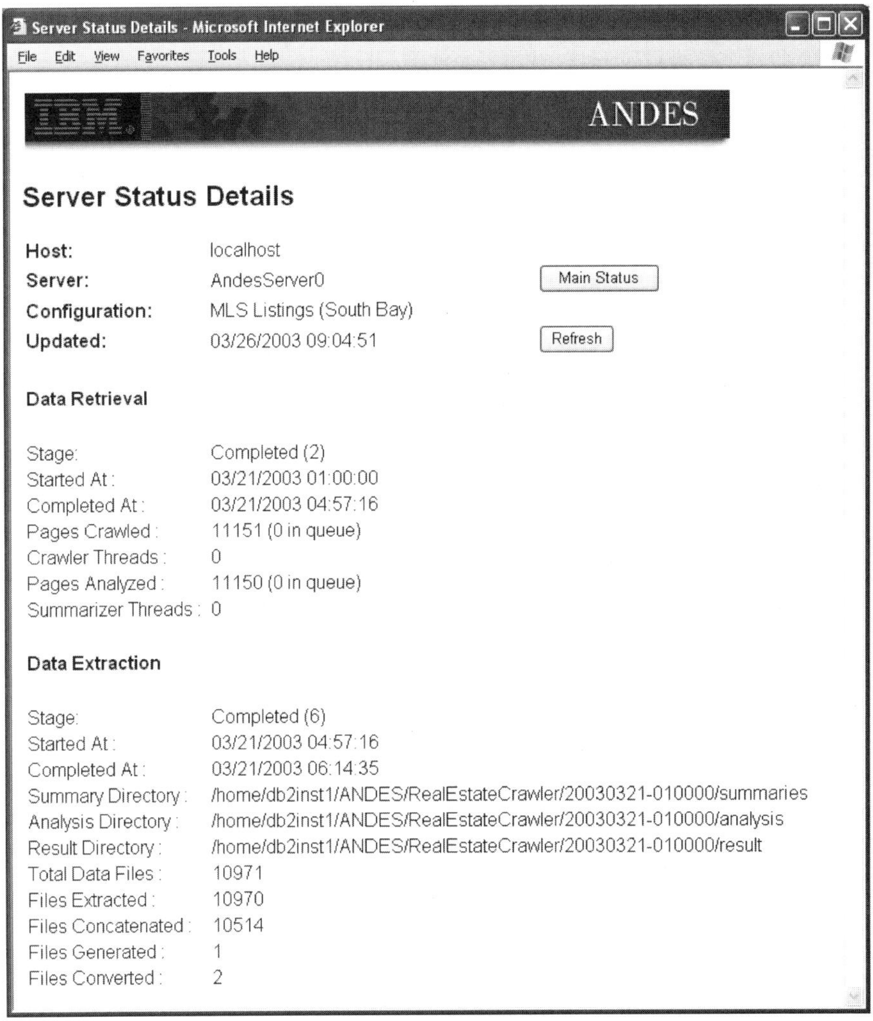

Figure 10. Detailed Status of a Crawling Task.

single-processor server. Dramatically higher throughput is achieved by parallelizing the network accesses, data extraction, and database processing.

It is also essential that the system be capable of monitoring itself and alerting the administrator when problems are encountered. Table 1 shows an email message generated by the ANDES system for a deployed news crawler. The system tracks the number of Web pages crawled and extracted in each run. Significant deviations in these numbers trigger the system to send an email message warning the system administrator that attention may be required.

Table 1 Email message notifying the administrator that a deviation was detected in the number of pages crawled and extracted

```
Warning: Last execution of configuration "CNet News" extracted
data from 3013 pages while the previous crawl extracted data
from 3350 pages.

Statistics Report
=================
Started              Completed            Pages  Files  Concatenated

02/27/2003 22:01:01  02/27/2003 23:08:13 3013   2698          2698
02/20/2003 22:00:00  02/20/2003 23:14:42 3350   3033          3033
02/13/2003 01:02:02  02/13/2003 02:22:59 3614   3261          3261
02/06/2003 01:01:01  02/06/2003 02:17:01 3169   2829          2829
01/30/2003 01:00:00  01/30/2003 02:58:07 3345   3014          3013
01/23/2003 01:03:03  01/23/2003 02:28:51 3728   3377          3374
01/16/2003 01:02:02  01/16/2003 02:18:50 3437   3134          3132
01/09/2003 01:01:01  01/09/2003 02:05:18 2865   2626          2624
01/02/2003 01:00:00  01/02/2003 02:43:53 4650   4223          4221
12/26/2002 01:01:01  12/26/2002 02:30:45 4036   3677          3675
12/20/2002 12:07:11  12/20/2002 13:34:41 3927   3611          3609
12/16/2002 11:20:44  12/16/2002 12:33:54 3218   2966          2966
12/14/2002 01:01:01  12/14/2002 02:41:18 2073   1913          1913
12/07/2002 01:00:00  12/07/2002 01:33:06 2288   2109          2109
11/30/2002 01:01:01  11/30/2002 03:27:33 2558   2364          2363
11/23/2002 01:00:00  11/23/2002 02:13:52 2729   2489          2488
11/16/2002 01:02:02  11/16/2002 03:05:17 2336   2141          2141
11/09/2002 01:01:01  11/09/2002 01:38:00 2394   2226          2226
11/02/2002 01:00:00  11/02/2002 01:52:45 2639   2429          2429
10/26/2002 01:00:00  10/26/2002 02:34:51 2072   1905          1905
10/21/2002 13:15:36  10/21/2002 13:50:23 1875   1734          1734
```

Given that Web sites are autonomous and can change at any time, data extraction errors are likely to occur at some point during the lifetime of the system. Significant deviations in the number of pages crawled and extracted compared to previous crawls cause the system to issue an alert to the system administrator via email. For instance, if the navigation rules of a Web site change, the Data Retriever may get only half the number of target HTML pages compared to a previous crawl. When this happens, the administrator is notified, who will then take a closer look to determine what the appropriate action is. The corrective action may be to adjust the crawling configuration or data extraction patterns. On the other hand, the change may just be a result of less data being available on the Web site. In that case, no change is required in the data extraction system.

4.7. Pattern designer

The Pattern Designer component is a tool used by an extraction engineer to design extraction templates. The tool helps the user analyze one or more sample HTML pages to come up with a set of robust extraction patterns. Graphical design tools are most powerful. A sample screenshot of our InFact tool is shown in Figure 11. The user loads an HTML page into the tool and uses its search function to find occurrences of the

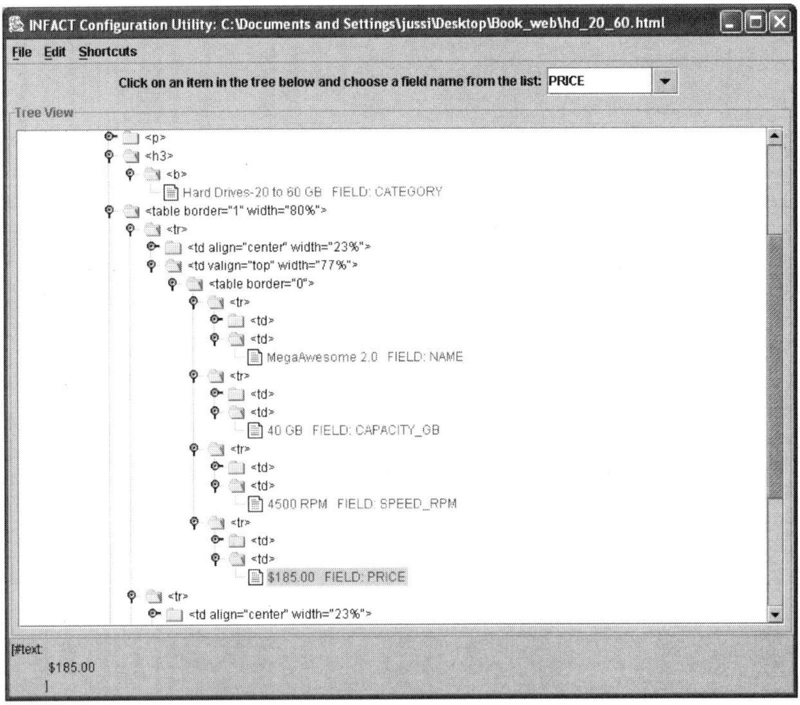

Figure 11. Screenshot of InFact Extraction Pattern Generator.

data that need to be extracted. The occurrences are then labeled with a descriptive name. Data that is repeated on multiple table rows or columns can be marked as a repetitive field, in which case the tool generates an extraction expression that iterates over those rows or columns. More advanced extraction pattern types are discussed in the next section.

5. DATA EXTRACTION PRINCIPLES

5.1. Extraction templates

As mentioned earlier, the majority of interesting Web content that is delivered as HTML Web pages is generated through some sort of template-based technology. The good news for data extractors is that this means that most of the pages to extract will have the same general structure and nearly the same markup. This consistency can easily be used to our advantage in order to robustly extract the more interesting content that does vary across these pages.

Given that most Web pages are constructed using a template technology, it seems almost intuitive that these pages are ready candidates for processing by further templates. In fact, the data extraction process can be largely viewed as an extension to the

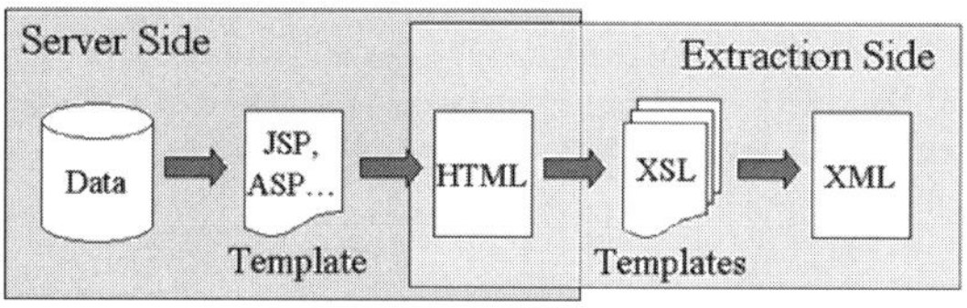

Figure 12. Process for Transformation of Server Data to Extracted Data.

mechanism that delivered the content in the first place. Web data that was transformed into a Web page with a template is simply then transformed with another template back into a data-centric form, as illustrated in Figure 12. While this technique can properly be termed an exercise in reverse engineering, the fact that the extraction mechanism is so like the creation mechanism simplifies the process immensely. As it turns out, creating the extraction templates is a far simpler task than creating the templates that produced the original Web pages.

Of course, we are still left with the task of determining what technology to use as the backbone for extraction templates. The best choice for this technology would be one that can easily represent and manipulate Web pages, that provides navigation through the hierarchical structure of HTML, that allows for robust pattern matching in the document, and that produces results that integrate easily with the back-end system into which we are porting the extracted data. XSL meets all of these criteria and is preferred over other alternatives such as W3QL [18] and WebSQL [23] because it offers one large bonus: it has become a de facto standard for working with Web-based technologies and most developers working in this sector are already familiar with its workings.

To illustrate that XSL is in fact a solid general choice for representing extraction templates consider its advantages. First, XSL was designed to work with other XML-like languages. This includes HTML once it has been tidied up. Second, XSL relies on a technology called XPath to work with its input. The sole purpose of XPath is to provide a robust way of navigating XML documents using a compact notation. This aspect of XSL is ideal for creating templates designed for reverse engineering. An XPath expression can traverse an HTML document recursively (as in XWRAP [22], WebL [5], and Informia [3]) and express predicates (WebLog [21]), context and delimiter patterns (WHISK [30]), and token features (SRV [7]). XSL is not limited to absolute path names like the HTML Extraction Language in W4F [29] and WIDL [2]. XSL stylesheets can also perform complex computations that require recursive function calls [15].

Perhaps the only drawback to the use of XSL is its lack of support for regular expressions, a way of extracting data from portions of text that have no mark-up using a compact notation that matches certain expressions. However, before becoming discouraged by this news consider that the coming version update to XSL will add regular expression matching to the technology, and even now that functionality can be added to XSL using a mechanism called XSL extensions.

A final advantage to using XSL for our templates is its flexible output mechanism. Once the extraction patterns have been written, it is easy to adjust the output to reflect the requirements of the back-end system. As discussed previously, the required output format may be XML, Comma Separated Values, SQL commands, or something else.

5.2. Extracting XML data from HTML

From its infancy in the early 1990's until just a few years ago, the HTML language evolved continuously, introducing increasingly complex design elements. Design elements such as tables within tables, frames, and image maps, were among the early additions. Later came client-side scripting, including its handling of mouse events (e.g. mousing-over an image), which improved the interactivity of Web sites and allowed them to function more like real applications.

In recent years, however, the makeup of HTML has stabilized and Web developers have shifted their focus to more programmatic Web standards such as XML and Web Services. Today, HTML no longer evolves as a language and, apart from incompatibilities that exist between the HTML features supported by different browsers, it is fair to say that HTML itself and related development and design tools are mature and produce consistent output.

As a result of these developments, it is reasonable to assume that certain design paradigms in Web sites are programmed using a consistent and predictable set of HTML constructs. For instance, excepting complex graphics and client-side scripting, there is only one way to create a pull-down menu on a Web page: using the <select> and <option> tags. Similarly, text input boxes, radio buttons, and check boxes are specified using a well-established set of HTML tags. We will later explain how we can make use of this consistency in developing a forward-looking robustness when creating extraction patterns.

The predictability of some HTML features does not remove the inherent uncertainty that accompanies the most critical aspect of page design for data extraction, namely page layout. Page layout is defined almost exclusively with nested <table>, <tr>, <td>, <div>, and <frame> tags. As anyone who has observed the evolution of the Web in recent years can attest, Web pages have become increasingly more complex, with whole sections of a page being assigned to serve various business and technical needs; consider the wealth of advertising, standard headers/footers, navigation sidebars, polls, and search bars on Web pages today.

As a consequence of the increasing structuredness of Web pages, over time the "main content" of the page is pushed deeper and deeper down the HTML tree. This means that more often than not, the interesting data is found somewhere in a deeply nested table, and raises the issue of how to find that "interesting" data in a robust manner.

5.3. Pattern creation

There are several different approaches to creating the templates for extracting Web data. A lot a research is being put into automating the creation of the patterns that make up these templates. While it is always possible for a developer to manually write these templates, the assistance of an automated algorithm can substantially add to that developer's productivity.

The most interesting automated tools for finding relevant data and creating patterns to get to that data involve processes of machine learning. In machine learning algorithms, the computer looks at source Web pages many times over, continually refining its findings until satisfied with the results. This process can be done with or without human supervision, and while work in this area is still in early stages of development, it has produced some reliable results [17][20][27].

Other automated systems work with general pattern matching or structural analysis of the source Web pages to suggest patterns for inclusion in the extraction template. Some of these systems have graphical user interfaces attached to enable the extractor to better see what kind of data will be extracted and to work with selecting and editing the suggested patterns.

Unfortunately, no amount of automation will ever completely remove the human user from the process. While it is possible for a computer application looking at several similar Web pages to suggest data of interest and the patterns to extract them, the application will undoubtedly make suggestions of uninteresting data or will miss data that is interesting.

No matter the process being used, the principles of creating data extraction patterns are the same: reverse engineering the template that created the Web page and keeping the pattern as robust to incremental changes to that original template as possible. Since we are not privy to the original template, our only method of reconstructing it is to analyze the similarities and differences found amongst several pages created by the same template. These pages are easy to recognize. With few exceptions they are always found on the same site, can be picked out by visual inspection, and are organized together either by an index page or a search component.

5.4. Sample pattern analysis

To best understand this process we will now step through the creation of an extraction template using a fictitious example site introduced in Section 3, an on-line electronics retailer named Acme Gizmo Superstore. While fictitious and a bit simple in form, this site's composition is indicative of many existing commercial Web sites.

Imagine the following scenario: You are a new hire to the technology department of Brick & Mortar, a well establish electronics retailer. Of late Brick & Mortar executives have been worried about their competition's ability to adjust prices quickly, especially in the hard drive market, and thus undercut the company's profits. They want you to come up with an automated way of adjusting to Acme's price changes on a daily basis. Your best option is to extract the information from the most automated source Acme has, its Web site.

Getting back to pattern creation, your first task is to examine Acme's site and group together pages that come from the same template. In this scenario we will focus that grouping around pages having to do with hard drives. Samplings of the pages for the site are shown in Figure 3 through Figure 5.

```
<html>
<body>
<table>
  <tr> ... </tr>
  <tr> ... </tr>
  <tr>
    <td> ... </td>
    <td>
      <h3><b>Hard Drives - 40 to 80 GB</b></h3>
      <table>
        <tr>
          <td><img src="../images/hd1.jpg"></td>
          <td>
            <table>
              <tr>
                <td><b>Manufacturer</b>:</td>
                <td>
                  <a href="http://www.zygnotdrives.com">
                    Zygnot Hard Drives
                  </a>
                </td>
              </tr>
              <tr>
                <td><b>Name</b>:</td>
                <td>MegaAwesome 2.0</td>
              </tr>
              <tr>
                <td><b>Capacity</b>:</td>
                <td>60 GB</td>
              </tr>
              <tr>
                <td><b>Speed</b>:</td>
                <td>5400 RPM</td>
              </tr>
              <tr>
                <td><b>Price</b>:</td>
                <td>$75.00</td>
              </tr>
            </table>
...
</body>
</html>
```

Figure 13. Source Code for HTML Page Shown in Figure 4.

Notice that the first page (Figure 3) is an index, or catalog, into categories of the products. This page differs significantly from the others, all of which provide product details. It is clear from inspection that all of the pages but the first come from a common template. The catalog page most likely also comes from a template, just a different one from the product details template, and thus must be considered separately.

Now examine a portion of the source code (Figure 13) making up one of the product pages (Figure 4). A list of four hard drive products is shown, with detailed information about each to the left of a picture of the product. An examination of the source code from the page shows that all of the product content is stored within an inner <table> element. For illustration, let us first try to extract the URLs of the manufacturers of the various hard drives on the page.

There are several patterns we could choose from to get to these links. If we wanted to be very specific we could use the following patterns (note the increasing number inside the <tr> element):

```
<xsl:value-of select="html/body/table/tr[3]/td[2]/table/tr[1]/td[2]/tr/td[2]/a/@href"/>
<xsl:value-of select="html/body/table/tr[3]/td[2]/table/tr[2]/td[2]/tr/td[2]/a/@href"/>
<xsl:value-of select="html/body/table/tr[3]/td[2]/table/tr[3]/td[2]/tr/td[2]/a/@href"/>
<xsl:value-of select="html/body/table/tr[3]/td[2]/table/tr[4]/td[2]/tr/td[2]/a/@href"/>
```

These patterns direct us node by node down the HTML source tree to the links that we are looking for. These are not good patterns to use for several reasons. First, they are completely tied to the existing structure of the page. If the Acme site were to add or remove even one node in the pattern, the entire template would fail. Second, they do not take into account that number of hard drives contained on the page may change.

To fix the latter problem, we need only surround our pattern with a loop:

```
<xsl:for-each select="html/body/table/tr[3]/td[2]/table/tr">
 <xsl:value-of select="td[2]/tr/td[2]/a/@href"/>
</xsl:for-each>
```

This resolves our dependence on a fixed number of links, but still we are completely tied to the existing structure of the source page.

An alternate approach would be to free ourselves from the structure completely. Consider the following pattern:

```
<xsl:for-each select="//a">
 <xsl:value-of select="@href"/>
</xsl:for-each>
```

This approach is perhaps too flexible, as all links in the page will now be included in our result set and we will be forced to implement some sort filtering before we can follow or store those links.

A better approach is to come up with an anchoring point in the page that we think has little likelihood of changing and then jumping from that point to the data we wish to extract. Look again at the source code for this page and notice that all of our links are contained in <a> tags within a table containing the text "Manufacturer." We will use this text be establish an anchor on this table and then we will hop down to the links from that point as shown in Figure 14.

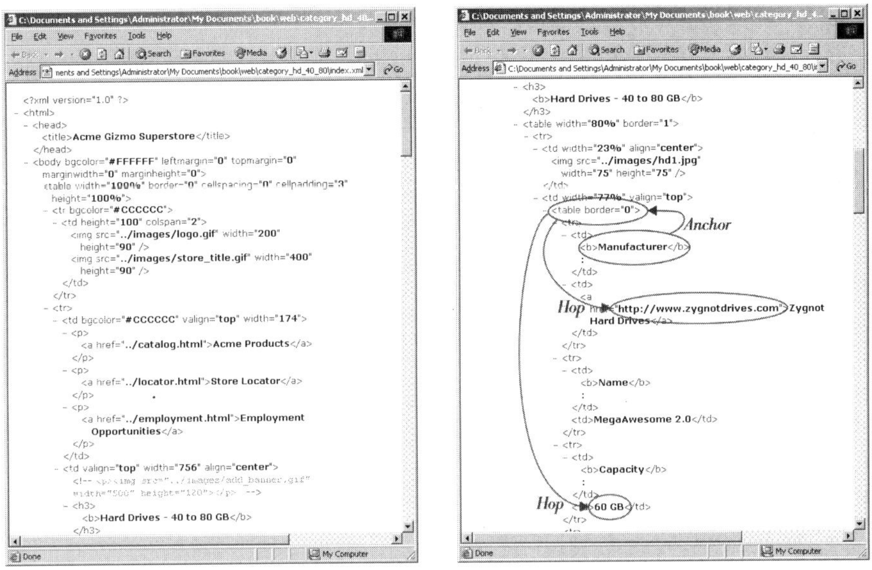

Figure 14. Example of Anchors and Hops for ACME Gizmo Superstore Web Site.

Our pattern now becomes:

```
<xsl:for-each select="//table[normalize-string(tr/td) ='Manufacturer']">
  <xsl:value-of select="tr/td[2]/a/@href"/>
</xsl:for-each>
```

There are two patterns in the above example. The first establishes an anchoring point on the relevant subtrees of the source HTML at a <table> element, and the second hops from the anchor to the value we wish to extract. Notice that by removing any dependency on content outside of the anchoring table much of the content of the source of this Web page could change, and the expression would still work.

A further advantage to this approach is that by separating data hops from their anchors, the patterns making up the anchors can be reused for other data extraction on the page. In the hard drive example, all relevant information about the various drives is contained in within the <table> element set by our marked. To extract further information about the drive we need only insert more hop expressions, as the following indicates:

```
<xsl:for-each select="//table[normalize-string(tr/td) ='Manufacturer']">
  <xsl:variable name="manufacturerURL" select="tr/td[2]/a/@href"/>
  <xsl:variable name="productName" select="tr[2]/td[2]"/>
  <xsl:variable name="price" select="substring-after(tr[5]/td[2],'$')"/>
</xsl:for-each>
```

The best advantage realized by using this technique for creating extraction patterns is the robustness and dependability of your extraction templates. The examples above merely illustrate a principle in its simplest form. To extend the concept, anchors could be chained together (e.g. an anchor to the <td> element containing the text "Price" can be chained under the anchor establishing the <table> element to remove the dependency in the example above of price being in the fifth <td> element) and could make use of the more advanced features of XSL. We leave these exercises to the reader to apply to their own extraction needs.

6. CONCLUSION

In this chapter we have discussed the important role Web data plays in modern business enterprises. Whether it is product catalogs and price listings, financial reports, service offerings, news reports, or other published information, Web data has become an indispensable ingredient for the decision process of modern companies. Our discussion has focused on ways in which such data can be extracted and integrated into the internal process of a company. We view Web data extraction as a data transformation effort and advocate a method based on reverse templates that utilize the full power of XML technologies, among them XSL stylesheets and XPath expressions.

Web data extraction is not without its pitfalls. One has to recognize the legal and technical limitations of any such effort. While information on the Web is public, proper consideration has to be given to the appropriateness of an extraction effort. Adhering to existing agreements such as the Robot Exclusion Standard and adopting solid internal ground rules for crawling scope, method, and timing ensure continued success of the effort.

Technical challenges range from overcoming crawling obstacles (HTML forms, scripts, and session handling) to designing extraction patterns that are robust and continue to work even if the structure of the source Web page changes. We have described numerous techniques for dealing with these challenges and have demonstrated by way of a sample Web data extraction task how those techniques might be used.

Based on our experience and empirical evidence gathered over the past several years, we observe that Web data extraction is both feasible and profitable to business enterprises. We believe that XML technologies provide the right tools for the task. The continued investment of the Information Technology industry in XML storage and query capabilities guarantee the continued increase in the power and pervasiveness of XML across industries.

BIBLIOGRAPHY

1. Active Server Pages, Microsoft Developer Network, http://msdn.microsoft.com/library/default.asp?url=/nhp/default.asp?contentid=28000522.
2. Charles Allen. WIDL: Application Integration with XML. World Wide Web Journal 2(4), November 1997.
3. Maria Luisa Barja, Tore Bratvold, Jussi Myllymaki, and Gabriele Sonnenberger. Informia: a Mediator for Integrated Access to Heterogeneous Information Sources. Proceedings of the ACM Conference on Information and Knowledge Management (CIKM), Washington, DC, November 1998.
4. CGI: Common Gateway Interface. October 1999. http://www.w3.org/CGI/.

5. Compaq Computer. Compaq's Web Language. http://www.research.digital.com/SRC/WebL/index.html.
6. Erik Espe. Blockade of site aims to keep firms from "deep linking." Silicon Valley/San Jose Business Journal. http://sanjose.bizjournals.com/sanjose/stories/1999/11/15/story3.html
7. Dayne Freitag. Information Extraction from HTML: Application of a General Machine Learning Approach. Proceedings of the Conference on Artificial Intelligence (AAAI), pp. 517–523, September 1998.
8. Ashish Gupta, Venky Harinarayan, and Anand Rajaraman. Virtual Database Technology. ACM SIGMOD Record, vol. 26, no. 4, December 1997.
9. Joachim Hammer, Hector Garcia-Molina, Junghoo Cho, Arturo Crespo, and Rohan Aranha. Extracting Semistructured Information from the Web. Proceedings of the Workshop on Management of Semistructured Data, Tucson, Arizona, 1997.
10. HTML 4.01 Specification, W3C Recommendation, December 1999. http://www.w3.org/TR/html4/.
11. Hypertext Transfer Protocol—HTTP/1.1, RFC 2616, The Internet Society, June 1999. ftp://ftp.isi.edu/in-notes/rfc2616.txt.
12. HTTP State Management Mechanism, RFC 2109, http://www.ietf.org/rfc/rfc2109.txt.
13. International Business Machines. DB2 XML Extender. http://www.ibm.com/software/data/db2/extenders/xmlext/index.html.
14. Jared Jackson and Jussi Myllymaki. Web-Based Data Mining. IBM developerWorks, June 2001. http://www-106.ibm.com/developerworks/Web/library/wa-wbdm/?dwzone=web.
15. Jared Jackson. Use Recursion Effectively in XSL. IBM developerWorks, October http://www-106.ibm.com/developerworks/xml/library/x-xslrecur/?dwzone=xml.
16. JavaServer Pages 2.0 Specification (JSR-000152), Java Community Process, http://jcp.org/aboutJava/communityprocess/first/jsr152/index3.html.
17. Craig A. Knoblock, Kristina Lerman, Steven Minton, and Ion Muslea. Accurately and Reliably Extracting Data from the Web: A Machine Learning Approach. IEEE Data Engineering Bulletin, vol. 23, no. 4, pp. 33–41, 2000.
18. David Konopnicki and Oded Shmueli. W3QS: A Query System for the World Wide Web. Proceedings of the International Conference on Very Large Data Bases (VLDB), pp. 54–65, Zurich, Switzerland, September 1995.
19. Martijn Koster. A Standard for Robot Exclusion. http://www.robotstxt.org/wc/norobots.html
20. Nicholas Kushmerick. Gleaning the Web. IEEE Intelligent Systems, vol. 14, no. 2, pp. 20–22, March/April 1999.
21. Laks V. S. Lakshmanan, Fereidoon Sadri, and Iyer N. Subramanian. A Declarative Language for Querying and Restructuring the Web. Proceedings of the 6th International Workshop on Research Issues in Data Engineering (RIDE), February 1996.
22. Ling Liu, Calton Pu, and Wei Han. XWRAP: An XML-Enabled Wrapper Construction System for Web Information Sources. Proceedings of the International Conference on Data Engineering (ICDE), San Diego, California, February 2000.
23. Alberto Mendelzon, George Mihaila, and Tova Milo. Querying the World Wide Web. International Journal on Digital Libraries, vol. 1, no. 1, pp. 54–67, 1997.
24. Jussi Myllymaki. Effective Web Data Extraction with Standard XML Technologies. Proceedings of the Tenth International World Wide Web Conference, Hong Kong, May 2001.
25. Jussi Myllymaki and Jared Jackson. Robust Web Data Extraction with XML Path Expressions. IBM Research Report RJ 10245, May 2002.
26. Lucian Popa, Mauricio A. Hernández, Yannis Velegrakis and R. J. Miller. Mapping XML and Relational Schemas with CLIO. System Demonstration, IEEE Data Engineering Conference, 2002.
27. Sriram Raghavan and Hector Garcia-Molina. Crawling the Hidden Web. Proceedings of the International Conference on Very Large Databases (VLDB), 2001.
28. Berthier Ribeiro-Neto, Alberto H.F. Laender, and Altigran S. da Silva. Extracting Semi-Structured Data Through Examples. Proceedings of the ACM Conference on Information and Knowledge Management (CIKM), Kansas City, Missouri, November 1999.
29. Arnaud Sahuguet and Fabien Azavant. Building Light-Weight Wrappers for Legacy Web Data-Sources Using W4F. Proceedings of the International Conference on Very Large Data Bases (VLDB), Edinburgh, Scotland, September 1999.
30. Stephen Soderland. Learning Information Extraction Rules for Semi-structured and Free Text. Machine Learning, vol. 34, no. 1, pp. 233–272, 1999.

31. Simple Object Access Protocol (SOAP) 1.1, W3C Note, May 2000. http://www.w3.org/TR/SOAP/.
32. Marc Songini. IBM: All Searches Start at Grand Central, Network World, November 11, 1997.
33. HTML Tidy. http://www.w3.org/People/Raggett/tidy/.
34. Web Content Accessibility Guidelines 1.0. W3C Recommendation, May 1999. http://www.w3.org/TR/WAI-WEBCONTENT/.
35. XHTML: The Extensible HyperText Markup Language, W3C Recommendation, January 2000. http://www.w3.org/TR/xhtml1.
36. Extensible Markup Language (XML), W3C Recommendation, February 1998. http://www.w3.org/TR/REC-xml.
37. XQuery 1.0: An XML Query Language. W3C Working Draft, November 2002. http://www.w3.org/TR/xquery/.
38. XML Schema Part 0: Primer, W3C Working Draft, April 2000. http://www.w3.org/TR/xmlschema-0/.
39. XML Path Language (XPath), W3C Recommendation, November 1999. http://www.w3.org/TR/xpath.html.
40. XSL Transformations (XSLT), W3C Recommendation, November 1999. http://www.w3.org/TR/xslt.html.

PRODUCT LIFE CYCLE MANAGEMENT IN THE DIGITAL AGE

JÖRG NIEMANN AND E. WESTKÄMPER

1. INTRODUCTION

The development of modern products is being decisively influenced by the application of technologies contributing towards increasing efficiency. Products are becoming complex highly-integrated systems with internal technical intelligence enabling the user to utilize them reliably, economically and successfully even in the fringe ranges of technology. As a result, business strategies are aiming more and more towards perfecting technical systems, optimizing product usage and maximizing added value over the entire life time of a product. In this context, the total management of product life cycles associated with the integration of information and communications systems is becoming a key success factor for industrial companies. [1, 2]

When manufacturing technical products, industrial corporations generally direct their strategies at economic targets. Their main business lies in developing, producing and operating products either for individual customers or for complete sectors of the market. Service and maintenance are considered by many companies to be necessary to achieve lasting business relationships with customers.

As a result, industrial manufacturing companies are concentrating their businesses more and more on engineering, assembly and services. They are following new paradigms in order to add value by customer orientation, systems management and services in the life of products. [1, 3]

Manufacturers of machines and other industrial fields such as the automobile industry have reduced their own capacities down to the main or core technologies and final assembly. The manufacturing of parts and components is performed by suppliers or specialized companies. More and more often, profit is becoming a result of business operations in design, engineering, final assembly and service. These phases of production are the core competencies of companies which produce strong market or customer-oriented products and add value during a product's life cycle. [4]

The functionalities of products are defined in the processes of design and engineering. By assembling, maintaining and disassembling real configurations, the functionality of products and their specific or characteristic properties for usage are determined (as-built) or altered. In the usage phase, special know-how concerned with the design and characteristic properties is required, such as specific process knowledge for optimizing utilization and performance. Increasing technical complexity is promoting product-near services and manufacturer assistance. This brings about new business models for marketing only the functionality of capital-intensive products rather than selling the products themselves.

Behind these tendencies, there is a new paradigm: in order to add value and maximize utilization, products are linked in the manufacturer's network from beginning to end. For this paradigm, manufacturers need life cycle management (LCM) systems, tools and technologies. Assembly and disassembly play the key roles in life cycle management. This will be demonstrated below with a focus on high-value technical products or capital-intensive goods, such as machines for manufacturing or production purposes.

2. THE NEW PARADIGM OF LIFE CYCLE MANAGEMENT

Influenced by limited natural resources, the environment is becoming endangered due to emissions and more severe technical general conditions. Consequently, a change in strategies has taken place which takes not only economical aims but also ecological aspects into account in the design and utilization of technical products. Manufacturers have to accept more and more responsibility for the usability of their technical products and for their consequences of usage. However, many companies only follow statutory general conditions in pre-sales and after-sales in order to prevent them from losing their markets. There is a general impression that the cost-benefit ratio, especially in after-sales business, is insufficient. This also applies to industrial recycling. One main factor is the availability of actual information about the products and a lack of synergy between final assembly and after-sales operations. [3, 5, 6]

The concentration of all processes into the total life cycle of a product and the optimization of usage of each single technical product can be described as a new paradigm. Seen from a global point of view, (macro-economy), this is only logical. Seen from an operational point of view (micro-economy), it is proving difficult to initiate such strategies due to the fact that fundamental structural changes are required in products as well as in organization and production technologies and that the economic benefits involved are either uncertain or associated with risks. [3, 6]

But there is a future vision in life cycle management for optimizing the total utilization of each product and to reduce environmental impact to a minimum. In reality, the different types of products need to be taken into account. For some products, it makes economic sense to link them to the manufacturer's network as shown in Figure 1. If the

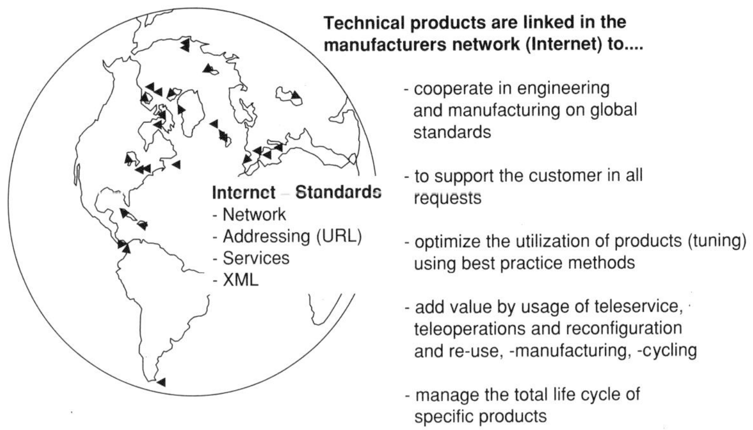

Technical products are linked in the manufacturers network (Internet) to....
- cooperate in engineering and manufacturing on global standards
- to support the customer in all requests
- optimize the utilization of products (tuning) using best practice methods
- add value by usage of teleservice, teleoperations and reconfiguration and re-use, -manufacturing, -cycling
- manage the total life cycle of specific products
Internet – Standards
- Network
- Addressing (URL)
- Services
- XML

Figure 1. The vision of life cycle management.

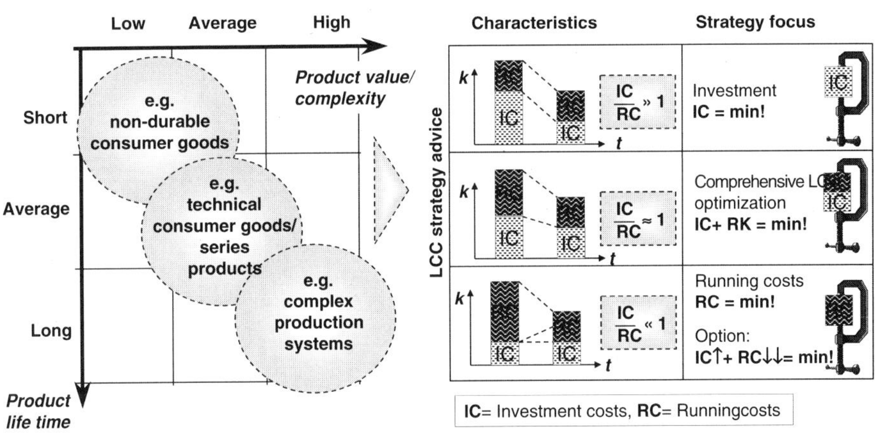

Figure 2. Strategic options for life cycle management.

futuristic vision is followed that all machines and high quality technical products will remain in the manufacturer's information network, the Internet then attains a central importance in total life cycle management.

The strategies followed by companies are significantly dependent upon the type of product concerned. In a first approximation, three categories with varying time scales and strategies may thus be defined (Figure 2). Technical consumer goods are usually mass-produced and manufactured in large series. The main emphasis of life cycle management here is placed on the rational organization of services, marketing and product recycling techniques. Robust techniques can be used for recycling due to the fact that the added value profit is low in relation to the value of the product.

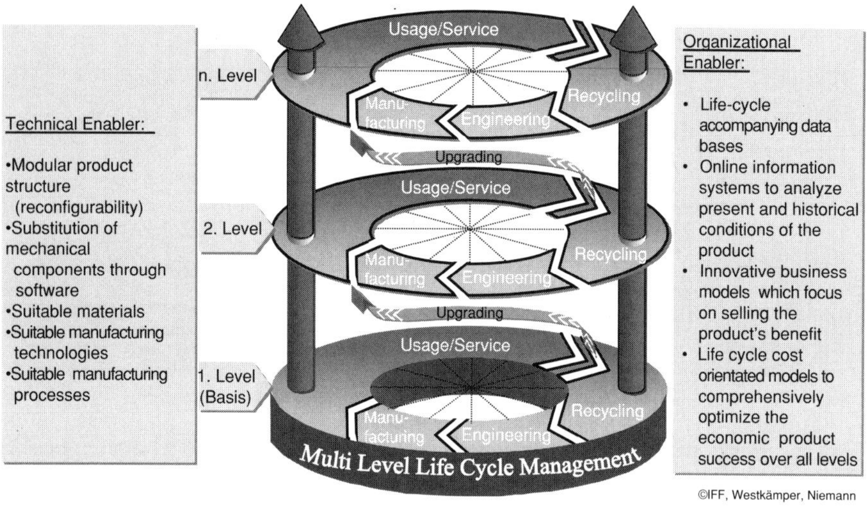

Figure 3. Products have several lives.

The second category is assigned to series products with limited numbers of variants. Life cycle management for these products includes services and maintenance as well as industrial recycling and the partial re-use of parts and components. High-quality capital goods have been assigned to the third category. The main emphases here include maximum utilization strategies, maintaining performance and additional added value in the field of after-sales. Industrial recycling only plays a minor economic role in this category of products. [7]

A forward-looking life cycle plan for the product is one example of a maximum utilization strategy. On completion of the usage phase, the owner is faced with the alternative of either scrapping/recycling the product or of upgrading it. On upgrading, the product is transformed so that it obtains a new operational status reflected in new product functions. Specific modifications in the form of software or hardware alterations are carried out on the product to equip it with advanced, extended or new functional features in comparison with its original condition. Consequently, the product can be improved, extended or be utilized to perform completely new tasks. When choosing to upgrade, a product almost starts a new life (Figure 3).

However, upgrading is not always possible due to either technical or economic circumstances. In order to be able to upgrade at a later point in time, far-sighted product planning is required which commences in the product engineering stage. In this early phase of development, the fundamental product features—including later modification possibilities—are fixed. Numerous technical and organizational measures decide whether a product can be successfully transformed to attain another level.

From the technical point of view, the modular design of a product's construction is of particular importance. The modular design of a product in accordance with the laws of system technology enables a variable and economically-viable re-design of a

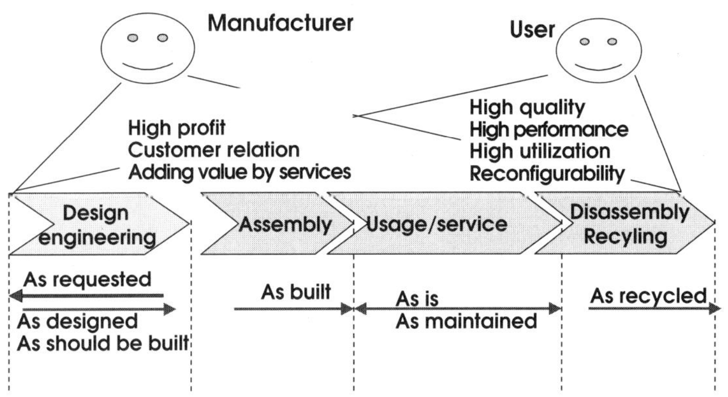

Figure 4. Views of manufacturers and users on the life cycle of technical products.

product throughout its entire lifetime. If the fact is taken into consideration that a product may be modified many times over or even altered completely during its lifetime, such product constructions not only bring about advantages for product maintenance but also create enormous potentials. The increasing substitution of mechanical components with software also supports the short-term usage of a product for variable task assignments; retrofitting times can be shortened due to the fact that modified software can be loaded in a much shorter space of time than hardware components can be exchanged. [8]

As far as organization is concerned, optimization can be supported using lifelong data acquisition. [5] Data-logging enables statistical analyses of the behavior of a product to be generated or for products or processes to be monitored online. The data obtained using this method is evaluated according to specific criteria and discloses optimization potentials. In this way, machines can be completely controlled so that, in the future, not only will it be possible to perform technical optimization but also to take economical factors into consideration and to carry out far-sighted planning thanks to "real" machine data.

2.1. Partnerships for sustainable product life cycles

Up till now, traditional manufacturing paradigms have focused on aspects of profit by manufacturing and selling products to the end-customer.

The new paradigm takes into account the life cycle of technical products and the optimization of value and benefits such as engineering, assembly, service, maintenance and disassembly. The objective is to reduce environmental losses and to fulfill public or governmental restrictions over the life cycle [2, 9, 10, 11, 12, 13].

Following the new paradigm of optimization and of adding value over the total life of products, a structural change in the relationship between manufacturer and user will subsequently take place. They have different views on the same business processes in the life of products, as shown in Figure 4.

Different views about one product are the result of 21st century industrial development. In the future, the holistic view will offer new ages of manufacturing. The main environmental views are not addressed in this paper because they are more important for mass-produced goods than for technical investment products.

2.1.1. Manufacturer's view

In general, the life cycle of products can be defined as the phases of design and engineering, manufacturing, assembly, usage, service, disassembly and recycling.

Further dimensions are defined in [1, 3, 9, 10, 14, 15, 16, 17] and depend on the specific structure of products and production. The main objective is to fulfill the requirements of markets and customers for the efficient utilization of manufacturing resources. The new view is adding value in the usage and recycling phases as a result of customer-near services including maintenance and disassembly for reconfiguration, reuse or recycling.

More than ever before, this view of the usage and recycling phases makes it necessary to take into account aspects of life cycle design and engineering or the capability of systems to be assembled, disassembled and diagnosed in all phases, especially in that of usage (as is).

This creates profitable product-oriented services throughout all operations by supporting the diagnostics of actual properties, as well as the partial disassembly and assembly for reconfiguration, upgrading and final disassembly for recycling.

2.1.2. Customer's view

In general, customers are interested in achieving a high utilization in the usage phase at the lowest cost, even if processes need to be changed. The requirement is for flexible manufacturing systems with minimal set-up times and costs which provide a guaranteed process performance. The high efficiency of the usage of complex technical products depends on specific skills and know-how concerned with the details of machines, mechatronic components, software and process optimization. This costly tendency can be overcome by using specific skilled services and assistance or support provided by manufacturers. Users prefer buying specialized services to reduce the fixed costs of products and the costs of inspection, maintenance and reconfiguration or upgrading.

The economic efficiency of capital-intensive products in industrial manufacturing depends on the requirements and profiles of products, technical requirements and capacities. These requirements are changing constantly with the result that manufacturing systems need to be permanently adapted. At present, there are no economic evaluation methods in existence for controlling life cycles and for finding the optimal point in time for the end of a product's life or even for calculating real life cycle costs [18, 19, 20, 21].

2.1.3. Life cycle objectives

The new paradigm of activating the product's cost-benefit is oriented according both to economic aspects and to fulfilling requirements for the environmental behavior of technical products by applying ecological criteria. It assumes that the concentration

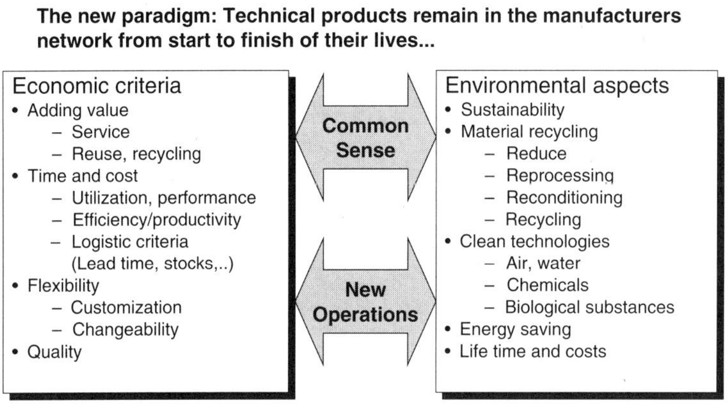

The new paradigm: Technical products remain in the manufacturers network from start to finish of their lives...
Economic criteria
• Adding value
– Service
– Reuse, recycling
• Time and cost
– Utilization, performance
– Efficiency/productivity
– Logistic criteria
(Lead time, stocks,..)
• Flexibility
– Customization
– Changeability
• Quality
Common Sense
New Operations
Environmental aspects
• Sustainability
• Material recycling
– Reduce
– Reprocessing
– Reconditioning
– Recycling
• Clean technologies
– Air, water
– Chemicals
– Biological substances
• Energy saving
• Life time and costs

Figure 5. Objectives of life cycle management.

on core competence and specialization offers new potentials to add value or to reduce the cost of usage by industrializing service and disassembly. A common understanding between manufacturers and users is a prerequisite in order to be able to activate potentials, to obtain the maximum benefit from each technical product during its life cycle and to fulfill economic and environmental objectives (Figure 5).

Common sense and active optimization demand technical solutions to link products at any point in time throughout their entire life cycle to the information networks of manufacturers and users. This can be achieved by implementing technical products in global IT networks and electronic services. It is evident today that we have the technologies to do this and to follow the technical trend for developing intelligent machines connected to communications systems. [7] Following the new paradigm, the vision is to permanently link products to manufacturers' networks. Communication is the platform for any product-oriented service with the aim of achieving maximum benefit over its life time.

2.2. Economical assessment of product life cycles

The following graph (Figure 6) represents the principal course of a product's value over its lifetime. During the comparatively short production phase, product value rises to sale price. Subsequent to wear and increasing failure rates, a drop in value occurs which can be partially compensated for by carrying out maintenance, repair and upgrading. If nothing else, recycling is at least able to maintain the material value. Higher values can only be achieved through re-use and re-manufacturing.

The economical feasibility of measures to maintain value and to recuperate remaining values at the end of a product's life is a function of product value at that particular point in the product's life cycle. Life cycle controlling (LCC) methods can be used to calculate the product value and pro-active assessment of future developments accurately.

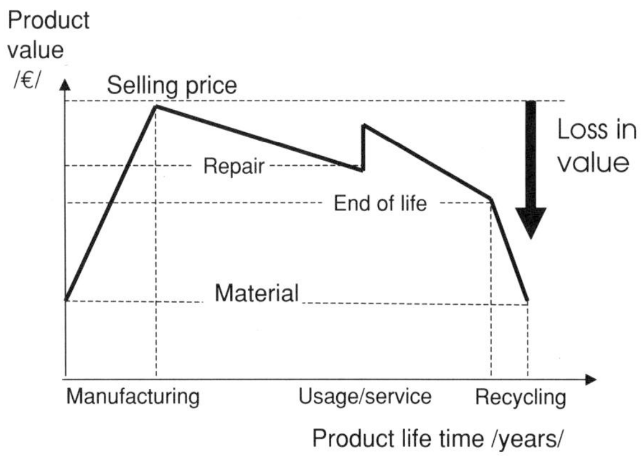

Figure 6. Product value during a life cycle.

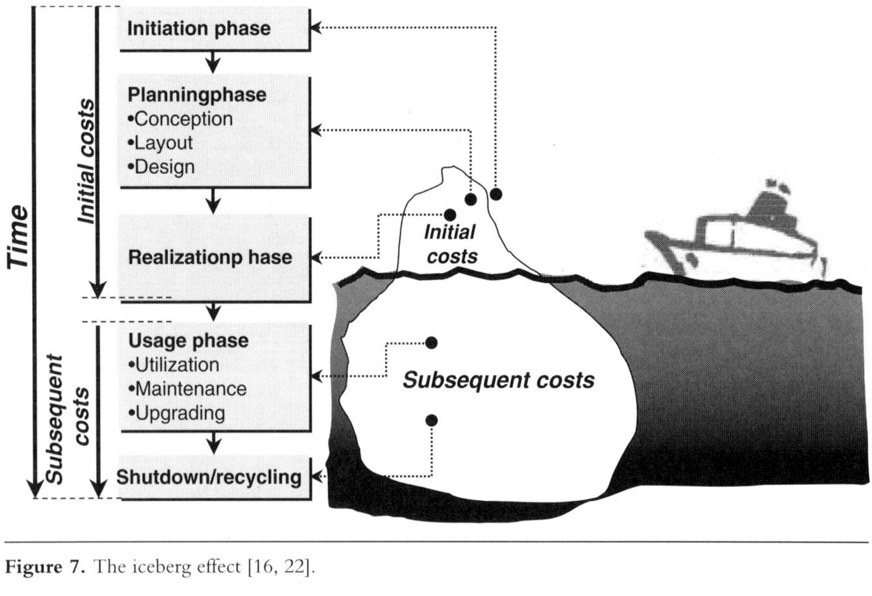

Figure 7. The iceberg effect [16, 22].

Pro-active assessment of future cost developments requires in-depth knowledge of possible developments. Costs [16] measured over an entire life cycle possess the structure of an iceberg (Figure 7).

The costs arising can be divided into initial costs and subsequent costs over the life time. As with an iceberg, only a small part of the entire (cost) block is initially visible. The main part is (initially) "hidden", but must to be taken into account in order to avoid "shipwreck". By assigning the different costs to specific life cycle phases, it becomes clear that the initial costs occur during the phases of initiation, planning and realization. During this period, the product is being manufactured. Subsequent costs mainly arise in the usage phase of a product. Due to the fact that most of the financial transactions are performed during this phase, an exact estimation of costs and revenues must be obtained. Studies have shown that a focus on minimized initial costs by ignoring (later) subsequent costs does not lead to minimized total life cycle costs. [22] Nevertheless, subsequent costs are essentially determined in the early phases of product design. One way of evaluating and analyzing these economic correlations is the method of life cycle controlling.

The main objective of a life cycle controlling analysis (LCC analysis) is to maximize the difference between life cycle costs and benefits (finally evaluated in profits). In the process, the life cycle costs can be roughly divided into the three sections of development costs, utility or service costs and recycling/reprocessing costs. Figure 8 shows an example of such a cost breakdown structure.

The passing through of these three phases is equally as important as the technical product life cycle. Analogous to costs, the life cycle profits can also be classified in a similar way to the individual phases. Firstly, the relevant cost and profit blocks are recorded in which the type of the individual positions turn out varyingly depending on the investment goods investigated. To assess total success in the life cycle, the positions are aggregated separately according to expenditure and profit spread out over all the phases. An example is given in Figure 8 which shows graphically the cumulated expenditure and profits during the life cycle of a machining center. If only marginally different functional solution options exist for a certain system design, a life cycle controlling analysis can help in finding the best economical variant. If—in later phases—the results of the life cycle controlling analysis which was carried out are periodically assessed critically and are used instead to optimize the design within an improvement cycle, a technically and economically optimized product is the final result. The method can be applied to plan and identify profit potentials over the entire product life cycle:

- Calculation of total cost for products (initial and subsequent cost)
- Identification of cost and revenue drivers
- Impact of outsourcing decisions
- Cash-flow analyses, Return on Investment
- Analysis of "what if" scenarios (prognosis)
- Optimal time for machine replacement
- Holistic investment budgeting
- Analysis of trade-offs between initial and subsequent costs
- Analysis of customer life time value (evaluating the value/profitability of each business relation).

By looking at the situation in the long-term, LCC analyses uncover hidden cost drivers as well as profit potentials during the entire life cycle. In this way, the analysis

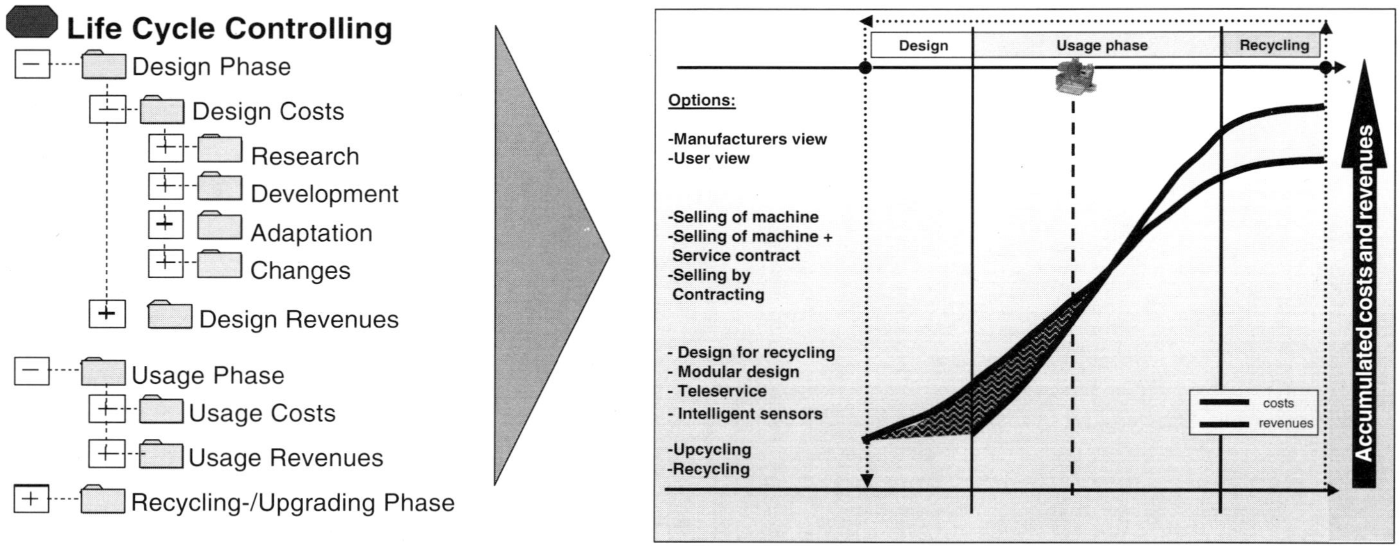

Life Cycle Controlling
Design Phase
Design Costs
Research
Development
Adaptation
Changes
Design Revenues
Usage Phase
Usage Costs
Usage Revenues
Recycling-/Upgrading Phase
Design
Usage phase
Recycling
Options:
-Manufacturers view
-User view
-Selling of machine
-Selling of machine + Service contract
-Selling by Contracting
- Design for recycling
- Modular design
- Teleservice
- Intelligent sensors
-Upcycling
-Recycling
costs
revenues
Accumulated costs and revenues

Figure 8. Method of life cycle controlling.

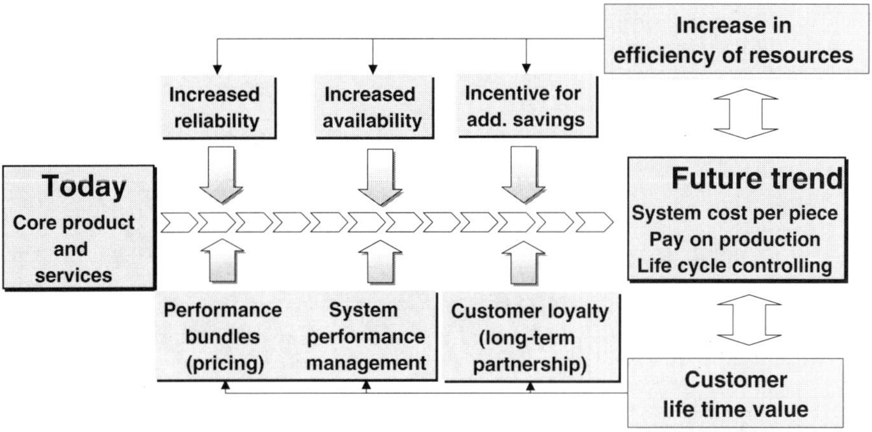

Figure 9. Performance potentials for system operators.

also supplies parameters for outsourcing strategies right up to calculations for modern full-service concepts and complete outsourcing.

3. THE DIGITAL AGE—ACTIVATING HIDDEN PERFORMANCE POTENTIALS

Today's traditional product business models see a product in the center of all activities which is surrounded by peripheral services. The (additional) services are offered by the supplier himself or by other service agents (third parties). These business models are actually changing towards so-called participative or even full-service concepts. This implies that the supplier extends (or sometimes has to extend ...) his operations over the product's life cycle. Modern business models require the supplier's guarantee of system cost per piece, or the customer only pays for the usage of a machine rather than for the purchase of the machine itself. This results in a dramatic change in the business relationships between product users and suppliers. In this way, the original equipment manufacturers (OEM's) transfer the production risks to their supplier. The supplier is responsible for the operation of a machine and is paid according to output (Figure 9).

On the other hand, in many industries, suppliers possess considerably more in-depth knowledge about machine operation that the OEM. In this way, they are able to drive and to operate their machines in the fringe ranges of performance and quality. They benefit from their long time experience and in-depth constructional knowledge. This enables them to improve machine reliability and availability in order to achieve a higher degree of productivity (resources' efficiency) compared to that of a machine operated by the OEM. Another stimulus to follow these new business relationships is the evaluation of a customer's value over the entire business relationship (customer life time value). Modern business models will create extensive and long-lasting business partnerships. Durability is based on the early integration of a partner right from the planning phases of the production systems. This allows the supplier to generate pricing

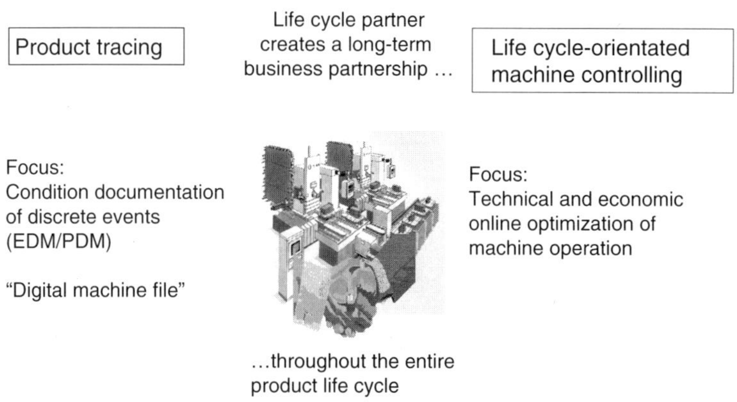

Figure 10. Digital life cycle product data management.

models according to the requested degree of service. The service package may include total system performance management (full-service provider) and the total control and responsibility of all production operations are then taken over by the supplier. In this way, the supplier mutates to become a system operator with a strong influence on the OEM performance (and profit) results.

Due to this integration, it becomes very difficult and costly to replace such a partner who was involved in the essential planning and scaling of the system. The system, the tasks to be performed, logistic chains and system management were all designed to achieve a maximum profit among all partners. Also, the knowledge and abilities of all the partners were distributed according to the working tasks, making it difficult to find another partner with exactly the same special knowledge profile.

The close integration of suppliers permits OEM's to minimize their production risks. However, at the same time production costs change from being originally fixed to become variable parameters. On the other hand, suppliers are able to extend their value chain and apply their special machine know-how to realize additional potentials. This constitutes the basis for a durable win-win relationship for both partners.

When implementing this strategy it becomes obvious that a supplier having to constantly guarantee life cycle costs or production system costs also needs online access to the system control. The supplier is required to permanently monitor his machines and to react at short notice in case of failures, machine break-downs or deviations in quality. Any irregular events directly worsten his profit situation. Most performance contracts (e.g., life cycle cost contracts) foresee penalties if the fixed performance criteria are not met but also monetary incentives for outstanding performance results over and above fixed ratios.

Digital life time tracking and (online) optimization is therefore imperatively required to meet the fixed performance criteria (Figure 10). A general model must cover the entire machine life cycle beginning with the machine design and ending with the machine "death" of recycling. Similar to a patient's file at a doctor's practice, this digital machine file can be considered as a document where all machine data and events have been logged. In accordance with the life cycle, the bill of materials (design data), dates of selling, inspections, changed parts etc. (usage data) and recycled parts (recycling data) are all recorded continuously.

The performance or service contracts also require online tele-operations to optimize machine operation and to attain fast reaction times in case of abnormal machine behavior. A direct look into the machine and its current performance parameters enables financial ratios to be constantly generated. The values can be used for life cycle-oriented machine controlling, including pro-active performance steering and profit management based on technical performance control.

3.1. Digital product tracing

Today, the Internet offers a great variety of usable tools for life cycle management. There are worldwide standards for the communication and exchange of data and information. The Internet uses tools, engines and robots (behind the interfaces) to recommend and search for information and knowledge. There are new standards for b2b (business to business) and b2c (business to consumer). Leading companies in the automotive and machine industries use the Internet as a platform for logistics and the administration of processes between OEM and suppliers.

Internet technologies offer a broad spectrum of tools for managing the link between manufacturers and users wherever they are located. Examples of this include the management of the logistics of component supply for assembly and maintenance or technical support in the usage phase. The basic architecture of the Internet and of intranets in companies' information technologies is illustrated in Figure 11. It shows three systems for internal, for service partner and for common information.

Security techniques (firewall, en- or decryption) have to be adapted to the needs of manufacturers and be able to be operated in closed areas with service partners. Both the architecture of a product's control systems and Internet availability at each work place are important for assembly and maintenance (partial disassembly and assembly).

The diagnosis of functions and the monitoring of usage can be integrated into these systems and linked to the Internet. The same diagnosis systems are required for final assembly as for maintenance. New internal information system architectures follow agents' theories.

3.2. Boosting utilization performance

Today's new machine control concepts provide access to machine data. The programmable logic controls (PLC) generally used are increasingly set up modularly which permits a flexible application. Combined with intelligent machine and field buses, they allow the realization of fractal machine control systems. Similar to nervous systems, ideally the control tasks are distributed among more central components such as master computers and among more decentralized components right down to the actor/sensor level [23, 24, 25, 26]. This concept is supported by the development trend towards PC-based controls.

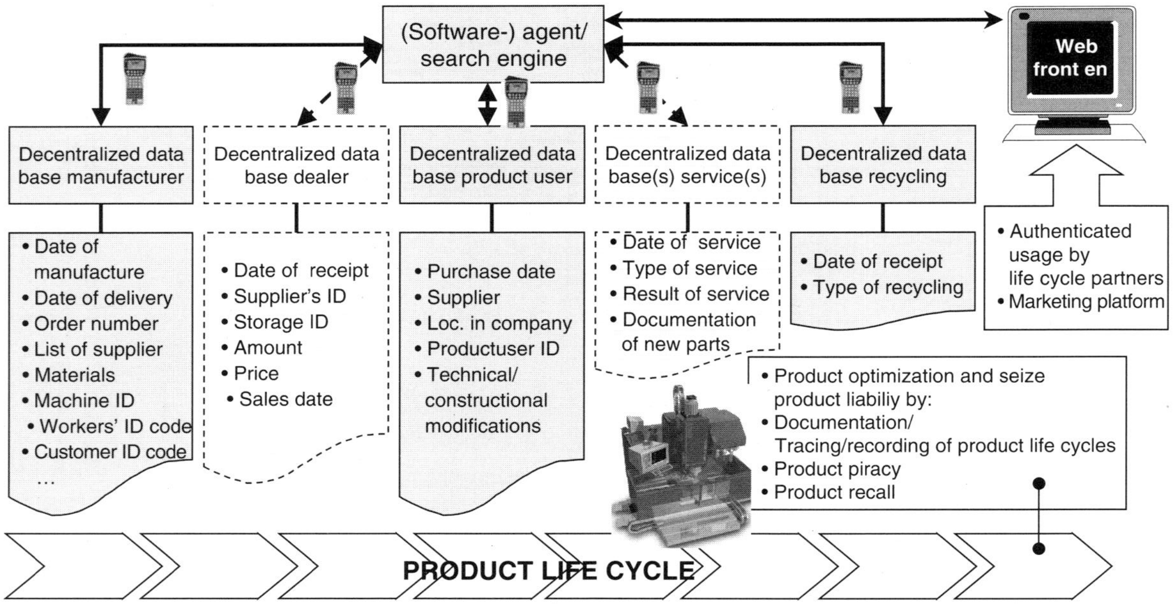

Figure 11. Traceability of products during an entire life cycle.

"Transparent" machine control over a long distance is practically state-of-the-art even though only a minority of machine manufacturers use this technology in order to provide support for their customers in a multitude of functions, such as putting a machine into operation, carrying out maintenance and even actual operation of a machine [27, 28]. There are a number of applications for remote machine control and service using telecommunication: the most common application is the access to the control software, e.g., for the purpose of analysis, error diagnosis or updating. Other applications result from the compression, transmission and evaluation of sensor data, e.g., for condition monitoring where sensors enable the mechanical wear of component parts to be monitored. Latest approaches focus on establishing life cycle data bases, track machine behavior and performance data.

Figure 12 shows a structure for the network of services based around a machine. The network is characterized by connections which allow the transfer of knowledge and information automatically as well as manual. The nodes serve as a provider, server and distributor of knowledge. In this way, complex structures are generated which consist of knowledge sinks and sources whereby communication via the web is made possible using transparent interfaces.

3.3. Workplaces on change

Modern information and communication technologies will also have a strong impact on the workplace of the future. Due to the availability of detailed process and machine information in digital format, the workplace of the future will provide both real and virtual information (Figure 13). The traditional workplace will be transformed into a "control cockpit" which provides all kinds of information presented in multimedia form.

Depending on the technical options concerned, requirements regarding the convergence of data structures and information must also be considered. Due to the limited ability of human beings to adequately process "mass data flows", all the information needs to be aggregated on a top level for the user.

Several "soft" technical requirements also need to be met in order to achieve working convenience. The "virtu-real" workplace is born and will serve as a powerful tool to improve efficiency in manufacturing. [29, 30]

3.4. Product data management for high data continuity

Appropriate strategies, methods and tools must be applied to reduce the lack of information in the early stages of a product's life cycle. Here, qualified activities and systems have to enable the transfer of know-how and information—for example with the help of communication networks based on reference models and simulation tools—to anticipate life cycle data such as system behavior or activities with a high degree of reliable information.

"The digital factory" ensures high data continuity for life cycle management and improves and accelerates all simultaneous engineering activities. Appropriate computer-aided tools for planning, analysis, assessment and simulation are used in order to include manufacturing data in early reuse studies, design reviews or manufacturing planning.

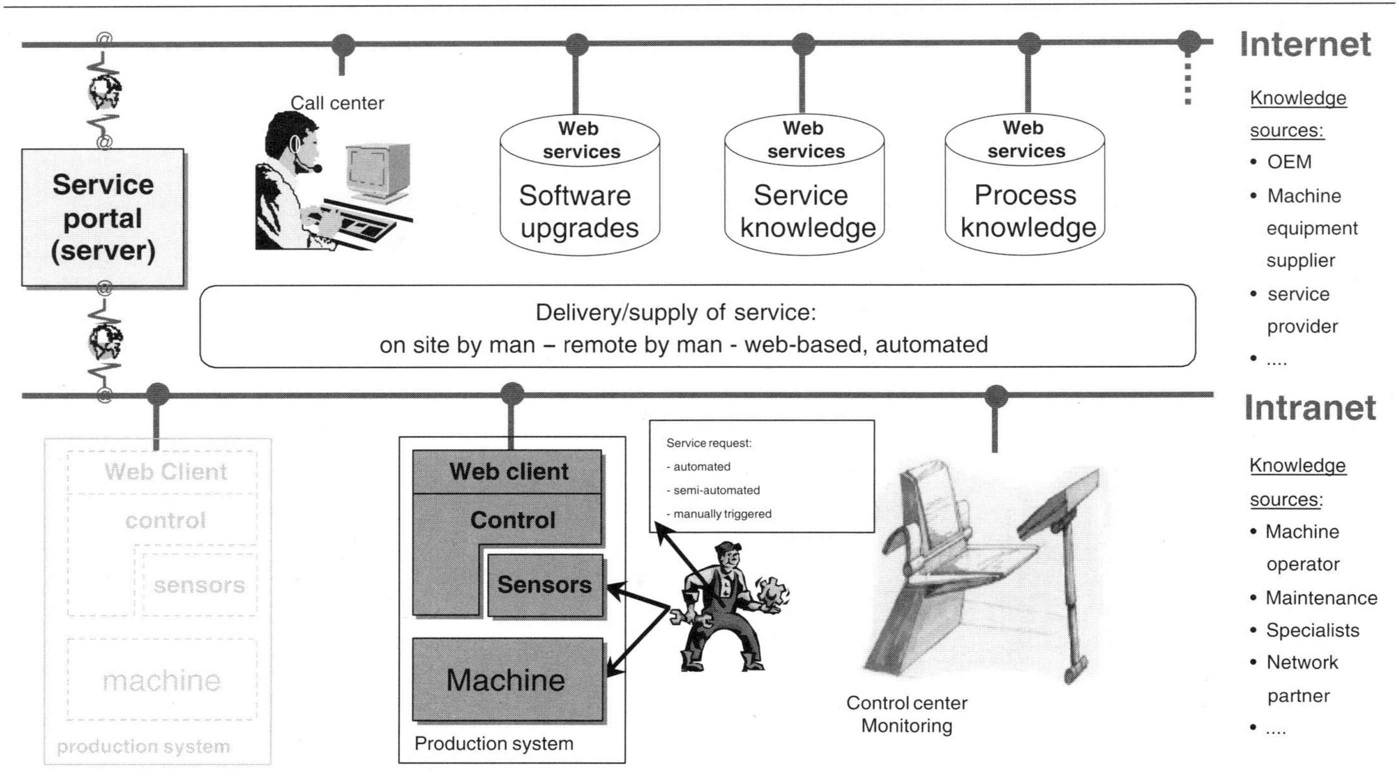

Figure 12. Knowledge sources and sinks for e-services.

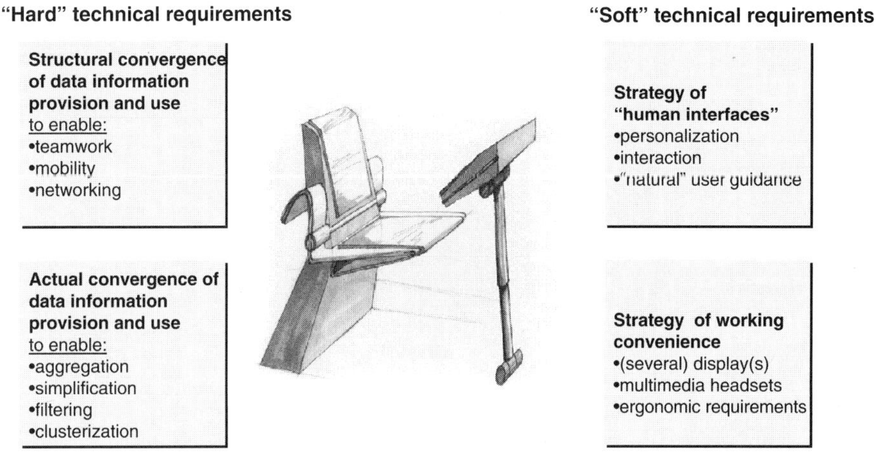

"Hard" technical requirements
"Soft" technical requirements
Structural convergence of data information provision and use
to enable:
•teamwork
•mobility
•networking
Actual convergence of data information provision and use
to enable:
•aggregation
•simplification
•filtering
•clusterization
Strategy of "human interfaces"
•personalization
•interaction
•"natural" user guidance
Strategy of working convenience
•(several) display(s)
•multimedia headsets
•ergonomic requirements

Figure 13. The "virtu-real" workplace.

A concurrent exchange of information expands interoperability and enables a better degree of communication between specialists. The result of regulations, increasing functions and the complexity of modern manufacturing systems are expanding the product stewardship of a producer. To ensure maximum performance and to secure processes during usage, the producer becomes more and more involved at this stage. The user or operator of a machine is supported by means of tele-service and tele-operations controlled by the producer. All these activities must follow the law of maximum economy. Optimizing a life cycle by assessing economical criteria requires the application of new cost accounting methods so that the share of costs and revenues can be determined.

The close co-operation of all business partners involved in a product's life cycle is a prerequisite for optimizing the design and operation of a product. To this end, configuration management and documentation must be organized in a way which takes into account all the needs of the different life cycle partners. The organization of documentation and data is essential for a clear and unambiguous product configuration at all stages in a life cycle as well for the realization of efficient technical support processes within life cycle management. This is essential for all activities performed by the different life cycle partners in the various phases of the product life cycle so that the same data is available.

An integrated information model is the key technical factor in determining the success of technical support processes (Figure 14). It is a life cycle-wide information reservoir not only of complete product data but also of data which is not directly related to the product but necessary for competent consulting in technical support processes. Reference models for the life cycle phases of the different life cycle partners, for the documents and data allocated to processes in these phases and also models of useful

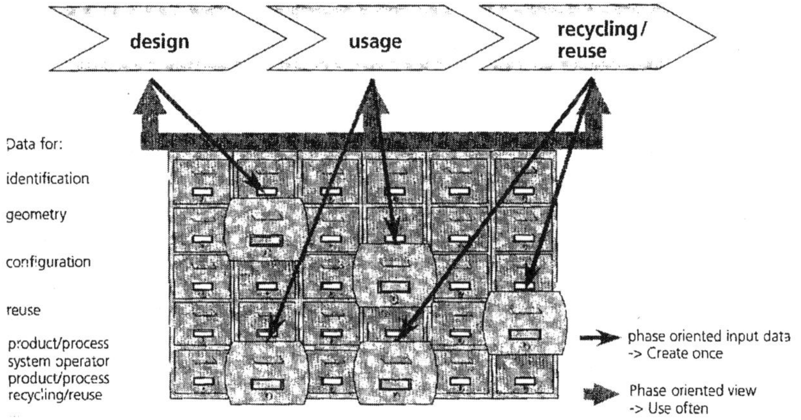

Figure 14. Integrated data model.

co-operation processes can all help to speed up agreements on life cycle management between partners and to implement an integrated information model faster.

Once the informational needs of the co-operation processes have been determined, the integrated information data model can then be conceived. For this, the detailed identification of data transferred with the documents in the co-operation processes is important. These activities and structures result in fundamental challenges in terms of information consistency, redundancy, reliability, efficiency and security.

4. ALLIANCES AND LIFE-LONG NETWORKS

Surveys estimate that over the next five years, up to 70% of the PPS systems used in today's companies will be replaced by integrated order management systems. In this field alone, huge potentials exist for reducing costs by implementing new methods and techniques. In the future, a high level of customer-orientated dynamics will have to be achieved in complex networked systems. Long-lasting improvement will only become possible if methods as well as structures are revised and integrated into networks.

Lengthy pathways and intensified work distribution are obstacles to agility and dynamics. For this reason, the objective of market-and customer-orientated businesses must be to reduce such restricting factors as lengthy administrative procedures, non-aligned interfaces or great distances in material flows. Production should only be carried out where there is a market for the product and where the cheapest resources are available. As a result, when organizing production networks, preference must be given to transformable structures with fast decision-making pathways. Preliminary ideas for creating such dynamics using virtual capacities are already in existence. These only permit the temporary inclusion and utilization of resources for a short time when required, see Figure 15. [31]

Methods for carrying out improvements exist due to the availability of faster, cheaper and, in principle, more open information and communications systems. These enable

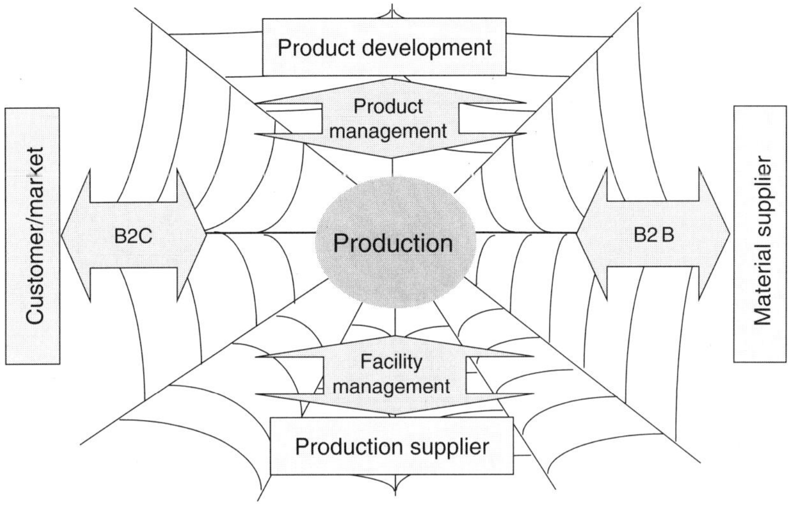

Figure 15. Network partners for production excellence.

the entire flow of information from customer to supplier to be completely integrated and production is only commenced on receipt of a customer order. Furthermore, formal and informal information can be made available to almost anywhere in the world. The process chains which are run through in an order sequence could be drastically accelerated using modern means.

By networking productions, there is a huge opportunity to uphold competitiveness, as this is targeted at achieving high synergic effects and simultaneously at attaining a high level of dynamics. History teaches us that those organizations which succeed are the ones which keep their networks transformable and adaptable and which are able to master these networks totally. Modern information and communications technologies provide the opportunity to use these possibilities in the interest of manufacturing technology. Subsequently, we should take this chance and develop it further. In order to demonstrate these ideas, a prototype of the "digital factory" has been developed (see Figure 21). The control center was located more than 300 miles away from the machining process.

In the future, it will be possible to extend this system and to integrate it into a web-based platform for holistic product support concerned with all aspects of performance optimization.

A web-based platform will provide the backbone for constantly-optimized machine operation (Figure 16). The platform will integrate the manufacturer, machine operator and various other providers from engineering services right up to and including additional research institutions. These strategic alliances will accompany a product for the duration its entire life cycle. Through this, the complete optimization of a single product becomes the focus of attention in all business activities. The decisive criterion

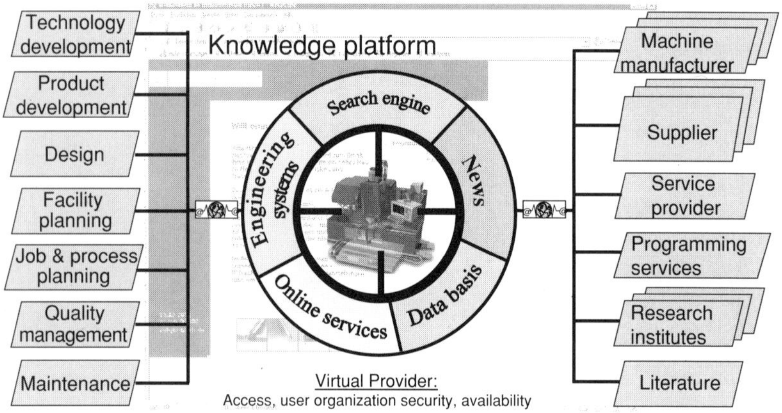

Figure 16. Networks and life-long partnerships.

for future market success will be the ability to establish, organize and promote such networks for product support. These networks will be created in order to monitor a product during its entire life-time. They may be extended or reduced while any desired service can be performed on demand. The ability to control and monitor machines digitally constitutes the foundations for mastering these constraints in the digital age. On the other hand, the machine-user will benefit from such holistic networks which help to optimize his machine or machine park. The additional benefit will generate surplus profits which the user will share among the network partners.

These alliances and networked partnerships will also be given a push from a dramatic acceleration in technical innovation cycles. Also, due to the fact that technical equipment, production processes, production sequences, goods and services all age faster in a highly-electronic environment, the long-term ownership of a production facility becomes less and less attractive. In order to be able to constantly maximize performance and precision, short-term access will become an ever-increasing option. Leasing, rental contracts or performance contracts will become more attractive than buying and owning. Accelerated innovation cycles and speeded-up product turnover will dictate conditions for the new network economy. Whereas the traditional market is characterized by the exchange of goods, the access to holistic concepts will include material aspects in a networked economy.

4.1. Product life-time value

In an economy where the possibility of short-term access to far-reaching resources forms the basis of commercial success, the entire potential of a product's life cycle moves into the center of strategic focus. It will no longer be a question of selling a single product to as many customers as possible, but rather of looking after a single customer and supplying him/her with as many products as possible.

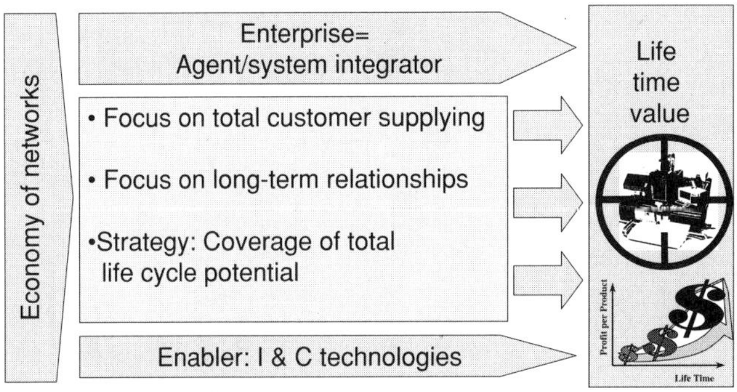

Figure 17. The paradigm of life-time value.

This new paradigm focuses primarily on the maximum exploitation of a single product instead of the maximization of total sales. Businesses will concentrate more on building up long-term relationships with individual customers. Success will be measured by the amount of value-adding realized to the customer or to the product(s) sold over the total duration of the relationship [32].

As a result, companies will only be able to exist if they are explicitly capable of increasing product profit by using other additional products. The paradigm of product life-time value, i.e. the evaluation of commercial success over the entire life span of a product, therefore demands an extreme focus to be placed on the requirements of individual customers (Figure 17). The linking-up of products to modern information and communications technology instruments offers here an excellent pre-requisite for researching and recording specific customer needs. Furthermore, for example, these technologies will also enable value-added services to be offered to the customer directly or machine optimizations to be carried out over great distances.

The change in paradigm no longer places the focus of attention on the maximum use of resources implemented by companies, but rather on the maximum technical and economical exploitation of products during their entire life cycle. This will also be forcefully demanded due to an alteration in society's conception of value with regard to environmental compatibility and to the closed circulation of materials. The technical conditions required for this already exist and will bring massive structural changes with them. Under the pressure of international competition, it is no longer possible for many companies to survive just by manufacturing and selling goods. Many enterprises transfer added-value activities more and more towards the area of product design, assembly and service.

4.2. Selling benefit instead of usage

The fields involved with the initial steps of processing basic materials or manufacturing parts, components and equipment are being dislocated. By using information

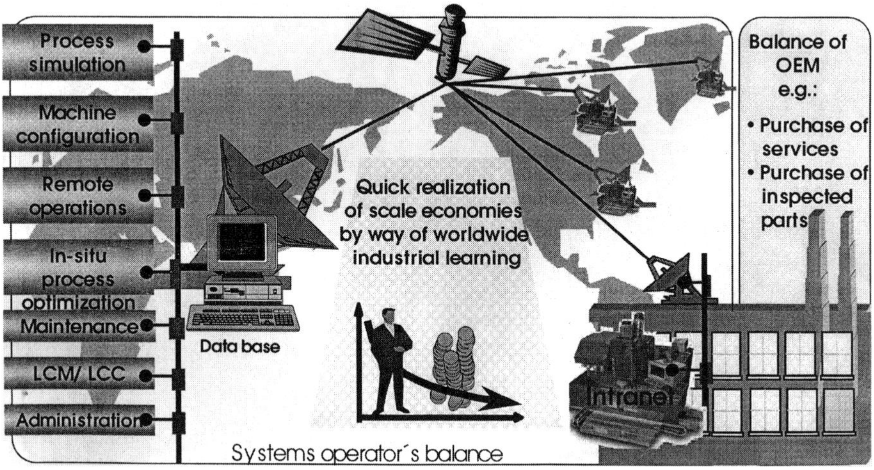

Figure 18. Systems operators and performance contracts.

and communications systems, suppliers will be involved in the development of products.

However, the so-called "system management" will remain in the hands of the manufacturers operating directly with the market. The area of after-sales where a long-term customer relationship can be established is gaining strategic importance. It will be possible to extend this development right up to the level of so-called performance contracts. Here, the manufacturers of technical products will also take over their operation and will only sell the usage of them (Figure 18). [30]

This leads no only to an increased responsibility on behalf of the manufacturer, but also to a stronger and more durable relationship with the OEM. The OEM, for example, purchases the service (instead of the machine) or pays only for inspected parts. This implies a conversion of fixed costs into variable costs for the OEM along with the extension of the value adding chain and an opportunity for the manufacturer to increase profits. The manufacturer becomes a system operator who offers his services worldwide. All machines are connected and operated by modern I&C technologies and controlled in a central surveillance center where all incoming data is collected, analyzed and evaluated. This center provides all modern technologies such as simulation, configuration and life cycle costing and revenue-forecasting tools.

The availability of these tools will allow system operators to benefit from scale economies. Once a data base has been set up, statistical performance evaluations can be made and the "best practice" determined. Through world-wide learning, system operators will be able to rapidly ascend the learning curve. By applying I&C technologies, new knowledge will be available immediately and it will be possible to implement it on all machines worldwide.

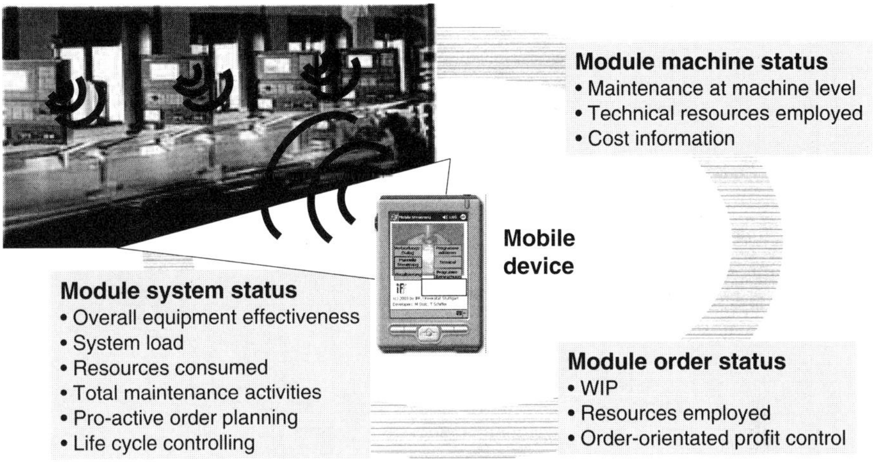

Figure 19. System elements of a controlling system for manufacturing systems.

5. INDUSTRIAL PROTOTYPES OF DIGITALLY NETWORKED PRODUCT LIFE CYCLE MANAGEMENT

5.1. Example of online process monitoring

In order to cost control a manufacturing system, various data from different sources is required. It is clear that the mastery of a system's behavior demands machine and machining data. This data can be easily acquired from the machine control system.

This offers the opportunity to access machines remotely for data logging via the Internet or telephone lines. The relevant machine data can be extracted from the data flow and serves as one input for in-situ cost monitoring and forecast. Various research projects have shown that optimal logistics play an important role in preventing performance losses. A second input is data from parts logistics; for a controlling system to be able to take these facts into account, such data needs to be integrated into the supervision system. A third group of data is directly related to the machine's environment. The order size, required quality, number of workers, calculated lead times etc. can all be taken directly from the work scheduling, bill of materials or order management. These data are static and can be extracted from various internal sources. Figure 19 and 20 describe the structure for a controlling system implemented on a precision machining center at the IFF, University of Stuttgart.

The data is monitored and visualized using a mobile handheld PC (PDA). The mobile PDA serves as a platform for production personnel in terms of technical machine control (failures, breakdowns etc.) and economic manufacturing surveillance (e.g., deviation to estimated cost, total cost and profit, etc.).

The measured data obtained from the monitored system gives a report of the actual machine status. Multiplied with cost coefficients according to the required processes, profit analyses can be made. A sensitivity analysis of different cost positions and a

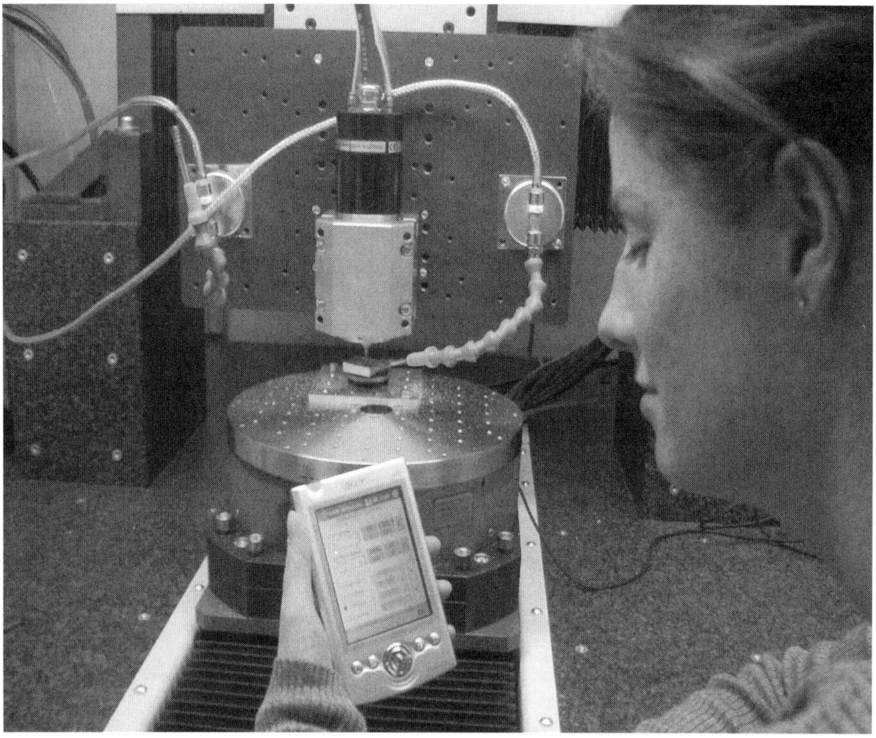

Figure 20. Management and control of a micro milling facility using a mobile device.

comparison between machine operation times and various breakdown times serve to identify hidden performance potentials. Even a forecasting module can be integrated in order to simulate future profits and performance under "status quo" conditions. All data concerned with the observed machining centers must be accumulated on a top level of production program planning to derive key actions in mid-term performance and resources planning.

5.2. Example of the digital factory of the future

As mentioned above, from the first idea to the realization, a multitude of influences and limiting conditions have an impact on the planning of production systems. The systems themselves also change rapidly during the planning phase. Because of this, the aim of the "communication platform digital factory" is the integrated representation and connection of planning and development processes in order to support the communication between man and machine (human-machine interface) and the persons associated with the planning (human-human interface).

Seen from an abstract point of view, it is necessary to provide a complete connection between the distributed real and virtual objects (machines) of a manufacturing system

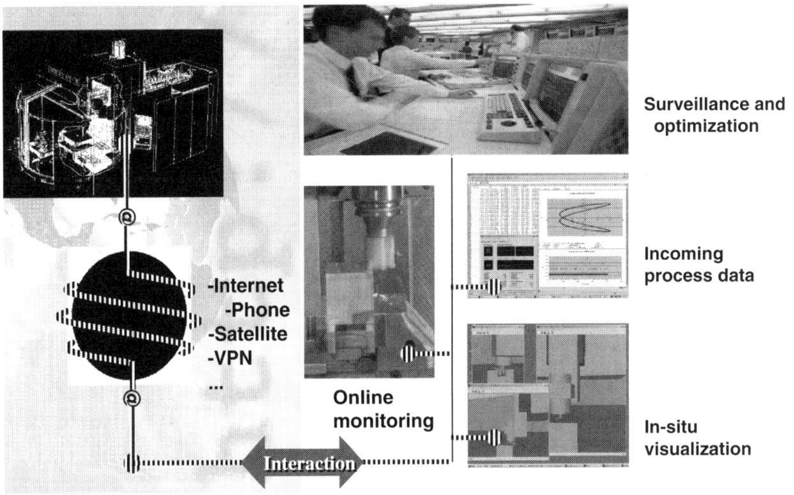

Figure 21. Prototype of the "digital factory".

on the basis of a bi-directional interactive information flow. Based on this flow, changes in the real object show up immediately on the virtual model and vice versa.

5.2.1. Structure of the platform

In order to demonstrate these ideas at the EXPO 2000, a "workplace of the future" was developed. With the help of this workplace it was possible for the visitors of the Global Dialogue to enter a configuration for a work piece in the virtual model and to watch the real manufacturing cell (at Hüller-Hille, Ludwigsburg) during the manufacturing process (Figure 21).

It was also possible to observe the alterations in the virtual model and to monitor some of the real machine's process parameters. The manufacturing process was not simulated, but the changes during the real process be visualized. As Figure 21 shows, the platform consists of three systems, a workplace for remote control of machine, an operations control centre of the real machine at the manufacturer's site and a communication system networking both systems.

The primary objective of the workplace was to directly support the user with all required and—if necessary—additional data which are essential for direct access to the machine. An interface was therefore implemented between the Siemens (S7) control system and the Specht manufacturing cell (Specht 500). Video cameras and microphones were installed within and outside the machine for audio-visual control. The interface allows to monitor the positions of axes as well as to read additional parameters about electric current or temperatures. Due to the internal Bus-structure of Siemens S7 additional sensors for e.g., forces or body sonic can be integrated. The central control center was located at the EXPO 2000 at Hannover whilst the machining centre was operated at Hüller-Hille in Ludwigsburg (distance: 300 miles).

5.2.2. Data transfer

Information was transferred on bundled telephone lines to Hanover in order to update the virtual model with the current data. To provide constant transmission rates and security against wrongful access, telephone lines were used instead of the Internet but by using TCP/IP as a transfer protocol, the system could also operate via internet. Communication was bi-directional to send update information for the visualizations in one direction and to send user inputs to control the machine in the other direction.

All the information from the machine was thus bundled in a "cockpit" in Hannover. It consisted of three screens on which the user could watch the machine's working status. One screen showed the view of the two video-cameras inside and outside the machine to provide an image of the real machine. The center screen was an active 3-D stereo projection on which the 3-D image of the virtual machine could be seen using shutter glasses. The third projection displayed the user input during product configuration and the process parameters during the manufacturing process. All but one of the computers used for the projections and networking were PCs. A Silicon Graphics Workstation (Onyx II) was required only for the high-level stereo-projection in combination with the rendering software "Vernissage" (developed by the Fraunhofer IPA).

5.3. Example for the web-based control of a technical consumer product

A new field of application of value-added services is formed by the management of technical consumer products. In co-operation with the Gebr. Joh. Vaillant GmbH, a newly-developed prototype was introduced at the EXPO 2000 in Hannover which permits the interactive control of a conventional heating system via the Internet.

5.3.1. System structure

The basis of the system's architecture is a developed web server which provides the read-out data of the heating system for global access via the Internet.

The server with the software is physically located at the site of the user's heating system. The interactive data exchange is secured by additional software which is implemented on a particular (dislocated) access terminal. The front end provides an input interface for access to the system and for setting parameters (Figure 22). In addition, the temperature and the flame are visually monitored via two web-cams.

In this way, the end-user is able to keep system data under surveillance in order to set desired temperatures and to time ignition. The manufacturer may offer this service as an added value or may even take charge entirely of the correct management of the heating system on site.

Such systems have a wide range of application, e.g., holiday houses, apartment blocks and public facilities.

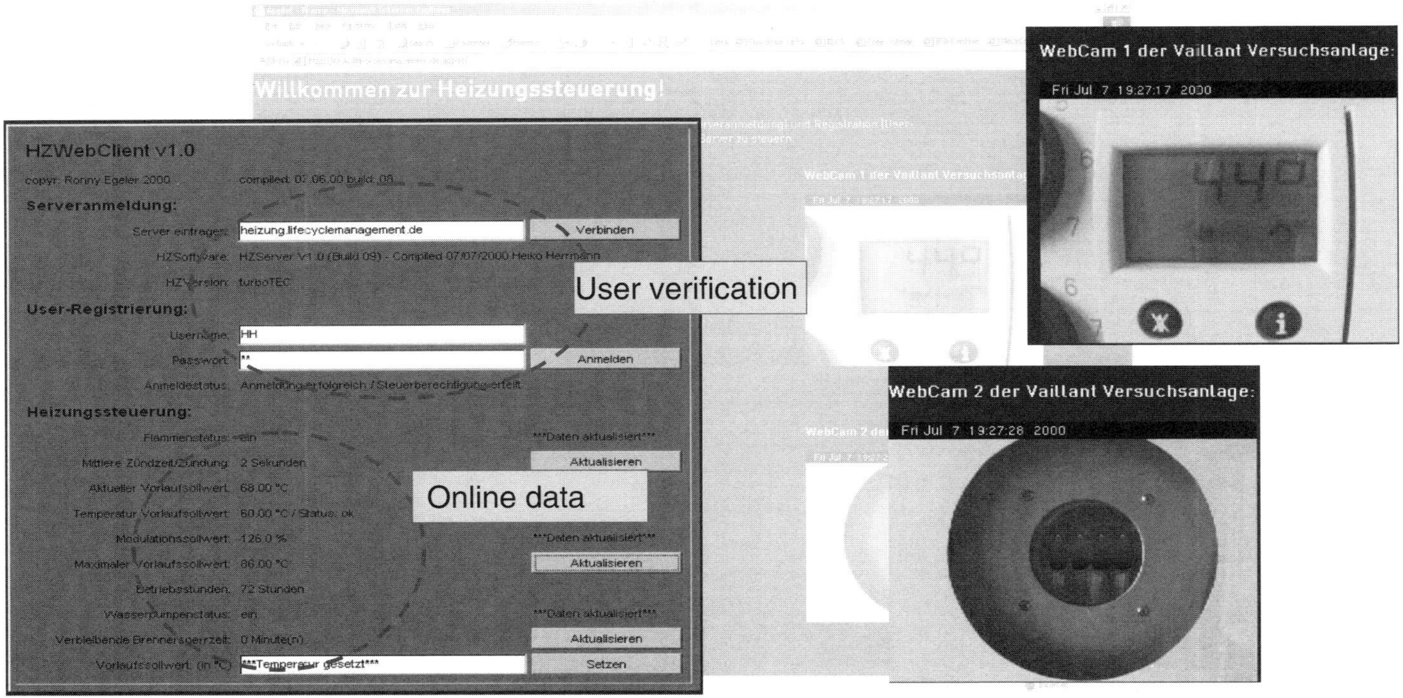

Figure 22. Control of a heating system via the Internet.

5.3.2. *Software-/Hardware architecture*

To control the heating, a java applet (HZWebClient) was generated which permits worldwide data access as part of a web page. The software contacts the server of the heating system (HZServer) and provides actual online data.

User verification is performed by way of a password ID. HZServer verifies the Client Computer and establishes a secure and reliable connection and data transfer.

As well as supplying the actual operational data, a failure protocol can be read should the system fail for any reason. In this way, the cause of the malfunction can be localized. HZServer provides a feature for generating such a failure protocol and for sending it to the user via e-mail.

The detailed protocol permits the failure to be rectified by using control commands or for the system to be reset for an operational restart. In the future, the entire operations management—including maintenance and failure reset—will be able to be performed either by the private user or be offered as a value-added service by the manufacturer. The latter will provide enormous extensions of business activities and open the gate for "mass business" with terrific potentials for value-added services.

5.3.3. *Extension of system bounds—a future vision*

Today's developments focus on activities to extend additional services for a wide range of products. Aiming at increasing profits, these value-added services can be characterized as a mixture of the horizontal and vertical integration of further functions.

The original product acts as a vehicle or platform to sell additional and/or more profitable products or services. An actual focus of research is models for realizing new potentials for value-added services. The digital linking of heating systems to distributed computer systems allows online access for status monitoring. The manufacturer is able to acquire all the data in a central control center so that they can be processed and evaluated with regard to specific aspects. The acquired knowledge constitutes a foundation for erecting a horizontal or vertical network (Figure 23).

Under the organization and direction of the heating manufacturer, it is conceivable that networks will take charge of installation, the delivery of the primary energy supply and services right up to the fulfillment of municipal services (e.g., emission control, chimney-sweeping services, etc.).

The network is controlled by applying modern communication and information technologies. The core benefit for customers is the subscription to an "all-inclusive package".

The heating system as a product mutates to an overall service platform for whose use the customer pays. The ownership of facility itself remains in the manufacturer's hands throughout the entire life cycle.

6. CONCLUSION AND OUTLOOK

Today, global competition demands guarantees from technical equipment manufacturers as far as the technical and economical performance of their products is concerned. Due to the increasing substitution of mechanical components with software, it has

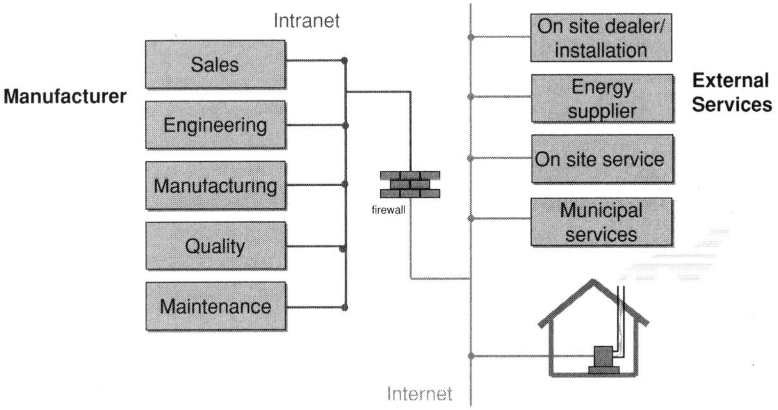

Figure 23. Net-based life cycle management of a technical consumer product.

become possible to read out data from machines and process control in-situ, i.e. during a process. In this way, the current status of the machine can be called up, monitored and analyzed online from anywhere in the world.

Modern technologies make it possible to couple actual process parameters with process data from the past, thus enabling the later process behavior to be forecast in advance in a simulation. The early recognition of inefficiencies and faults allows for in-situ process optimization even in the absolute fringe ranges of precision and performance. These enormous potentials can be translated into costs and virtual profit information so that the processes can be "controlled" with regard to their economical efficiency.

The transparent machine is becoming reality!

In modern system concepts, installations are operated in a distant network by teleoperations. It is possible that the installation may remain the property of the manufacturer and stay within his/her sphere of responsibility for its entire service life and that only the benefits or functions of the machine be sold. By integrating the knowledge sources of equipment manufacturers, machine outfitters and others, a markedly higher exploitation of the machine can be achieved.

To describe the maximum utilization of products as product profit is the greatest change in paradigm, as it breaks away from the traditional paradigms of growth- and resource-optimization. An emphasis is now being placed on the usage of customers or long-term business relationships and is therefore a viewpoint associated with life cycles. This results in a new dimension, as by considering the concept of customer life time value, the worth of a business relationship can be determined with the aid of a dynamic life cycle model. In the case of the customer-life-time value concept, the capital value of payments associated with such a relationship is seen as a business relationship assessment criterion. This new viewpoint is pursued by worldwide networks which have come into existence offering permanent product optimization support. As a result, the performance capability of a company will be expressed in the future by its short-term access to such networks, which may be and must be used to constantly optimize product usage in order for these companies to survive.

REFERENCES

[1] Seliger, G.: More use with fewer resources—a contribution towards sustainable development; Life Cycle Networks Chapman & Hall, London, Weinheim, New York, Tokio, Melbourne, Madras. 1997.

[2] Zülch, G., Schiller, E. F., Müller, R.: A disassembly information system; Life Cycle Networks Chapman & Hall, London, Weinheim, New York, Tokio, Melbourne, Madras. 1997.

[3] Westkämper, E., Alting, L., Arndt, G.: Life Cycle Management and Assessment: Approaches and Visions Towards Sustainable Manufacturing. In: CIRP Annals Manufacturing Technology 49 (2000), 2, S. 501–522.

[4] Feldmann, K.: Integrated Product Policy—Chance and Challenge: 9th CIRP International Seminar on the Life-Cycle Engineering, April 09–10, 2002, Erlangen, Germany. Bamberg: Meisenbach.

[5] Anderl, R., Daum, B., John, H., Pütter, C.: Cooperative product data modeling in life cycle networks; Life Cycle Networks Chapman & Hall, London, Weinheim, New York, Tokio, Melbourne, Madras. 1997.

[6] Alting, L., Hausschild, M., Wenzel, H.: Environmental Assessment of Products, Volume 1: Methodology, tools and case studies in product development, Chapman & Hall, London 1997.

[7] Brussel, H. van, Valckenaers, P. (Hrsg.): Katholieke Universiteit <Leuven>/Department of Mechanical Engineering/Production Engineering Machine Design Automation (PMA): Intelligent Manufacturing Systems 1999: Proceedings of the Second International Workshop on Intelligent Manufacturing Systems, September 22–24, 1999, Leuven, Belgium.

[8] Westkämper, E.: Technical Intelligence for Manufacturing. Third World Congress on Intelligent Manufacturing Processes and Systems. Cambridge, MA 2000.

[9] Alting, L., Jorgensen, J.: The Life Cycle Concept as a Basis for Sustainable Industrial Production, Annals of the CIRP, 1993, vol. 42(1): 163–167.

[10] Fullana, P., Puig, R.: Análisis del ciclo de vida. Rubes Editorial S. L., Barcelona 1997.

[11] Kondoh, S., Umeda, Y., Yoshikawa, H.: Development of upgradable cellular machines for environmentally conscious products, Annals of the CIRP, 1998, Vol. 47(1): 381–394.

[12] Sheng, P., Bennet, D., Thurwachter, S.: Environmental-based systems for planning of machining, Annals of the CIRP, 1998, Vol. 47(1): 409–414.

[13] Steinhilper, R.: Remanufacturing—The Ultimate Form of Recycling, Stuttgart: Fraunhofer IRB 1998.

[14] Alting, L., Legarth, J. B.: Life cycle engineering and design, CIRP keynote paper, Annals of the CIRP, 1995, Vol. 44(2).

[15] Harjula, T., Rapoza, B., Knight, W. A., Boothroyd, G.: Design for disassembly and the environment, Annals of the CIRP, 1996, Vol. 45(1): 109–114.

[16] Blanchard, B.: Design and manage to life cycle cost, Portland, Or.: M/A Pr., 1978.

[17] Niemann, J.: Life Cycle Management, In: Bullinger, H.-J. (Hrsg.), Warnecke, H. J. (Hrsg.), Westkämper E. (Hrsg.), Neue Organisationsformen im Unternehmen—Ein Handbuch für das moderne Management, 2. neu bearbeitete und erweiterte Auflage, Berlin u. a.: Springer Verlag 2003.

[18] Kirk, S. J., Dell'Isola, A. J.: Life Cycle Costing for design professionals, McGraw-Hill, Inc., In: Siegwart, H., Senti, R., 1995, Product Life Cycle Management, Die Gestaltung eines intrierten Produktlebenszyklus, Schäffer Poeschel Verlag 1995.

[19] Schimmelpfeng, K.: Lebenszyklus-orientiertes Produktionssystemcontrolling, Deutscher Universitäts-Verlag GmbH, Wiesbaden 2002, zugl. Habilitationsschrift, Universität Hannover, 2001.

[20] Westkämper, E., Niemann, J.: Life Cycle Controlling for Manufacturing systems in web-based environments, In: CIRP u.a.: CIRP Design Seminar: Proceedings, 16–18 May, Hong Kong 2002.

[21] Kemminer, J.: Lebenszyklusorientiertes Kosten- und Erlösmanagement, Gabler Verlag Wiesbaden 1999.

[22] Wübbenhorst, K. L.: Lebenszykluskosten, in: Schulte, C. (Hrsg.), Effektives Kostenmanagement, Methoden und Implementierung, Schäffer-Poeschel-Verlag, Stuttgart 1992, S. 245–271.

[23] Niemann, J., Galis, M., Abrudan, I., Stolz, M.: The Transparent Machine. In: Parsaei, H. R. (Hrsg.) u.a.; Integrated Technology Systems: Design and Manufacturing Automation for the 21st Century:

5th International Conference on Engineering Design and Automation, 5–8 August, 2001, Las Vegas, USA. Prospect (KY), USA, 2001, 180–185.
[24] Xie, S. Q., Huang, H., Tu, Y. L.: A www-based information management system for rapid and integrated mould product development, International journal of advanced manufacturing technology, 2002; 20(1), S. 50–57.
[25] Cantamessa, M., Valentini, C.: Planning and managing manufacturing capacity when demand is subject to diffusion effects, International journal of production economics, Jul 2000; 66(3), S. 227–240.
[26] Rehman, S., Guenov, M. D.: A methodology for modelling manufacturing costs at conceptual design, Computer and industrial engineering, Dec 1998, 35(3-4), S. 623–626.
[27] Pritschow, G. u. a.: Tendenzen in der Steuerungs-und Antriebstechnik; in: wt Werkstattstechnik 88 (1998) 1/2; Springer VDI Verlag, Düsseldorf.
[28] Berger, R., Krüger, J., Neubert, A.: Internet-basierter Teleservice; in: Industrie Management 6/98, GITO-Verlag, Berlin.
[29] Lippert, W. (Hrsg.): Future Office: Corporate Identity und Corporate Culture; Geist und Stil der Firma, Metropolitan-Verlag, Düsseldorf, Berlin 2001.
[30] Westkämper, E., Niemann, J., Stolz, M.: Advanced Life Cycle Management in Digital and Virtual Structures. In: Chryssolouris, George (Hrsg.); University of Patras/Dept. of Mechanical Engineering and Aeronautics/Lab. for Manufacturing Systems and Automation: Technology and Challenges for the 21st Century: CIRP 34th International Seminar on Manufacturing Systems, 16–18 May, 2001, Athens, Greece. Athens, Greece, 2001, S. 1–5.
[31] Ueda, K., Vaario, J., Takeshita, T., Hatono, I.: An Emergent Synthetic Approach to Suppy Network, CIRP Annals, 1999, Volume 48(1).
[32] Rifkin, J.: Access, das Verschwinden des Eigentums, 2. Auflage, Campus Verlag, Frankfurt/New York, 2000.

PRODUCT REDESIGN AND PRICING IN RESPONSE TO COMPETITOR ENTRY: A MARKETING-PRODUCTION PERSPECTIVE

GEORGE C. HADJINICOLA AND K. RAVI KUMAR

1. INTRODUCTION

Markets are dynamic environments where competing firms are engaging in a continuous struggle to maintain their market position. Often, firms that have established their presence in the market, are forced to confront new firms attempting to enter the market. In addition, firms have to deal with new products offered by existing competitors. Consider for example the case of the computer hardware industry. The intensity of competition has increased primarily because of the reduced product life-cycles since firms introduce in the market new products every six months. In such cases, incumbent firms are forced to react by offering a new product themselves, either of equal quality or capability at a lower price or a more enhanced product at a premium price. Such firm reactions to market entry imply the continuous redesign of products, a phenomenon that comes contrary to the marketing disbelief that continuous design changes are optimal. Robinson (1988) found that only 4% of the incumbent firms react aggressively with product redesigns during the first year of entry and only 20% do so during the second year of entry. However, such behavior is no longer valid in various industries, such as the electronics and computer hardware industries.

In general, incumbent firms have an arsenal of methods to defend their market position, the majority of which are defensive marketing strategies. Defensive marketing strategies have been very well researched and applied in the marketplace. Such strategies include changes in the marketing mix such as price reductions, increased advertising and distribution expenditures, and product redesign, often referred to as product repositioning. Defensive manufacturing strategies have also been applied such as maintaining excess capacity to signal price war in the event of entry, locating facilities in crucial areas to deter entry, acquiring flexible manufacturing technology to adapt the product mix in a speedy and cost-efficient manner in response to attacking products, and by adopting make-to-stock policies to be more responsive to customer needs. Nevertheless, defending the firm's position is not the sole responsibility of a single function. All functions should be involved in the decision-making process since functional decisions are interrelated and the level of coordination among the functions determines the success of the defensive strategy. Kumar and Hadjinicola (1996) provide a discussion on defensive marketing and manufacturing strategies as well as ways on how to coordinate the two functional strategies in defending the firm's market position.

In this paper, our effort is to address management's concerns when defending the firm's market position upon entry. In particular, we address the following question: "Upon the entry of a new competitor in the market, how should a firm change its product design and price when both marketing and production factors are considered?" Note that product design is also referred to as product position, and henceforth these two equivalent definitions will be used interchangeably. Product designs are a focal concern for production managers since product redesigns affect the production process and eventually the overall production cost. To address the above question, we need a modeling framework that incorporates elements from marketing and production. The presence of an equilibrium before and after entry is a prerequisite to examine the firm's reaction, since it shows that the incumbent firms have accommodated the entrant firm to offer its new product at a certain price.

The seminal paper by Hauser and Shugan (1983) which describes the "Defender" model, laid the groundwork for the prediction of market outcomes in dynamic competitive scenarios when there is market entry. The Defender scenario, which included consumer choice models, a profit optimization model for firms, and industry interaction models depicting competitive gaming behavior among firms, analyzed the reactions of incumbent firms with respect to price, product position, advertising and distribution. Hauser and Shugan's results on defensive response to entry include price reductions for markets where consumer tastes are uniformly distributed. They also identify the existence of cases where defensive response to entry implies price increase. Furthermore, they identify conditions for product repositioning away (product improvement) and towards the attack. Subsequently, Kumar and Sudharshan (1988) and Gruca et al. (1992) investigate full equilibrium reactions under functional response representation for advertising and distribution and corroborate defensive price reductions. In a similar vein, Ansari et al. (1994) deal with the issue of competitive pricing and positioning in an industry where consumer preferences are allowed to be non-uniform. They use the Defender model to evaluate static equilibrium outcomes in environments with two, three, and four firms entering simultaneously. They also allow these firms to enter sequentially and predict equilibrium outcomes for dynamic scenarios wherein entry-deterrent behavior is allowed. They show that under certain conditions, neither minimal nor maximal differentiation in product positioning may be the equilibrium outcome.

A drawback of the above stream of research is the inability to deal with positioning equilibrium for an arbitrary number of firms. For example, Hauser and Shugan's (1983) positioning results are in partial equilibrium even though Hauser and Wernerfelt (1988) establish the existence of equilibrium for prices in the Defender model. The absence of a proof for the existence of an equilibrium in product positions is coupled with the complexity in the model which makes the analytical extraction of equilibrium (assuming they exist) strategies impossible. For example, Ansari et al. (1994) have to resort to search procedures using symbolic algebra software to establish existence of, and determine, equilibria. The non-existence of positional equilibrium is suggested even in the three-firm case when consumer preferences are highly polarized.

Similarly, Kumar and Sudharshan (1988) and Gruca et al. (1992) do not "allow" repositioning, using the argument that in the short run, repositioning is very expensive; the original positioning equilibrium is ensured by using sequential entry of firms (Lane, 1980). Gruca et al. (1992) prove the existence of a Nash equilibrium in prices, advertising, and distribution expenditures. In addition, in the product positioning literature, the notion of sequential games has been used to ensure the existence of an equilibrium in prices and positions. In these games, firms first choose the product positions and then their prices (Vandenbosch and Weinberg, 1995). Carpenter (1989) performed a sensitivity analysis in a competitive environment and observed changes in prices upon a firm's product repositioning. In his analysis, the price equilibrium was obtained after product positions were chosen for a two-dimensional, two-brand market.

The economics literature on spatial competition includes work on the simultaneous existence of an equilibrium point in prices and product positions. Specifically, using the logit model an equilibrium can be shown to exist in prices and positions. This equilibrium though is puerile in terms of defensive reactions. The position chosen by all firms in this equilibrium is the same, the center of the market, and prices are equal for all firms. Therefore, using this modeling approach will not assist us in determining the reaction of incumbent firms upon entry, since the attacker would position himself in the center of the market and price his product at the same level as the incumbent firms. Anderson et al. (1992) present an excellent review on spatial competition and the existence of equilibria in prices and positions.

Other studies on defensive responses to entry have established the presence of equilibrium for various elements of the marketing mix. For example, Gruca and Sudharshan (1991) showed the presence of equilibrium using the multinomial logit model for prices and marketing effort (marketing expenditures). Shankar (1997) examined the market's pioneer reactions in price, advertising, and sales force in different competitive games (both Nash and leader-follower games). These studies do not consider product redesign upon entry. Finally, the literature on the quality-price competition problem establishes the equilibrium point in prices and quality for the incumbent and entrant firms (Shaked and Sutton, 1982; Moorthy, 1988; Karla et al., 1998), assuming a fixed cost for the product.

The aim of this paper is twofold. First, to present a model that incorporates marketing and production variables and shows the existence of a Nash equilibrium in prices and product positions. Note that the existing literature on reactions to entry mentioned above, does not explicitly use production variables. Instead, production comes in the picture through the constant per unit cost of production. Second, given that the market can reach an equilibrium point upon entry, examine the changes in product design and price that the incumbent firms should undertake. To accomplish the above, the paper includes a modeling framework that adopts notions from marketing such as ideal points to dictate the attraction of the product to consumers, market shares, and pricing issues. The model also incorporates the production cost of the product, that depends on the level of the product's attributes, and thus is not assumed to be constant.

Using this modeling framework, we show the existence of a Nash equilibrium in prices and product positions for any number of competing firms, whether firms enter the market sequentially or simultaneously. Given that the market can reach an equilibrium upon entry, we analytically show that incumbent firms should lower their prices and more importantly, redesign their product with features closer to the market's ideal point. Even though product redesign may not be undertaken immediately after the entry of a new competitor, the results of this paper set the long-term direction that a firm should have as its product design policy. Furthermore, numerical examples show that the profits of firms entering the market can be higher than the profits of incumbent firms. This occurs because the model allows firms to have different production capabilities through different costs for furnishing the products with their attributes.

The organization of the paper is follows. Section 2 presents the model formulation using the marketing and production variables. Section 3 describes and provides comments on the proof of the existence of a Nash equilibrium in prices and product positions. Section 4 presents the incumbent firms' product and price responses upon market entry. Section 5 includes numerical examples and sensitivity analysis. Finally, Section 6 contains a summary and directions for future research.

2. MODEL FORMULATION

Products can be abstractly represented as a set of coordinates in an attribute space. Each dimension in the attribute space designates a product characteristic, for example, the level of sweetness of a chocolate which translates into the per unit volume sugar content. Realizations of these attribute dimensions in the form of coordinates should be meaningful to both users and manufacturers. Shocker and Srinivasan (1974, p. 922) stated that attributes should be actionable, that is, "indicate specific actions the manufacturer must take to build the product." Under this framework, each consumer is assumed to have a set of most preferred attributes termed the *ideal point*. The greater the proximity of the product offering in the attribute space to the consumers' ideal point, the greater the product *attraction* (appeal), and in general, the propensity/probability that consumers will purchase the product. McFadden (1986) provides a review on deterministic and probabilistic choice models related to consumer buying behavior. Attraction has also been assumed to be a function of other factors such as price where, for example, attraction decreases when price increases.

2.1. Model notation

For the formulation of the model we use the following notation:

k : firm index
N : number of competing firms
i : attribute index
L : number of attributes
b : price elasticity of demand
Y : consumers' average income
Q : market sales potential
$\mathbf{x}^*$: an $L \times 1$ vector containing the attribute coordinates of the market's ideal point. Its elements are denoted by x_i^*
$\mathbf{W}$: an $L \times L$ diagonal matrix whose diagonal elements w_i, denote the weight consumers place on attribute i
$\boldsymbol{\beta}_\mathbf{k}$: an $L \times 1$ vector containing the costs for furnishing a product with one unit of a specific attribute by firm k. Its elements are denoted by β_{ki}
P_k : price of the product offered by firm k
$\mathbf{x}_\mathbf{k}$: an $L \times 1$ vector containing the attribute coordinates of the product offered by firm k. Its elements are denoted by x_{ki}.

2.2. Attraction and market share models

Market share models have been used to predict a firm's market share in a competitive environment and appear in linear, multiplicative, and exponential forms. These three forms of market share models are not *logically consistent* (McGuire et al., 1968), a property which states that market share models should predict market shares between zero and one and also sum to unity. As described by Cooper and Nakanishi (1988), logically consistent market share models use the relationship (us/(us+them)) to capture the market share of a firm in a competitive environment. Kotler (1965), for example, stated that the market share of a firm is equal to the ratio of its marketing effort (a function of price, advertising and distribution expenditures) to the sum of the marketing effort of all firms. Bell et al. (1975) consider the market share of a firm to be the ratio of the *attraction* that consumers feel towards a particular brand to the sum of the attractions of the brands of all competing firms.

We model competition between firms through Multiplicative Competitive Interaction (MCI) market share models, also known as attraction models (Gruca et al., 1992). These models have the advantage that with the use of linearizing transformations, their estimation can be achieved through simple econometric methods such as OLS and GLS (Nakanishi and Cooper, 1982). Specifically, we employ the model:

$$M_k = Attr_k \Big/ \sum_{k=1}^{N} Attr_k, \quad k = 1, \ldots, N, \tag{1}$$

where M_k is the market share and $Attr_k$ is the product attraction of firm k. Attraction can be viewed as a measure of the "willingness" of consumers to purchase a product, and in studies by Cooper and Nakanishi (1988), Kumar and Sudharshan (1988), and Gruca et al. (1992) has been modeled as:

$$Attr = f(\mathbf{x})g(P).$$

$f(\mathbf{x})$ is a function of the product position relative to the ideal point (the smaller the distance, the higher the value of the function). $g(P)$ is a downsloping function of price. In this model, we neglect the effects of advertising and distribution in order to simplify the analysis. Following Shocker and Srinivasan (1974) who modeled the distance of the product offering to the ideal point as a weighted Euclidean distance, we define the function $f_k(\mathbf{x_k})$ for firm k as:

$$f_k(\mathbf{x_k}) = 1 - \left[\sum_{i=1}^{L} w_i (x_i^* - x_{ki})^2 \bigg/ \sum_{i=1}^{L} w_i x_i^{*2}\right] = 1 - [(\mathbf{x}^* - \mathbf{x_k})' \mathbf{W}(\mathbf{x}^* - \mathbf{x_k})/(\mathbf{x}^{*'} \mathbf{W}\mathbf{x}^*)], \quad (2)$$

The functional form of $f_k(\mathbf{x_k})$ indicates that the smaller the distance to the ideal point, the larger the value of the function. We assume that $0 \leq \mathbf{x_k} \leq 2\mathbf{x}^*$ which further implies that $0 \leq f_k(\mathbf{x_k}) \leq 1$. The reason for restricting the space of the vector containing the coordinates of the product attributes is that the model presented in this paper is valid only in that range. One way to justify such a restriction is the fact that products which lie outside the above hyper-ellipsoid will have limited appeal to consumers and thus be unprofitable to produce.

In the product positioning literature, the optimal product position is usually derived after considering an ideal point for each and every consumer (Alberts and Brockoff, 1977). In order to simplify our analysis, we assume that the market has one ideal point (like Sudharshan et al., 1988 and Eliashberg and Manrai, 1992). This is a valid perspective when consumer ideal points are distributed around what is termed the market's ideal point or when considering the single ideal point as the median value of consumers' ideal points. Nevertheless, this is a limitation of this study.

We define the function $g_k(P_k) = (1 - (bP_k/Y))$, linearizing Gruca's et al. (1992) nonlinear function $g(P) = (Y - P)^b$. We assume that $P_k \leq Y/b$, where Y/b is the market's reservation price. This ensures a downsloping function of price, consistent with economic theory for competitive products. Under the above assumptions, it follows that $0 \leq g_k(P_k) \leq 1$, and since $0 \leq f_k(\mathbf{x_k}) \leq 1$ also follows that product attraction assumes values in [0, 1]. Summarizing, the product attraction for firm k is defined as:

$$Attr_k = f_k(\mathbf{x_k})g_k(P_k) = [1 - ((\mathbf{x}^* - \mathbf{x_k})' \mathbf{W}(\mathbf{x}^* - \mathbf{x_k})/(\mathbf{x}^{*'} \mathbf{W}\mathbf{x}^*))][1 - (bP_k/Y)]. \quad (3)$$

Note that with the above modelling framework, for a given price, attraction is the same for $x_{ki} = x_i^* + \Delta$ and $x_{ki} = x_i^* - \Delta$. This assumption is valid for attributes like the sweetness of a soft-drink or the width of a car where, regardless of price, a consumer will prefer an intermediate value to either low or high values. However, for attributes such as safety or fuel economy, the ideal point will be determined by a trade-off between the benefit from a high value of the attribute and the price the consumer will have to pay to get it. Thus, the decline in attraction at attribute values above the ideal point, even when price is the same, may not be valid. To compensate for this, for attributes like safety and fuel economy though, if price is not considered, the ideal point is determined by what is technologically possible and, as a consequence, the highest attribute value any firm can offer is bounded above by that ideal point.

2.3. Profit maximization objective

Firms are assumed to adopt a profit maximization objective with the profit function of firm k ($k = 1, \ldots, N$) given by:

$$\Pi_k = [P_k - \beta_{\mathbf{k}}' \cdot \mathbf{x_k}] M_k Q. \tag{4}$$

In this formulation, we assume that the cost of firm k to furnish a product with its attributes (given by $\mathbf{x_k}$) is given by $\beta_{\mathbf{k}}' \cdot \mathbf{x_k}$. This assumption implies that the cost of production depends on the nature of the product, determined by its position (coordinates) in the joint attribute space. This is based on the fact that furnishing a product with a larger quantity of a particular attribute should require higher cost.

Note that we assume a linear relationship between the cost of furnishing a product with its attributes (given by $\mathbf{x_k}$) and the magnitude of these attributes. Other authors, for example, Bachem and Simon (1981) and Choi et al. (1990) also present product positioning models that utilize a cost function which increases linearly with increasing attribute levels. Firm k will attempt to maximize its profits through the selection of its optimal product position and pricing policy. The profit maximization program of firm k is given by:

$$\max_{P_k, \mathbf{x_k}} \Pi_k, \quad k = 1, \ldots, N. \tag{5}$$

3. EXISTENCE OF A NASH EQUILIBRIUM

In our framework, N firms compete in a noncooperative way in a single market by selecting their price and product position. The notion of Nash equilibrium (Nash, 1951) in a noncooperative game states that, at Nash equilibrium no firm has the incentive to change its strategy. Friedman (1990, p. 64) describes an N-person noncooperative game and provides conditions and assumptions for the existence and uniqueness of a Nash equilibrium. Specifically, he shows that the existence of a Nash equilibrium is based on three conditions: (1) the strategy space of each player (firm) is compact and convex; (2) the payoff function of each player, in our case the profit function, is continuous; (3) the payoff function of each player is quasiconcave in its strategy, in our case its product's price and position. The lemmas that follow are used for the proof of the existence of a Nash equilibrium in prices and product positions for N firms competing in the same market.

Lemma 1. *If a Nash equilibrium in prices and product positions exists, then it will exist for* $\mathbf{x_k} \in (\mathbf{0}, \mathbf{x}^*),\ k = 1, \ldots, N.$

Proof of Lemma 1: See Appendix A. □

Lemma 1 establishes bounds on the product's attributes for the N firms in the case that a Nash equilibrium in product positions exists. If the product attribute levels tend to zero, implying no product offering, the firm in question attains zero profits regardless of the competing firms' prices and product positions. This establishes a disincentive for a firm to set the product attribute levels to zero, bounding the solution space of product attribute levels from below.

The lemma presents a more interesting result related to the upper bound of the solution space of the product attribute levels, namely the solution space is bounded by the consumers' ideal point. Intuitively, this occurs because a product with attribute levels above the ideal point is more expensive than a product equidistant to the ideal point and with attribute levels below the ideal point.

Lemma 2. *If a Nash equilibrium in prices and positions exists, then it will exist for* $P_k \in (0, Y/b),\ k = 1, \ldots, N.$

Proof of Lemma 2: See Appendix A. □

In a similar fashion as in Lemma 1, Lemma 2 establishes the solution region for prices for a possible Nash equilibrium in prices and product positions. At the limiting price Y/b, which represents the maximum price consumers can bear (reservation price), profits drop to zero regardless of the competing firms' product and pricing strategy. This, as discussed before, discourages the firm to price its product at such a high price. The lower bound follows from the fact that price has to be positive.

Lemma 3. *For* $\mathbf{x_k} \in (\mathbf{0}, \mathbf{x}^*)$, $P_k \in (0, Y/b)$, *and if* $P_k - \boldsymbol{\beta}_{\mathbf{k}}' \cdot \mathbf{x_k} \geq 0$, *the following hold true: (i)* $\partial^2\Pi_k/\partial x_{ki}^2 < 0$ *and (ii)* $\partial^2\Pi_k/\partial P_k^2 < 0$.

Proof of Lemma 3: See Appendix A. □

Lemma 3 presents the necessary conditions, those in Lemmas 1 and 2 and that the price of the product must be greater or equal to the production cost, that ensure that the second derivative of the profit function with respect to price and individual product attributes are negative. This is a necessary condition for maximization programs and guarantees quasi-concavity of the profit function, a necessary condition for the existence of a Nash equilibrium.

Note that Lemma 3 has been derived using a linear cost function that relates the cost of the product with its attribute levels. However, other cost functions such as convex or concave functions can be used, as long as the conditions are identified which ensure that the second derivatives of the objective function with respect to price and individual product attributes are negative. This will ensure the existence of a Nash equilibrium after entry occurs.

Theorem 1 *Consider the game with N players whose profit functions are given as in (4) on the compact and convex set* $S_k = \{[0+\epsilon, Y/b - \epsilon] \times [\mathbf{0}+\epsilon, \mathbf{x}^* - \epsilon] : P_k \in [0+\epsilon, Y/b - \epsilon], \mathbf{x_k} \in [\mathbf{0}+\epsilon, \mathbf{x}^* - \epsilon], P_k - \beta_{\mathbf{k}}' \cdot \mathbf{x_k} \geq 0, \}$ *where* ϵ *is an infinitesimal value. Then, there exists a unique Nash equilibrium in prices and product positions in* $S_1 \times \cdots \times S_N$.

Proof of Theorem 1: See Appendix A. □

The lemmas and theorem of this section present the result that a Nash equilibrium in both prices and product positions does exist. The existence of Nash in product positions has been addressed in a number of studies such as Hotelling (1929), Graitson (1982), and Gabszewicz and Thisse (1986). More recent discussion on the issue can be found in Hauser (1988), Ansari et al. (1994), and Anderson et al. (1992). These studies on spatial competition focus on a market where consumer preferences are assumed to be distributed, in most cases uniformly, in a one-dimensional space. Hotelling (1929) showed that under fixed prices, firms would tend to position their products in the center of the distribution in order to capture the maximum possible market share. Incorporation of prices into Hotelling's framework shows that a simultaneous price and product position Nash equilibrium may not exist due to price undercutting.

The results obtained in this study come contrary to the work on spatial competition primarily due to three differences present in the problem formulation. First, the literature on spatial competition assumes a distribution of consumer preferences whereas in this study we use a single ideal point, specifically the mode or median of the distribution. Second, in spatial competition, utility functions lead to consumer choice. Aggregation of individual choices leads to product demand. In this study, attraction functions are the building blocks of choice. Attractions from all competitors form each competitor's market share. Third, in spatial competition demand functions depend on price ordering and relative product positions. This results in discontinuous profit functions. In this study, demand functions do not depend on price or product position ordering, resulting in continuous market share and profit functions. The continuity of market share, and profit functions is the underlying factor leading to a Nash equilibrium in prices and product positions. In particular, the market share function is everywhere defined, positive and continuous, yielding positive profit margins. In the case where the firms have the same production capabilities, the Nash solution will be symmetric, i.e. me-too products and pricing. More importantly, the firms can obtain non-zero profits in a symmetric equilibrium. In spatial competition, such a scenario would have led to intense price competition and absence of equilibrium. We also show that since the objective function is strictly quasiconcave in price and product position, the obtained Nash equilibrium is unique (Friedman, 1990).

4. PRODUCT AND PRICE RESPONSES TO MARKET ENTRY

The existence of the Nash equilibrium, proven in the previous section, is independent of the number of firms present in the market. This means that a market at equilibrium, will once again reach a new equilibrium upon entry of a new competitor. Note that the proof of the existence of a Nash equilibrium in prices and product positions does not restrict the entry to sequential (one firm enters at a time), and it can accommodate the case where two or more firms enter the market simultaneously.

The fact that the market can reach an equilibrium point enables us to determine how incumbent firms will redesign and price their products after entry occurs. In general, upon market entry, an incumbent firm can respond in one of four ways concerning product design and price: (1) decrease price/decrease product features; (2) decrease price/increase product features; (3) increase price/decrease product features; and (4) increase price/increase product features. Note that an increase in the product's features implies that the product design moves closer to the market's ideal point. The lemmas and theorem that follow will identify the optimal defensive marketing strategy.

Lemma 4. *If at the Nash equilibrium in prices and product positions, we treat the market share as an exogenous parameter, then the price of firm k increases (decreases) when the exogenous market share increases (decreases).*

Proof of Lemma 4: See Appendix B. □

Lemma 5. *If at the Nash equilibrium in prices and product positions, we treat the market share as an exogenous parameter, then the product attribute i of firm k decreases (increases) when the exogenous market share increases (decreases).*

Proof of Lemma 5: See Appendix B. □

Lemmas 4 and 5 indicate that when competing firms have reached a Nash equilibrium, upon a change in an incumbent's market share, its optimal price and product position reaction will move in opposite directions. This implies that upon entry, and thus change in the incumbents' market share, incumbents will react in one of two ways: increase price and decrease product attribute values or decrease price and increase product attribute values. Such a market share change may be forced on the incumbent firms by either an entrant firm that captures some of the incumbents' market share or by an existing firm whose repricing or repositioning actions alter the other incumbent firms market share.

Consider for example the case where a firm enters the market successfully. Presumably, the entrant firm will capture some market share from the incumbent firms. The reduction of the incumbent firms' market share, according to the above lemmas, will result in the defensive mechanism of reducing prices. By decreasing their prices, incumbent firms try to improve their attraction. Similarly, incumbent firms will increase their products' features so as to increase their products' attraction.

Note that from equations (1) and (3) which describe the market share of firm k, we see that as the price of a firm increases and/or the product position decreases, the market share decreases. This at first sight contradicts the results of Lemmas 4 and 5. However, we need to point out that the above lemmas are derived under the assumption that the market share is an exogenous parameter and not a function of price and product position. The reason for doing this is to observe the direction of change of the Nash equilibrium prices and product positions upon a change in the market share.

Theorem 2 *Consider a market where a Nash equilibrium in prices and product positions exists for the firms already in the market. Upon viable market entry, the incumbent firms will respond by decreasing their prices and redesign their products by increasing their features.*

Proof of Theorem 2: See Appendix B. □

The important result presented in Theorem 2 is that incumbent firms respond to market entry by redesigning their products. This redesign is characterized by an increase in the features of the product which further implies that the firm will design a product closer to the market's ideal point. Incumbent firms will increase the features of their products in an effort to increase the attraction of their product which will assist them in retaining some of the market share lost to the entrant firm(s). Hauser and Shugan (1983) also suggest that upon entry, product improvement by the incumbent firms is an optimal strategy, even though their result was not obtain in the presence of full equilibrium after entry. Redesigning a product immediately after the entry of a new competitor in the market may not be plausible. Nevertheless, the results of this paper show managers that in the long-run, products should be redesigned in response to market entry. In addition, Theorem 2 suggests that upon entry, incumbent firms should reduce their price. The reduction of price upon entry is consistent with the findings of the work of Hauser and Shugan (1983), Kumar and Sudharshan (1988), Gruca, et al. (1992), and Karla et al. (1998). Incumbent firms, in their attempt to sustain the attraction of their products in the presence of new competition, decrease their price.

Theorem 2 implies that every time a firm enters the market, the price and product position of the incumbent firms changes. This is different from the work of Lane (1980) who examines the cases of exogenous entry (the number of firms entering the market is exogenously given) and endogenous entry (firms enter the market as long as they derive positive profits). In Lane's paper, the position (price and product) that firms choose to enter the market remains the same when later entrants flood the market. Firms choose their positions with the foresight of later entrants. Sequential entry and fixed product positions were chosen by Lane in order to accommodate an equilibrium in product positions. The model in this paper allows the entry of any number of firms whether sequentially (one firm enters the market at a time) or simultaneously (two of more firms enter the market at a time). This stems from the fact that a Nash equilibrium exists for any number of firms, as long as they all derive positive profits.

5. NUMERICAL EXAMPLE AND SENSITIVITY ANALYSIS

To illustrate product redesign and price changes upon market entry, we initially consider a market with two competing firms whose products have a single attribute. The market with its two firms, has reached its equilibrium point in prices and product positions.

Table 1 Nash equilibrium product positions, prices, and profits for competing firms

Firm (k)	Product (x_{k1})	Price (P_k)	Market Share (M_k)	Profit (Π_k)
1	3.9348	44.7390	0.5183	5732.53
2	3.3520	44.5979	0.4817	4991.93
1	4.1522	41.4046	0.3627	3601.50
2	3.5776	41.7808	0.3327	3098.69
3	3.1099	41.9675	0.3046	2698.61
1	4.2472	39.6066	0.2642	2465.66
2	3.6805	40.2911	0.2407	2112.22
3	3.2059	40.7160	0.2190	1832.50
4	4.5578	39.1263	0.2761	2674.76
1	4.2927	38.6517	0.2068	1865.39
2	3.7309	39.5052	0.1878	1595.35
3	3.2536	40.0607	0.1704	1382.09
4	4.5963	38.0729	0.2165	2025.44
5	4.6579	37.9432	0.2185	2059.61

We then consider the case where a firm or firms enter the market. For the numerical example, the following set of parameter values is used:

$$b = 1.6 \quad Y = 100 \quad Q = 300 \quad w_1 = 1.0 \quad x_1^* = 5.5$$
$$\beta_{11} = 2.0 \quad \beta_{21} = 3.0 \quad \beta_{31} = 4.0 \quad \beta_{41} = 1.5 \quad \beta_{51} = 1.4$$

Table 1 presents the Nash equilibrium in prices and product positions for the cases where the market has 2, 3, 4, and 5 competing firms. These values are obtained from the solution of the set of nonlinear first order conditions of all competing firms, in terms of their prices and product positions, using *Newton's successive relaxation method* (Schwartz, 1989, p. 224).

If we consider the case where two firms are present in the market and then the third firm enters the market, we observe that firms 1 and 2 reduce their prices and redesign their products by increasing their features. Similarly, we can observe the same defensive reaction when firms 1, 2, and 3 are in the market and firm 4 enters, or when firms 1, 2, 3, and 4 are in the market and firm 5 enters.

Note that the above scenario implies sequential entry where one firm enters the market at a time. If though two firms enter the market at a time, for example firms 1 and 2 are in the market and firms 3 and 4 enter the market, then the prices and product positions that would constitute the Nash equilibrium are the same as in the case where firms 3 and 4 enter the market sequentially. In the case of sequential entry, firms 1 and 2 would change their prices and redesign their products when firm 3 enters the market. Subsequently, firms 1, 2 and 3 would change again their prices and redesign their products to reach the Nash equilibrium with four firms. These values are given in Table 1. The reason why prices and product positions are not affected by the mode of entry but by the number of firms is that every time a firm enters, the Nash equilibrium is recomputed for the specific number of firms present in the market.

From the results of Table 1, we see that the profits of the incumbent firms decrease when firms enter the market. This is intuitive since the new entrant captures some market share. Furthermore, incumbent firms, according to Theorem 2, will lower their prices, and increase the features of their products which implies an increase in the products' cost. From Table 1, we also see that the profits of later entrants can be higher than the profits of incumbent firms, see for example the case where firms 1, 2, and 3 are in the market and firm 4 enters the market. This phenomenon occurs because the model allows firms to have different production capabilities. Specifically, the model allows firms to have different costs for furnishing their products with their attributes. As a result, if a later entrant firm's technology allows him to have lower costs for producing its product than the incumbent firms, then this firm can obtain higher profits upon entry than the incumbent firms.

Markets are dynamic environments characterized by changes in the factors affecting the performance of the firm. Such factors may be firm-specific or market-specific. To assess the impact that the model's parameters have on the prices and product positions of the competing firms at the equilibrium point, we define $\partial\Pi/\partial x_{ki} = q_{ki}$ and $\partial\Pi/\partial P_k = p_k$ for $k = 1, \ldots, N$ and $i = 1, \ldots, L$. These functions can be derived from the profit functions of each competing firm. The first order conditions imply that $q_{ki} = 0$ and $p_k = 0$. Using the chain rule, total differentiation of the above functions with respect to one of the parameters, e.g. θ, gives a system of equations which can be presented in matrix form. For the sake of demonstration, we present this matrix for the case where two firms are competing ($k = 1, 2$) and the products have L attribute ($i = 1, \ldots, L$). The methodology can be easily generalized for cases with any number of competing firms.

$$\begin{bmatrix}
\partial p_1/\partial P_1 & \partial p_1/\partial P_2 & \partial p_1/\partial x_{11} & \cdots & \partial p_1/\partial x_{1L} & \partial p_1/\partial x_{21} & \cdots & \partial p_1/\partial x_{2L} \\
\partial p_2/\partial P_1 & \partial p_2/\partial P_2 & \partial p_2/\partial x_{11} & \cdots & \partial p_2/\partial x_{1L} & \partial p_2/\partial x_{21} & \cdots & \partial p_2/\partial x_{2L} \\
\partial q_{11}/\partial P_1 & \partial q_{11}/\partial P_2 & \partial q_{11}/\partial x_{11} & \cdots & \partial q_{11}/\partial x_{1L} & \partial q_{11}/\partial x_{21} & \cdots & \partial q_{11}/\partial x_{2L} \\
\vdots & \vdots & \vdots & \cdots & \vdots & \vdots & \cdots & \vdots \\
\partial q_{1L}/\partial P_1 & \partial q_{1L}/\partial P_2 & \partial q_{1L}/\partial x_{1L} & \cdots & \partial q_{1L}/\partial x_{1L} & \partial q_{1L}/\partial x_{21} & \cdots & \partial q_{1L}/\partial x_{2L} \\
\partial q_{21}/\partial P_1 & \partial q_{21}/\partial P_2 & \partial q_{21}/\partial x_{11} & \cdots & \partial q_{21}/\partial x_{1L} & \partial q_{21}/\partial x_{21} & \cdots & \partial q_{21}/\partial x_{2L} \\
\vdots & \vdots & \vdots & \cdots & \vdots & \vdots & \cdots & \vdots \\
\partial q_{2L}/\partial P_1 & \partial q_{2L}/\partial P_2 & \partial q_{2L}/\partial x_{1L} & \cdots & \partial q_{2L}/\partial x_{1L} & \partial q_{2L}/\partial x_{21} & \cdots & \partial q_{2L}/\partial x_{2L}
\end{bmatrix}$$

$$\times \begin{bmatrix}
\partial P_1/\partial\theta \\
\partial P_2/\partial\theta \\
\partial x_{11}/\partial\theta \\
\vdots \\
\partial x_{1L}/\partial\theta \\
\partial x_{21}/\partial\theta \\
\vdots \\
\partial x_{2L}/\partial\theta
\end{bmatrix} = -\begin{bmatrix}
\partial p_1/\partial\theta \\
\partial p_2/\partial\theta \\
\partial q_{11}/\partial\theta \\
\vdots \\
\partial q_{1L}/\partial\theta \\
\partial q_{21}/\partial\theta \\
\vdots \\
\partial q_{2L}/\partial\theta
\end{bmatrix}.$$

The above system of equations can be written as $\mathbf{Ax} = -\mathbf{b}$. The vector $\mathbf{x}$ contains the directions of change at the optimal profit point of all variables such as prices and product positions with respect to some parameter θ. This parameter can be a market-specific parameter such as b, Y, w_i, Q, as well as a firm-specific parameter such as β_{ki}. The direction of change of the variables with respect to the parameter can not be stated explicitly, because of the complexity of the functions and dimension of the problem. Numerical techniques can assist us to determine the direction of change of the variables with respect to the parameters.

Figures 1 and 2 demonstrate the direction of change of the product positions and prices of three firms, when the cost of furnishing attribute dimension 1 of firm 3 increases, and when price sensitivity increases. For the computations presented in the figures if the parameters are not treated as variables, they assume the values given at the beginning of this section. Figure 1 shows that as the cost of furnishing the attribute dimension 1 of firm 3 increases, the increase in cost is reflected in a higher price and a product design with features further away from the ideal point, for firm 3, inevitably leading to lower profits. The two competing firms respond to firm 3's increased price (due to higher production cost) by increasing their own prices and designing their products further away from the ideal point, enabling them to obtain higher prices. Figure 2. shows that as the price sensitivity increases, all competing firms reduce their prices and design products with lower features. In other words, the firms offer products with less features and lower prices in an effort to attract the price sensitive consumers. This of course leads to lower profits. The above discussion clearly shows that the modeling framework presented in this paper follows traditional economic laws.

6. CONCLUSION

Firms are often called to make decisions on how to respond to the entry of a new competitor in the market. The incumbent firms' functions are called to devise defensive strategies in order to confront the entrant firm. As such, defensive marketing and manufacturing strategies are visible in practice. In this paper, we examine the issue of product redesign and pricing upon the entry of a new competitor in the market when both marketing and production variables are considered.

We employ a model that adopts marketing notions such as market shares and ideal points. The model also incorporates production costs where the cost of the product increases linearly with increasing product attribute levels. The modeling framework facilitates the existence of a Nash equilibrium in prices and product positions for any number of competing firms, unlike other spatial location models. The equilibrium exists whether firms enter the market sequentially or simultaneously. Given that the market can reach an equilibrium upon entry, we show that incumbent firms should lower their prices and more importantly, redesign their product with features closer to the market's ideal point. In addition, through a sensitivity analysis we demonstrate how the model's firm-specific and market-specific parameters affect product designs and prices. A numerical example demonstrates that because of varying production capabilities, entrant firms may obtain higher profits than the incumbent firms.

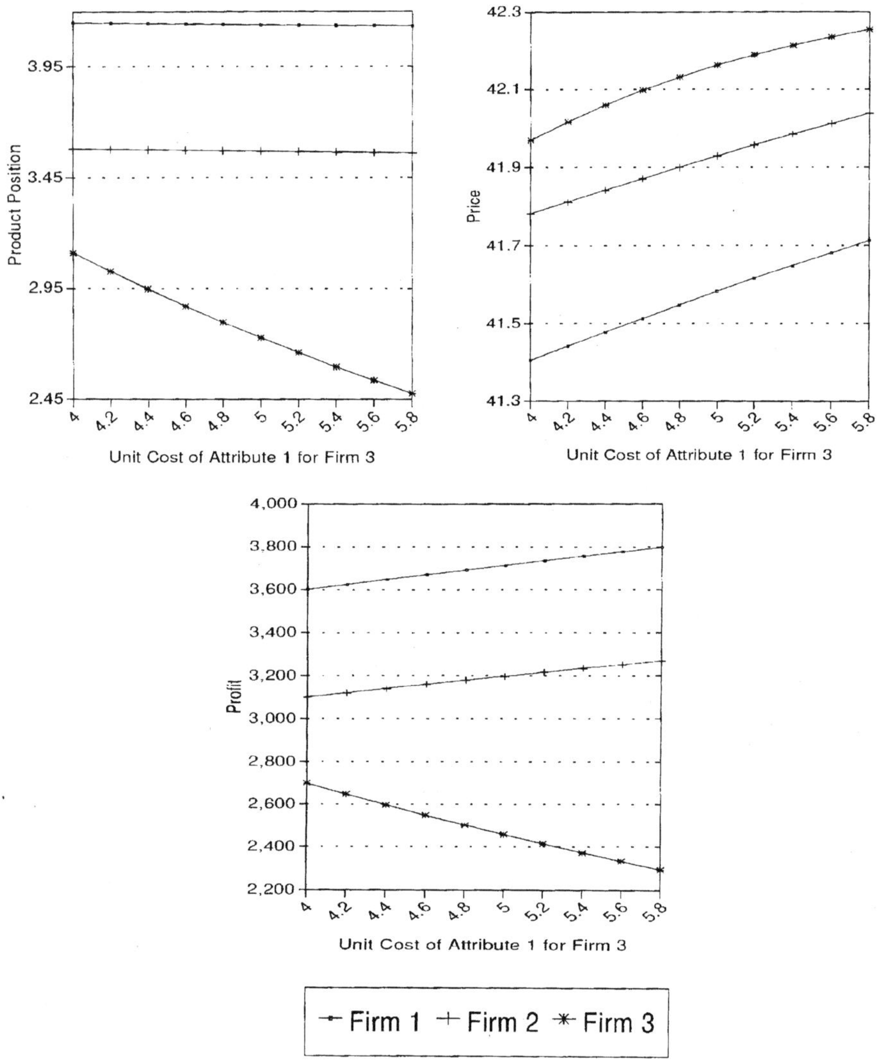

Figure 1. Nash equilibrium product positions, prices, and profits when the cost of furnishing the attribute dimension 1 of firm 3 (β_{31}) changes.

Research can be extended in several directions. First, product redesign is closely related with the stage that the product has reached in its product life-cycle. Therefore, the type of product redesign upon entry must be examined in conjunction with the product's life-cycle. Second, the modeling framework can be used to evaluate incumbent product redesigns when firms operate in segmented markets where more ideal points need to be considered, and more than one products need to be offered. Issues

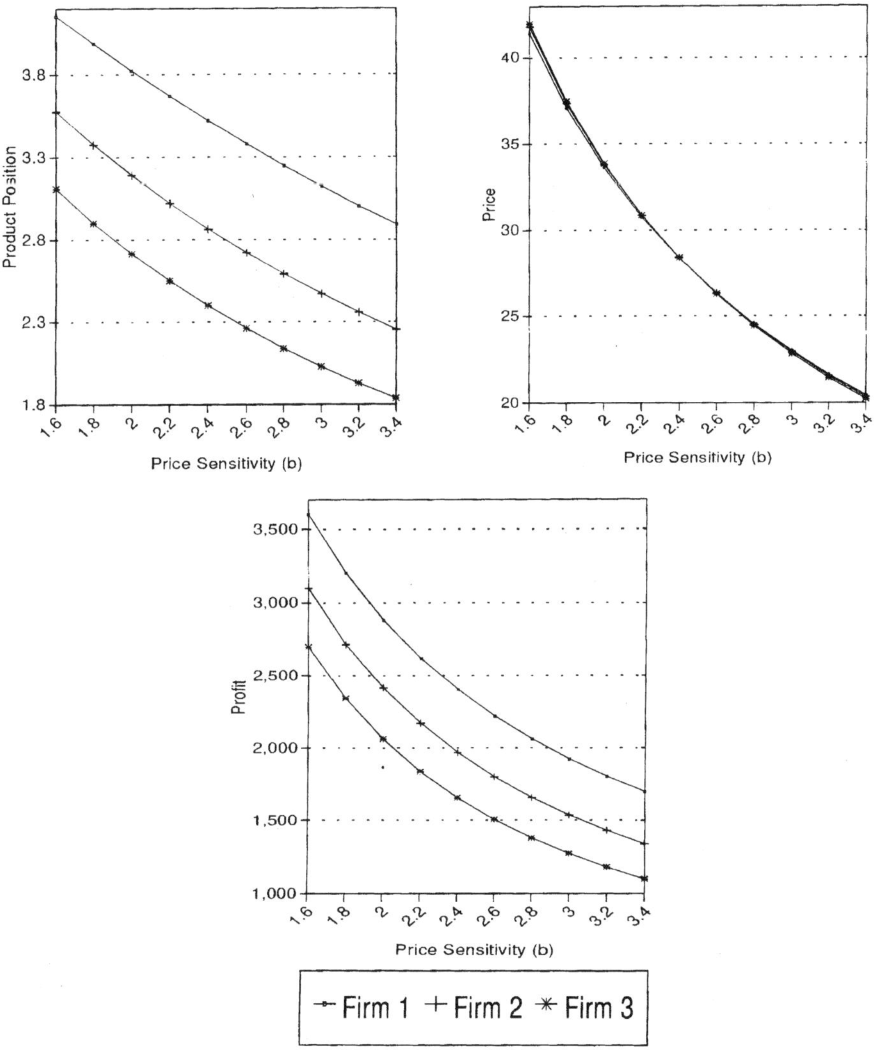

Figure 2. Nash equilibrium product positions, prices, and profits when the price sensitivity (b) changes.

to be examined here include the possibility of abandoning a segment upon the entry of a strong competitor. Third, the modeling framework could be used to examine the impact of the number of competitors on product diversity, prices, and industry profitability. Finally, the major theorems in this paper characterize the new product positions and prices upon entry without considering the redesign process and its associated time frames. Therefore, a direction of future research could examine how sensitive the new product positions are when the above factors are taken into consideration.

APPENDIX A

Proof of Lemma 1: Using (4) we get

$$\lim_{\mathbf{x_k}\to\mathbf{0}} \Pi_k = \lim_{\mathbf{x_k}\to\mathbf{0}} [P_k - \beta'_{\mathbf{k}} \cdot \mathbf{x_k}] M_k Q = Q\left\{\lim_{\mathbf{x_k}\to\mathbf{0}} [P_k - \beta'_{\mathbf{k}} \cdot \mathbf{x_k}]\right\}\left\{\lim_{\mathbf{x_k}\to\mathbf{0}} M_k\right\} = QP_k \times 0 = 0, \quad (6)$$

as long as at least one of the other firms offers a product with attractiveness greater than zero. Next note that for a given P_k, attractiveness is symmetric in attribute value around the ideal point of that attribute. Thus, for any given $x_{ki} > x_i^*$, there is an $x_{ki} < x_i^*$ which generates the same market share at a lower cost, i.e., gives a higher profit. This establishes that $\mathbf{x_k} < \mathbf{x}^*$. To show that $\mathbf{x}^*$ is not included in the solution set, let $\Pi_k = \pi_k(M_k(\mathbf{x_k}), \mathbf{x_k})$. Then for an attribute dimension i follows that

$$\frac{\partial \Pi_k}{\partial x_{ki}} = \frac{\partial \pi_k}{\partial M_k}\frac{\partial M_k}{\partial x_{ki}} + \frac{\partial \pi_k}{\partial x_{ki}}, \quad (7)$$

Using (4) and (7) we obtain the first order condition

$$\partial \Pi_k / \partial x_{ki} = [P_k - \beta'_{\mathbf{k}} \cdot \mathbf{x_k}](\partial M_k / \partial x_{ki}) Q - \beta_{ki} M_k Q = 0. \quad (8)$$

Rearranging and simplifying (8) we obtain

$$[P_k - \beta'_{\mathbf{k}} \cdot \mathbf{x_k}] = \beta_{ki} M_k / (\partial M_k / \partial x_{ki}). \quad (9)$$

For the problem to have a solution, the left hand side of (9), which represents the profit margin, must be non-negative. Therefore, the right hand side of (9) must be non-negative as well. Using the fact that if a solution exists it is implied that $M_k > 0$, $1 - M_k > 0$, the right hand side of (9) should satisfy

$$\beta_{ki} / (\partial M_k / \partial x_{ki}) \geq 0. \quad (10)$$

From (1) and (3) follows that

$$\partial M_k / \partial x_{ki} = (\partial M_k / \partial f_k)(\partial f_k / \partial x_{ki}), \quad (11)$$

and that if a solution exists that

$$\partial M_k / \partial f_k = M_k(1 - M_k) / f_k > 0. \quad (12)$$

Furthermore, using (2) we derive

$$\partial f_k / \partial x_{ki} = [-2w_i(x_{ki} - x_i^*)] \Big/ \sum_{i=1}^{L} w_i (x_i^*)^2. \quad (13)$$

If $x_{ki} = x_i^*$ then from (13) follows that $\partial f_k(x_i^*)/\partial x_{ki} = 0$ and therefore, from (11) that $\partial M_k(x_i^*)/\partial x_{ki} = 0$. This implies that (8) gives, $\partial \Pi_k(x_i^*)/\partial x_{ki} = -\beta_{ki} M_k Q < 0$. Since the first order condition in (8) is not met, the point x_{ki}^*, $i = 1, \ldots, L$, may not be included in the solution set. □

Proof of Lemma 2: Using (4) we get

$$\lim_{P_k \to Y/b} \Pi_k = \lim_{P_k \to Y/b} [P_k - \beta_{\mathbf{k}}' \cdot \mathbf{x_k}] M_k Q = Q\left\{\lim_{P_k \to Y/b} [P_k - \beta_{\mathbf{k}}' \cdot \mathbf{x_k}]\right\}\left\{\lim_{P_k \to Y/b} M_k\right\}$$
$$= Q[(Y/b) - \beta_{\mathbf{k}}' \cdot \mathbf{x_k}] \times 0 = 0, \tag{14}$$

unless all other firms offer products with zero attractiveness. From Lemma 1 we know that a solution may exists for $\mathbf{x_k} \in (\mathbf{0}, \mathbf{x}^*)$. In this region, if a solution exists, it is implied that $P_k - \beta_{\mathbf{k}}' \cdot \mathbf{x_k} \geq 0$. Since $\mathbf{x_k} > \mathbf{0}$ then it also follows that for a solution to exist $P_k > 0$. □

Proof of Lemma 3: From (8) we obtain

$$\partial^2 \Pi_k/\partial x_{ki}^2 = [P_k - \beta_{\mathbf{k}}' \cdot \mathbf{x_k}]\left(\partial^2 M_k/\partial x_{ki}^2\right) Q - 2\beta_{ki}(\partial M_k/\partial x_{ki}) Q. \tag{15}$$

Using (11) we get

$$\frac{\partial^2 M_k}{\partial x_{ki}^2} = \frac{\partial}{\partial x_{ki}}\left[\frac{\partial M_k}{\partial f_k}\right]\frac{\partial f_k}{\partial x_{ki}} + \frac{\partial M_k}{\partial f_k}\frac{\partial^2 f_k}{\partial x_{ki}^2} = \frac{\partial}{\partial f_k}\left[\frac{\partial M_k}{\partial f_k}\right]\left[\frac{\partial f_k}{\partial x_{ki}}\right]^2 + \frac{\partial M_k}{\partial f_k}\frac{\partial^2 f_k}{\partial x_{ki}^2} \tag{16}$$

From (12) we obtain that for $x_{ki} \in (0, x_i^*)$ and $P_k \in (0, Y/b)$

$$\frac{\partial}{\partial f_k}\left[\frac{\partial M_k}{\partial f_k}\right] = \frac{-2M_k^2(1 - M_k)}{f_k^2} < 0. \tag{17}$$

Furthermore, we know that for $x_{ki} \in (0, x^*)$

$$\partial f_k/\partial x_{ki} = [-2w_i(x_{ki} - x_i^*)] \Big/ \sum_{i=1}^{L} w_i(x_i^*)^2 > 0, \tag{18}$$

and that

$$\partial^2 f_k/\partial x_{ki}^2 = (-2w_i) \Big/ \sum_{i=1}^{L} w_i(x_i^*)^2 < 0. \tag{19}$$

Equations (12), (17), (18), and (19), combined with (16) yield that for $x_{ki} \in (0, x_i^*)$ and $P_k \in (0, Y/b)$

$$\partial^2 M_k/\partial x_{ki}^2 < 0. \tag{20}$$

For $x_{ki} \in (0, x^*)$ and $P_k \in (0, Y/b)$ we know that $M_k > 0$. In this region, (11), (12), and (13) imply that $\partial M_k/\partial x_{ki} > 0$. These facts combined with (20) in (15) and if $P_k \geq \beta'_{\mathbf{k}} \cdot \mathbf{x_k}$, yield that

$$\partial^2 \Pi_k/\partial x_{ki}^2 < 0. \tag{21}$$

Using (4) we obtain the first order condition with respect to price

$$\partial \Pi_k/\partial P_k = [P_k - \beta'_{\mathbf{k}} \cdot \mathbf{x_k}](\partial M_k/\partial P_k)Q + M_k Q = 0. \tag{22}$$

From (1) and (3) follows that for $x_{ki} \in (0, x_i^*)$ and $P_k \in (0, Y/b)$

$$\partial M_k/\partial P_k = M_k(1 - M_k)(-b/Y)/[1 - (b P_k/Y)] < 0. \tag{23}$$

Using (23) we obtain that for $x_{ki} \in (0, x_i^*)$ and $P_k \in (0, Y/b)$

$$\partial^2 M_k/\partial P_k^2 = \left[-2M_k^2(1 - M_k)(b/Y)^2\right]/[1 - (b P_k/Y)]^2 < 0. \tag{24}$$

Using (22) we obtain

$$\partial^2 \Pi_k/\partial P_k^2 = [P_k - \beta'_{\mathbf{k}} \cdot \mathbf{x_k}]\left(\partial^2 M_k/\partial P_k^2\right) Q + 2(\partial M_k/\partial P_k)Q. \tag{25}$$

Using (23) and (24) in (25) for $x_{ki} \in (0, x_i^*)$ and $P_k \in (0, Y/b)$, and if $P_k \geq \beta'_{\mathbf{k}} \cdot \mathbf{x_k}$, we conclude that in this region $\partial^2 \Pi_k/\partial P_k^2 < 0$. □

Proof of Theorem 1:
For the proof of Theorem 1 the following three theorems will be used: □

Theorem 3 *The set* $S_k = \{[0 + \epsilon, Y/b - \epsilon] \times [\mathbf{0} + \epsilon, \mathbf{x}^* - \epsilon] : P_k \in [0 + \epsilon, Y/b - \epsilon],$ $\mathbf{x_k} \in [\mathbf{0} + \epsilon, \mathbf{x}^* - \epsilon],\ P_k - \beta'_{\mathbf{k}} \cdot \mathbf{x_k} \geq 0\}$ *is compact and convex.*

Proof of Theorem 3:
Consider the set $S_k = \{[0 + \epsilon, Y/b - \epsilon] \times [\mathbf{0} + \epsilon, \mathbf{x}^* - \epsilon] : P_k \in [0 + \epsilon, Y/b - \epsilon],$ $\mathbf{x_k} \in [\mathbf{0} + \epsilon, \mathbf{x}^* - \epsilon],\ P_k - \beta'_{\mathbf{k}} \cdot \mathbf{x_k} \geq 0\}$. This set is compact since it is closed and bounded.

Let $(P_k, x_{k1}, \ldots, x_{kL})$ and $(P'_k, x'_{k1}, \ldots, x'_{kL}) \in S_k$. This implies that $0 + \epsilon \leq P_k \leq (Y/b) - \epsilon$, $0 + \epsilon \leq P'_k \leq (Y/b) - \epsilon$, $0 + \epsilon \leq x_{ki} \leq x_{ki}^* - \epsilon$, and $0 + \epsilon \leq x'_{ki} \leq x_{ki}^* - \epsilon$, for $i = 1, \ldots, L$. In addition, the following hold true: $P_k \geq \sum_{i=1}^{L} \beta_i x_{ki}$ and $P'_k \geq \sum_{i=1}^{L} \beta_i x'_{ki}$. Take $0 < \lambda < 1$. Then from the above also holds that $\lambda\epsilon + (1 - \lambda)\epsilon = \epsilon \leq \lambda P_k + (1 - \lambda)P'_k \leq \lambda(Y/b - \epsilon) + (1 - \lambda)(Y/b - \epsilon)$ $= Y/b - \epsilon$, and that $\lambda\epsilon + (1 - \lambda)\epsilon = \epsilon \leq \lambda x_{ki} + (1 - \lambda)x'_{ki} \leq \lambda(x_{ki}^* - \epsilon) + (1 - \lambda)$ $(x_{ki}^* - \epsilon) = x_{ki}^* - \epsilon$. In addition, the following holds true $\lambda P_k + (1 - \lambda)P'_k \geq \lambda \sum_{i=1}^{L} \beta_i x_{ki} + (1 - \lambda)\sum_{i=1}^{L} \beta_i x'_{ki} = \sum_{i=1}^{L} \beta_i(\lambda x_{ki} + (1 - \lambda)x'_{ki})$. Therefore, the vector

$\lambda(P_k, x_{k1}, \ldots, x_{kL}) + (1-\lambda)(P'_k, x'_{k1}, \ldots, x'_{kL}) = (\lambda P_k + (1-\lambda)P'_k, \lambda x_{ki} + (1-\lambda)$ $x'_{ki}, \ldots, \lambda x_{kL} + (1-\lambda)x'_{kL}) \in S_k$. This shows that S_k is a convex set. □

Theorem 4 *Let f be a differentiable function defined on the open convex set $C \subset R^n$. Then f is strictly quasiconcave if and only if for every $x^0 \in C$ and $v \in R^n$ such that $v'v = 1$ and $v'\nabla f(x^0) = 0$ the function $f(t) = f(x^0 + tv)$ does not attain a local minimum at $t = 0$. If f is twice differentiable then a necessary and sufficient condition for strict quasiconcavity of f is that for every $x^0 \in C$ and $v \in R^n$ such that $v'\nabla f(x^0) = 0$, and $v'v = 1$, either $v'\nabla^2 f(x^0) < 0$ or $v'\nabla^2 f(x^0) = 0$ and $F(t) = F(x^0 + tv)$ does not attain a local minimum at $t = 0$.*

Proof of Theorem 4:
Theorem 4 and its proof can be found in Avriel et al. (1988, p. 78). □

Theorem 5 *A twice differentiable function $f : R^n \to R$ does not attain a local minimum at x^0 if $\partial f^2(x^0)/\partial x_i^2 < 0$, $i = 1, \ldots n$.*

Proof of Theorem 5:
From Bazaraa and Shetty (1979, p. 125) we know that the necessary conditions for x^0 to be a local minimum of $f : R^n \to R$ is $\nabla f(x^0) = 0$ and that the Hessian matrix is positive semidefinite. From Noble and Daniel (1977, p. 427) we know that a necessary condition for a matrix to be positive semidefinite is that the diagonal elements of the matrix must be non-negative. Now, if $\partial f^2(x^0)/\partial x_i^2 < 0$, $i = 1, \ldots, n$ which correspond to the diagonal elements of the Hessian, then by Noble and Daniel (1977) the Hessian is not a positive semi-definite matrix, and therefore, by Bazarra and Sethi (1979), the function f does not attain a local minimum. □

The profit function Π_k given in (4) is continuous, differentiable and bounded in S_k which by Theorem 3 is a compact and convex region. Lemma 3 shows that in S_k the following hold true: (i) $\partial^2\Pi_k/\partial P_k^2 < 0$, (ii) $\partial^2\Pi_k/\partial x_{ki}^2 < 0$. From the results in Lemma 3 and Theorem 5 follows that the profit function Π_k does not attain a local minimum. Furthermore, since the second partial derivatives are negative in S_k (Lemma 3), then by Theorem 4 the profit function Π_k is strictly quasiconcave in prices and product position. By Friedman's (1990) theorem on the existence of a Nash equilibrium for an N-person game, it follows that there exists a unique Nash equilibrium in prices and product position in $S_1 \times \cdots \times S_N$. □

APPENDIX B

Proof of Lemma 4: Using (23) in (22) and after simplifying we obtain

$$\partial\Pi_k/\partial P_k = h_k(M_k(P_k), P_k) = \{M_k Q/[1 - (b P_k/Y)]\}\{[P_k - \beta'_{\mathbf{k}} \cdot \mathbf{x_k}] \times (1 - M_k)(-b/Y) + [1 - (b P_k/Y)]\} = 0. \tag{26}$$

From Lemma 3 we know that for $\mathbf{x_k} \in (\mathbf{0}, \mathbf{x}^*)$, $P_k \in (0, Y/b)$, and if $P_k - \beta'_{\mathbf{k}} \cdot \mathbf{x_k} \geq 0$, then $\partial^2 \Pi_k / \partial P_k^2 = \partial h_k / \partial P_k < 0$. Let the market share of firm k be an exogenous parameter defined as m_k. From (26) we get

$$\partial h_k / \partial m_k = \{m_k Q / [1 - (b P_k / Y)]\}[P_k - \beta'_{\mathbf{k}} \cdot \mathbf{x_k}](b/Y) > 0, \tag{27}$$

since in S_k, $P_k - \beta'_{\mathbf{k}} \cdot \mathbf{x_k} \geq 0$. Total differentiation of (26) yields that

$$\frac{\partial P_k}{\partial m_k} = -\frac{\partial h_k / \partial m_k}{\partial h_k / \partial P_k}. \tag{28}$$

Using (27) and (28) the fact that in S_k, $\partial h_k / \partial P_k < 0$, follows that at Nash equilibrium $\partial P_k / \partial m_k > 0$. □

Proof of Lemma 5: Using (8) let $\partial \Pi_k / \partial x_{ki} = q_k(M_k(x_{ki}), x_{ki}) = 0$. Using (11), (12), and (18) in (8) and after simplifying we obtain

$$q_k(M_k(x_{ki}), x_{ki}) = [P_k - \beta'_{\mathbf{k}} \cdot \mathbf{x_k}]\left[-2w_i(x_{ki} - x_i^*) \Big/ \sum_{i=1}^{L} w_i (x_i^*)^2\right][(1 - M_k)/f_k] - \beta_{ki} = 0. \tag{29}$$

Let the market share of firm k be an exogenous parameter defined as m_k. From (29) we obtain

$$\partial q_k / \partial m_k = [P_k - \beta'_{\mathbf{k}} \cdot \mathbf{x_k}]\left[-2w_i(x_{ki} - x_i^*) \Big/ \sum_{i=1}^{L} w_i (x_i^*)^2\right][-1/f_k] < 0. \tag{30}$$

The result in (30) follows from (18), and the fact that in S_k $P_k - \beta'_{\mathbf{k}} \cdot \mathbf{x_k} \geq 0$ and $f_k > 0$. Total differentiation of (29) yields that

$$\frac{\partial x_{ki}}{\partial m_k} = -\frac{\partial q_k / \partial m_k}{\partial q_k / \partial x_{ki}}. \tag{31}$$

From Lemma 3 we know that for $\mathbf{x_k} \in (\mathbf{0}, \mathbf{x}^*)$, $P_k \in (0, Y/b)$, and if $P_k - \beta'_{\mathbf{k}} \cdot \mathbf{x_k} \geq 0$, then $\partial^2 \Pi_k / \partial x_{ki}^2 = \partial q_k / \partial x_{ki} < 0$. Using this fact, (30) and (31), follows that at Nash equilibrium $\partial x_{ki} / \partial m_k < 0$. □

Proof of Theorem 2:

Step 1: Assume that entry occurs and that the entrant has positive attraction and gains positive market share. This implies a change in the market share of the incumbent firms. From Lemmas 4 and 5 follows that at Nash equilibrium prior to entry, when the market share changes, price and product position move in different directions. This implies that upon entry, and thus change of the incumbents' market share, incumbents will react in one of two ways: increase price and decrease product position or decrease price and increase product position.

Step 2: Consider incumbent j. Assume that upon entry incumbent j increases prices (P_j) and decreases product position on attribute dimension i (x_{ji}). By Lemmas 4 and 5 follows that M_j increases.

Step 3: If P_j increases and x_{ji} decreases it follows that $Attr_j$ decreases. Let $Attr_{entrant}$ be the attraction of the entrant firm. Then,

$$M_j = Attr_j \Bigg/ \left[Attr_j + \sum_{k \neq j} Attr_k + Attr_{entrant} \right].$$

From step 3 we know that $Attr_j$ has decreased and from step 2 that M_j has increased. Since $Attr_{entrant} > 0$, it is implied that the attraction of another incumbent r has decreased.

Step 4: Since $Attr_r$ has decreased, using the direction of change of prices and product position depicted by Lemmas 4 and 5, it is implied that P_r increases and x_{ri} increases. From the above and the lemmas also follows that M_r increases. This implies that upon entry all incumbent firms will increase price, decrease product position and gain higher market share than before the entry. This can not occur proving that the only way to react upon entry is with a decrease in price and increase in product position. □

REFERENCES

Albers, S. and Brockhoff, K. 1977, A procedure for new product positioning in an attribute space, European Journal of Operational Research 1, 230–238.

Anderson, S. P., de Palma, A. and Thisse, J.-F., 1992, Discrete choice theory of product differentiation (The MIT Press, Cambridge).

Ansari, A., Economides, N. and Ghosh, A. 1994, Competitive positioning in markets with nonuniform preferences, Marketing Science 13, 248–273.

Avriel, M., Diewert, W. E. Schaible, S. and Zang, I. 1988, Generalized concavity (Plenum Press, New York).

Bachem, A. and Simon, H. 1981. A product positioning model with costs and prices, European Journal of Operational Research 7, 362–370.

Bazarra, M. S. and Shetty, C. M. 1979, Nonlinear programming: Theory and algorithms (John Wiley and Sons, New York).

Bell, D. E., Keeney, R. L. and Little, J. D. C., 1975, A market share theorem, Journal of Marketing Research 12, 136–141.

Carpenter, G. S., 1989, Perceptual position and competitive brand strategy in a two-dimensional two-brand market, Management Science 35, 1029–1044.

Choi, S. C., Desarbo, W. S. and Harker, P. T. 1990, Product positioning under price competition, Management Science 36, 175–199.

Cooper, L. G. and Nakanishi, M. 1988, Market share analysis (Kluwer Academic Press, Boston).

Eliashberg, J. and Manrai, A. K. 1992, Optimal positioning of new-product concepts: Some analytical implications and empirical results, European Journal of Operational Research 63, 376–397.

Friedman, J. W., 1990, Game theory with applications to economics (Oxford University Press, New York).

Gabszewicz, J. J. and Thisse, J.-F. 1986, Spatial competition and the location of firms, Fundamentals of Pure and Applied Economics 5, 1–71.

Graitson, D., 1982, Spatial competition a la Hotelling: A selective survey, Journal of Industrial Economics 31, 13–25.

Gruca, T. S., Kumar, K. R. and Sudharshan, D. 1992, An equilibrium analysis of defensive responses to entry using a coupled response function model, Marketing Science 11, 348–358.

Gruca, T. S., Sudharshan, D. 1991, Equilibrium characteristics of multinomial logit market share models, Journal of Marketing Research, 28, 480–483.

Hauser, J. R., 1988, Competitive price and positioning strategies, Marketing Science 7, 76–91.

Hauser, J. R. and Shugan, S. M. 1983, Defensive marketing strategies, Marketing Science 2, 319–360.
Hauser, J. R. and Wernerfelt, B. 1988, Existence and uniqueness of price equilibria in defender, Marketing Science 7, 92–93.
Hotelling, H., 1929, Stability in competition, Economic Journal 39, 41–47.
Karla, A., Rajiv, S., and Srinivasan, K., 1998, Response to competitive entry: a rationale for delayed defensive reaction, Marketing Science, 17, 380–405.
Kotler, P., 1965, Competitive strategies for new product marketing over the life cycle, Management Science 12, B-104–B-119.
Kumar, K. R. and Hadjinicola, G. C., 1996, Resource allocation to defensive marketing and manufacturing strategies, European Journal of Operational Research, 94, 453–466.
Kumar, K. R. and Sudharshan, D. 1988, Defensive marketing strategies: An equilibrium analysis based on decoupled response function models, Management Science 34, 805–815.
Lane, W. J., 1980, Product differentiation in a market with endogenous sequential entry, The Bell Journal of Economics 11, 237–260.
McFadden, D., 1986, The choice theory approach to market research, Marketing Science 5, 275–297.
McGuire, T. W., Farley, J. W., Lucas Jr. R. E., and Ring, L. W. 1968, Estimation and inference for linear models in which subsets of the dependent variables are constrained, Journal of the American Statistical Association 63, 1201–1213.
Moorthy, K. S., 1988, Product and price competition in a duopoly, Marketing Science, 7, 141–168.
Nakanishi, M. and Cooper, L. G. 1982, Simplified estimation procedures for MCI models, Marketing Science 1, 314–322.
Nash, J., 1951, Non-cooperative games, Annals of Mathematics 54, 286–295.
Noble, B. and Daniel, J. W. 1970, Applied linear algebra (Prentice Hall, Englewoods Cliffs).
Robinson, W. T., 1988, Marketing mix reactions to entry, Marketing Science 7, 368–385.
Schwartz, H. R., 1989, Numerical analysis: a comprehensive introduction (John Wiley and Sons, New York).
Shaked, A. and Sutton, J., 1982, Relaxing price competition through product differentiation, Review of Economic Studies, 49, 3–13.
Shankar, V., 1997, Pioneer's marketing mix reactions to entry in different competitive game structures: theoretical analysis and empirical illustration, Marketing Science, 16, 271–293.
Shocker, A. D. and Shrinivasan, V. 1974, A consumer-based methodology for the identification of new product ideas, Management Science 20, 921–937.
Sudharshan, D., May, J. H. and Gruca, T. 1988, DIFFSTRAT: An analytical procedure for generating optimal new product concepts for a differentiated-type strategy, European Journal of Operational Research 36, 50–65.
Vandenbosch, M. B. and Weinberg, C. B. 1995, Product and price competition in a two-dimensional vertical differentiation model, Marketing Science 14, 224–249.

KNOWLEDGE DISCOVERY BY MEANS OF INTELLIGENT INFORMATION INFRASTRUCTURE METHODS AND THEIR APPLICATIONS

HENRY C. W. LAU, CHRISTINA W. Y. WONG, AND ANDREW NING

INTRODUCTION

In today's competitive environment, enterprises have set up Internet connections to promote their corporate business in the global marketplace. Nevertheless, a survey shows that only 5% of those connections allow direct data integration with corporate databases, i.e., without any manual input of data (New Era of Networks, Inc., 2000). Conventional methods such as mail, fax, and e-mail messages (all of them are *not* "format-specific") are still the main communication media in the business environment. Primarily, Internet connections are playing the role of information hubs and have not yet become "the gateway for information and data interchange" (Staab, et al., 2000).

Information infrastructure refering to the Internet connection or corporate network with data communication capability, has become an emerging platform to enable business partners, customers, and employees of enterprises to access and interchange corporate data from dispersed locations all over the world. In general, information infrastructure is a browser-based gateway that allows users to gather, share, and disseminate data through a single Internet connection easily and interactively. The benefits of the information infrastructure include (i) improvement of business-to-customer as well as business-to-business relationships, (ii) reduction of administration costs, and (iii) minimization of inventories of supplies and replacement of parts, etc. In addition, the information infrastructure can help automate manual data processing procedures and integrate the computer document system, and data warehouse of enterprises. Numbers of knowledge discovery by means of intelligent information infrastructure methods and applications are introduced in this chapter that help to address the importance and benefits of an information infrastructure for knowledge discovery.

Neural Online Analytical Processing System (NOLAPS)

Recently, data mining technology, which aims at the conversion of clusters of complex data into useful information, has been under active research (Berson and Smith, 1997; Michael and Bel, 1999; Robert, Joseph, and David, 1999; Peterson, 2000). Data mining, in general, identifies and characterizes interrelationships among multivariable dimensions without requiring human effort to formulate specific questions. In other words, data mining is concerned with discovering new, meaningful information, so that decision-makers can learn as much as they can from their valuable data assets. Data mining tools require different data formats in relational and multidimensional database systems. The shared data access interface of data mining tools will enable easier exchange of information among different sources. There are many commercial products for data mining and a typical example of such product is Microsoft SQL server that has incorporated the On-Line Analytical Processing (OLAP) technology, which provides a service for accessing, viewing, and analyzing on large volume of data with high flexibility and performance (Thomsen, 1999; Peterson, 2000). OLAP, which is based on data mining technology, has been developed by software companies and commercial products, such as the OLAP server by Microsoft, are now available in the market. OLAP provides a service for accessing, viewing, and analyzing on large volumes of data with high flexibility and performance. It can be used as a decision-support facility with the capability to properly manage the raw data for various purposes, thereby detecting opportunities and suggesting business strategies.

However, an OLAP application is not without pitfalls. Although OLAP is able to provide numerical and statistical analysis of data in an efficient and timely way, it lacks the predictive capability, such as the projection of possible outcomes based on the past history of events so as to decide on the action to be taken. In this respect, it seems necessary that a certain "ingredient" of intelligence element needs to be added to OLAP to enable the self-learning capability of the whole system.

Neural network is a technology that has typically been used for prediction, clustering, classification, and alerting of abnormal pattern (Haykin, 1994; Tandem Computers Incorporated, 1997). Parroting the operation of the human brain, neural network technology comprises many simple processing units connected by adaptive weights. They create predictive networks by considering a "training set" of actual records. In theory, the formation of neural network is similar to the formation of neural pathways in the brain as a task is practiced. Also, a neural network refines its network with each new input it considers. To predict a future scenario, the neural network technology is able to work with a training set of data from the past history of records. It will use the training set to build a network, based on which the neural network is able to predict future scenario by supplying a set of attributes. Like the OLAP technology, there are many commercial products that have incorporated neural network technology, such as EasyNN (2000), Neurem (2000), and Qnet (2000). The inclusion of computational intelligence knowledge into a data mining technology can significantly enhance the "machine learning" capability of the system and is undoubtedly an issue that is justified to be addressed.

In creating decision-support functionality, a mechanism, which is able to combine and coordinate many sets of diversified data into a unified and consistent body of useful information, is required. In larger organizations, many different types of users with varied needs must utilize the same massive data warehouse to retrieve the right information for the right purpose. Although data warehouse is referred as a very large repository of historical data pertaining to an organization, data mining is more concerned with the collection, management, and distribution of organized data in an effective way. The nature of a data warehouse includes integrated data, detailed and summarized data, historical data, and metadata. Integrated data enable the data miner to easily and quickly look across the vistas of data. Detailed data is important when the data miner wishes to examine data in its most detailed manner, whereas historical data is essential because important information nuggets are hidden in this type of data. OLAP is an example of architectural extension of the data warehouse.

OLAP refers to the technique of performing complex analysis over the information stored in a data warehouse. Moreover, there is currently no universally accepted conceptual model for OLAP. Merwe and Solms (1998) address this issue by proposing a model of a data cube and algebra to support OLAP operations on this cube. The model they present is simple and intuitive, and the algebra provides a means to concisely express complex OLAP queries.

Therefore, after the setup of a data warehouse, the attention is usually switched to the area of data mining, which aims to extract new and meaningful information. In other words, a pool of 'useful information' that has been stored in a company data warehouse becomes 'intelligent information', thereby allowing decision-makers to learn as much as they can from their valuable data assets. In this respect, neural network can be deployed to enhance the intelligence level of the OLAP application.

Neural network searches for hidden relationships, patterns, correlation, and interdependencies in large databases that traditional information gathering methods (such as report creation and user querying) may have overlooked. The responsibility of the neural network is to provide the desired change of parameters based on what the network has been trained on. Intrinsically, a sufficient amount of data sample is a key factor in order to obtain accurate feedback from the trained network. As neural network is meant to learn relationships between data sets by simply having sample data represented to their input and output layers (Herrmann, 1995), the training of the network with input and output layers mapped to relevant realistic values with the purpose to develop the correlation between these two groups of data will not, in principle, contradict the basic principle of neural network.

With a trained network available, the recommended action can be obtained with the purpose to rectify some hidden problems, should that occur at a later stage. Therefore, in the training process of the neural network, the nodes of the input layer of the neural network represent the data from the OLAP and those of the output layer represent the predictions and extrapolations. The data flow of the NOLAPS has been depicted

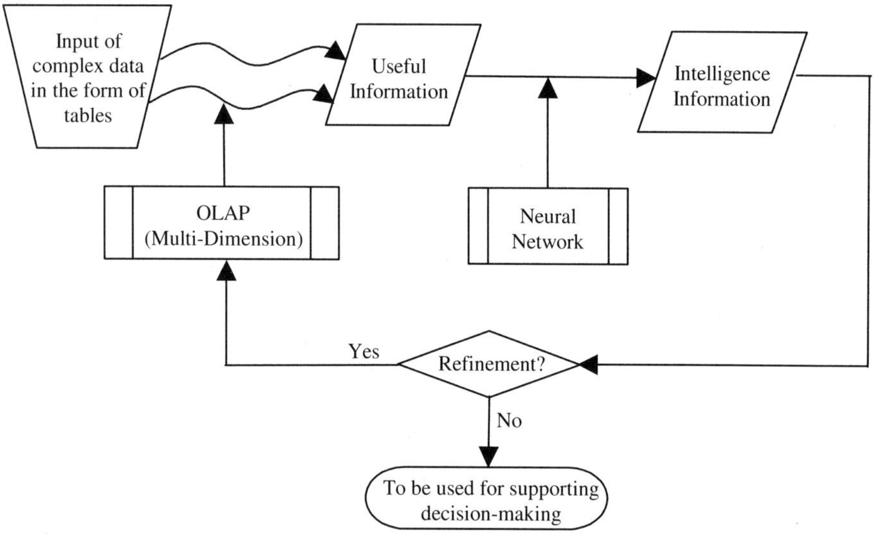

Figure 1. Information flow of NOLAP.

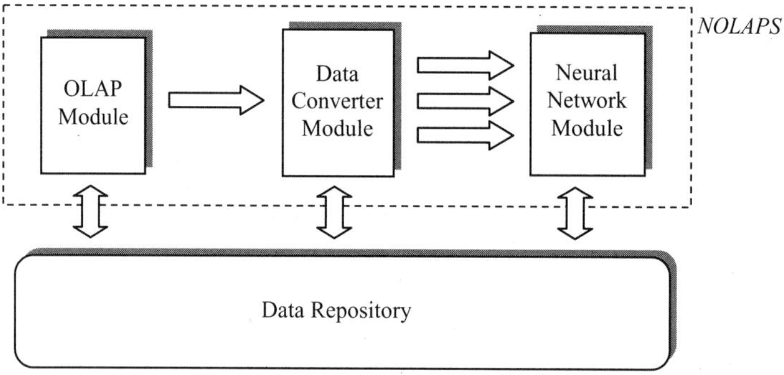

Figure 2. Infrastructure of NOLAPS.

in Figure 1. It should be noted that the output information from the OLAP could be used to refine the OLAP data cube so as to continually update the database over time.

The data interchange within the NOLAPS encompasses three modules, namely OLAP module, Data Conversion (DC) module, and Neural Network (NN) module (Figure 2). The data repository that aims to support efficient data interchange among the three modules, is essential for the coordination and updating of information from various sources.

As for the OLAP module, it consists of descriptive data (dimensions) and quantitative value (measures), both of which generate the OLAP data cube by building up two elements, namely, fact table and dimension (Erik, George, and Dick, 1999). In the fact table, the required data and user-defined methods for analysis are specified clearly. In the descriptive data of OLAP, the different dimension levels are defined for further computational use on different views of OLAP data cube. Typical dimension includes location, company, and time, whereas typical measure includes price, sales, and profit. With a multidimensional view of data, the OLAP module provides the foundation for analytical processing through flexible access to information. In particular, this distinct feature can be used to compute a complex query and analyze data on reports, thereby achieving the viewing of data in different dimensions in a more easy and efficient way.

Case example of neural online analytical processing system

A prototype system has been developed, based on the framework of the NOLAPS. Pursuing the NOLAPS infrastructure that has been defined in the previous section, the OLAP module has generated a pool of useful data and accordingly, the NN module has created a reliably trained NN. Next, five latest track records of a company have been gathered and listed as follows.

Performance Score Point (PSP) ranging from 1 (least point) to 7 (highest point) is used to assess the company as shown below.

Company A	Product quality PSP	Product cost PSP	Delivery schedule PSP
Latest record	3.5	6.5	6.6
2nd latest record	4.7	5.5	5.4
3rd latest record	5.0	5.1	4.8
4th latest record	5.6	4.1	4.4
5th latest record	4.0	4.0	3.0

After such information has been input, the NN module gives an assessment report back to user, thus supporting user to take action if deemed necessary. In the following table, "0" output from the NN node indicates a negative suggestion to the associated statement and "1" is the positive suggestion, whereas "0.5" indicates that there is not enough data to justify a firm suggestion.

Company A	Output from NN module
Potentially competent	0.5
Suggested to be replaced	0
Service quality is compromised to meet the quoted price	1
Further assessment of company performance is required	1
Delivery time seems to be inconsistent due to certain company problems	1

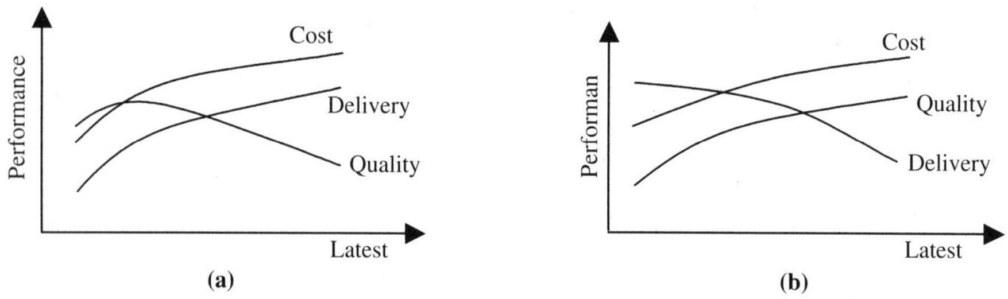

Figure 3. Performance of a company on the basis of past records.

On the basis of NN output results as shown in the table, Company A seems to have a problem in meeting the delivery schedules, and it is suggested that further assessment regarding the company's performance is needed. On the basis of the suggestion of this assessment report, Company A has been approached to find out the reason behind the continual downgrade of performance in terms of product quality. After an organized investigation of the issue, it has been found that several of the senior staff of the product quality assurance group have left the company to start their own business. Because of this unexpected change, the company has suffered an unprecedented "brain-drain", resulting in the sudden decline of quality level of certain mainstream products.

Because of this situation, Company A has been suggested to adopt some best practices related to quality assurance. In this case, the Total Quality Management (TQM) practice has been adopted and some necessary tools have also been acquired to implement such practice in the company. At this stage, it is still difficult to tell if the company could significantly reverse the downturn performance in terms of product quality. However, because of the signal generated from the NOLAPS, the problem of a business partner has been alerted and a quick decision has been made with supporting assessment report, thus avoiding the loss of a trusted business partner, which can in turn weaken the overall performance of the VEN.

This case example indicates that the introduction of the NN module to the OLAP module is able to significantly upgrade the decision-support functionality. However, the result obtained, so far, is by no means perfect although it demonstrates that the suggested NOLAPS is basically viable and, therefore, it is justifiable to have further investigation along this line of research.

Neural Fuzzy Model

Fuzzy logic is a superset of conventional (Boolean) logic that has been extended to handle the concept of partial truth, i.e., truth values between 'completely true' and 'completely false'. According to Zadeh (1965, 1993, 1996), rather than regarding fuzzy theory as a single theory, people should regard the process of "fuzzification" as a methodology to generalize any specific theory from a crisp (discrete) to a continuous (fuzzy) form. In particular, fuzzy logic has been deployed to replace the role of

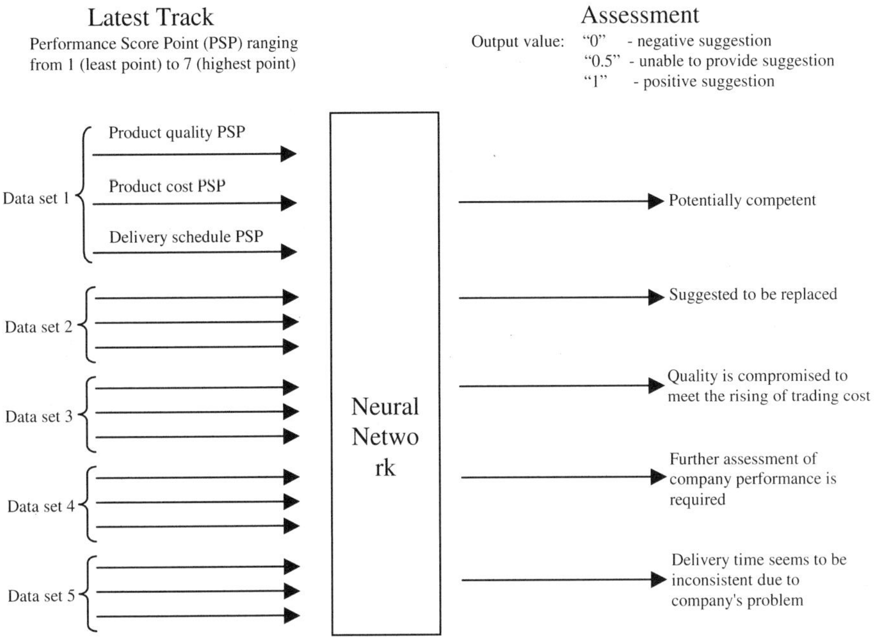

Figure 4. Mapping of input and output nodes of Neural Network (NN) module of the NOLAPS.

mathematical model with another that is built from a number of rules with fuzzy variables such as output temperature and fuzzy terms, such as relatively high and reasonably low (Buchanan, 1989; Leung and Lam, 1988; Orchard, 1994; Burns, 1997).

Parameter-based control can be applied to situations where the output values are influenced by the input parameters. Related research in the area pertaining to the parameter-based control, adopting a "nonconventional" approach, indicates that the study is focused on the provision of fuzzy logic inference techniques. In an environment where there are multiple input and output parameters interacting with each others, many authors suggest that a fuzzy logic inference architecture can be employed to deal with the complex control issues (Leung & Lam, 1988; Mizumoto, Fukami, and Tanaka, 1979; Whalen & Schott, 1983; Kaufman, 1975; Chiueh, 1992; Nguyen, 2000). Driankov et al. (1996) suggests the computational structure of a fuzzy knowledge base controller (FKBC) to handle parameter-based control, which encompasses five computational steps including input scaling (normalization), fuzzification of inputs, inference or rule firing, defuzzification of outputs, and output denormalization. It is not the intention of this chapter to justify any detailed analysis, methodologies, and techniques behind the fuzzy inference architectures covered in the above articles. However, most of the techniques described are very useful in understanding the design and operations of the fuzzy inference architecture on which the development of a fuzzy expert system can be based.

Although most of the fuzzy rules of these techniques are being set on the basis of experience, past history, and theoretical background, it is obvious that more can be done regarding the formulation of an algorithmic solution and the structure finding from existing data, which may lead to any generation of rules. In this respect, NN has the ability to learn the relationship among input and output data sets through a training process, thus enabling to "induce" output data if a new set of input data is made available. Although it can be said that NN cannot do anything that cannot be done using traditional computing techniques, yet they can handle some tasks that would otherwise be very difficult. For example, the rules generated by the NN training process are more acceptable than those decided by expert knowledge that may not be independent and fair (Zahedi, 1991; Zahedi, 1993).

The deployment of fuzzy logic principles involves fuzzy rules being set on the basis of past experience and trial result of operations. Instead of specifying exact numeric value, fuzzy rules support the use of statements with linguistic terms. And while fuzzy logic systems allow the use of linguistic terms representing data sets in the reasoning process, NN is able to discover connections between data sets by simply having sample data represented to its input and output layers (Haykin, 1999). NN can be regarded as a processing device, and it usually has some sort of "training" rule whereby the weights of connections are adjusted on the basis of presented patterns.

To enhance machine intelligence, an integrated neural-fuzzy model, which aims to make use of benefits generated by the synergy of NN and fuzzy logic intelligence techniques. The main feature of the neural-fuzzy model is that it uses the trained NN to generate 'If-Then' rules, which are then fuzzified prior to undergoing a fuzzy inferencing process, resulting in the generation of new process parameters for enhancing machine intelligence. The neural-fuzzy system described here adopts inductive learning through the network, indicating that the system induces the information in its knowledge base by example. That induced information is then fuzzified and fed to the fuzzy logic system prior to fuzzy reasoning process. The significance of the neural-fuzzy model is that it attempts to formulate a technique for eliminating the knowledge acquisition bottleneck, thus enhancing the intelligent monitoring of a parameter-based control situation.

Demonstration of Neural-Fuzzy Model

Neural network (NN)

The responsibility of the NN model element is to provide the desired change of parameters on the basis of what the network has been trained on. Intrinsically, a sufficient amount of data sample is a key factor to obtain accurate feedback from the trained network. In actual situations, recommended action about the required change of parameters to cope with the dimensional inconsistency is essential. In view of this situation, NN can be regarded as a better option, if the dimensional values are mapped to the nodes of the input layer and heat-transfer parameters are mapped to the output layer nodes, thus resulting in a control model that is the reverse of the heat-transfer model. In the light of the fact that in an actual thermal system design, the required overall heat transfer is first determined from the system analysis. Then the rib geometry is chosen according to the nearest overall heat-transfer performance determined from experimental investigations. Very often the difference between the designed overall heat transfer and the experimental-performance data can be quite significant.

With a NN, the correlation between the deviations of heat-transfer parameters in response to the deviations of the occurring dimensional values can be trained on the basis of a wide spectrum of actual sample data. As NN is intended to learn relationships between data sets by simply having sample data represented to their input and output layers (Herrmann, 1995), the training of a network with input and output layers mapped to dimensional deviation values and heat-transfer deviation values respectively, with the purpose to develop the correlation between these two groups of data will not contradict the basic principle of NN.

With a trained network available, it is possible that recommended action about the change of parameters can be obtained with the purpose to optimize the design of rib geometry, should that occur at a later stage. Therefore, in the training process of the NN, the nodes of the input layer of the NN represent the deviation of the dimensional values and those of the output layer represent the deviation of the heat-transfer parameters.

Fuzzy logic reasoning

If there is dimensional inconsistency on the heat-transfer model, the values at the nodes from the NN (representing the parameter deviations) may provide some hints for possible dimensional correction. With the availability of this information, a fuzzy logic approach can then be employed to provide a modified set of recommended parameter change on the basis of original output values from the NN. The motive for using fuzzy logic reasoning in this model is to take advantage of its ability to deal with imprecision terms that fit ideally in the parameter-based control situations, where terms such as "rib spacing could be increased slightly" are used. Furthermore, the vagueness and uncertainty of human expressions is well modeled in the fuzzy sets, and a pseudo-verbal representation, similar to an expert's formulation, can be achieved.

During fuzzy reasoning process, the input and output values of the NN are generally fuzzified into linguistic terms so that fuzzy rules can be developed. The method of obtaining the corresponding output membership values from the "fired" fuzzy rule is called fuzzy logic reasoning. Many reasoning strategies have been developed, including Sup-bounded-product (Mizumoto, 1981), Super-drastic-product (Mizumoto, 1979; Mizumoto, 1981; Mizumoto, 1990), Sup-min (Mamdani, 1974), and Sup-product (Kaufman, 1975). Because it is not the intention of this chapter to present a review of fuzzy logic reasoning strategies, the mentioned reasoning strategies are not further explained. The Sup-product strategy is adopted due to its simplicity and relatively less calculation time.

After the fuzzification process with the generation of fuzzy rules, it is necessary to have a defuzzification process. The defuzzification process is a process of mapping from a space of inferred fuzzy control results to a space of nonfuzzy control action in a crisp form. In fact, a defuzzification strategy is aimed at generating a nonfuzzy control action that best represents the possibility distribution of the inferred fuzzy control results. The Mean of Maximum (MOM) and Centre of Area (COA) are two common defuzzification methods in fuzzy control systems, and the latter method is selected in this neural-fuzzy model to defuzzify the reasoned fuzzy output (the parameters value). Proposed parameter change is carried out and the dimensional outcome, resulting from the change is checked against the expected dimension.

Cross-platform intelligent information infrastructure

The real challenge for the implementation of information infrastructure in enterprises is to achieve *seamless* data interchange in the sense that data from various sources with dissimilar formats can integrate directly with the database system of any individual company in a fully automatic way, i.e., without any human intervention. In this respect, DC and mapping of data-fields to match the formats of various enterprises are the prerequisites of meeting this data integration criterion.

Since 1996, the new eXtensible Markup Language (XML) has been developed for overcoming the limitations of HTML, and has received worldwide acceptance in terms of data interchange in the Internet-based information systems. In XML files, the content of data and the presentation of data are separated. Thus, various formats of data specified by XML are able to be transferred through the Internet and used on different platforms (Microsoft Corporation, 2000). In brief, XML is a subset of Standard Generalized Markup Language (SGML) which is an international standard (ISO 8879) for defining and representing documents in an application-independent form (Salminen, et al., 2000).

To be able to realize the potential of information infrastructure as an effective data processing gateway, data mining technology needs to be incorporated. In brief, data mining is seen as a technological approach that provides sophisticated analysis based on a set of complex data, enabling the management of different data formats in various database systems. The shared data access interface of data mining tools will enable exchange of data as well as results among various computer systems. The typical example of data mining tool is OLAP that provides a service for accessing, viewing, and analyzing on large volumes of data with high flexibility and performance. The essential characteristic of OLAP is that it performs a numerical and statistical analysis of data, which are organized in the form of multidimensions (as opposed to the two-dimensional format of traditional relational data tables).

Cross-platform intelligent information infrastructure allows users to access and retrieve data of any database format from distributed sources, followed by the automate assimilation of the data in the user's own database system. The information infrastructure also allows collaboration and data sharing and provides users with the ability to generate business transactions, reports, and dynamic updates through the common interface. On the basis of robust XML data interchange open standard, the information infrastructure can integrate virtually with all existing systems and database in real time and distrbute data automatically to the required destinations. To enable users to

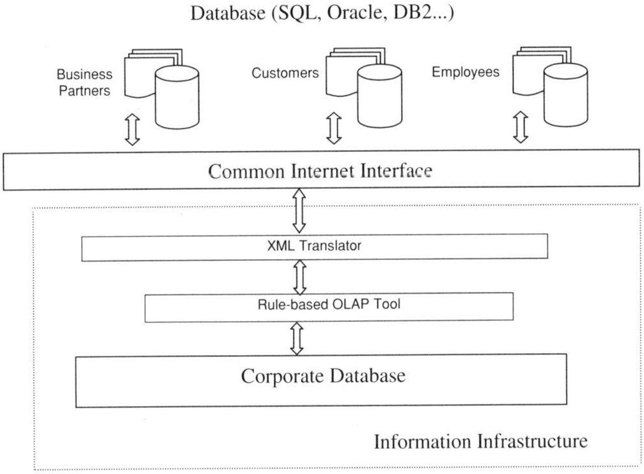

Figure 5. Outline of cross-platform intelligent informaton infrastructure.

access timely information efficiently, an OLAP tool with intelligent functionality such as rule-based reasoning is required.

Figure 5 shows the configuration of the information infrastructure, which is a client-server system. The clients are users' (business partners, customers, employees) desktops who connect to the common interface using Internet browers. Thus, users can quickly access and retrieve all information and data needed through the information infrastructure, i.e., the Internet server with the XML and the intelligent OLAP facilities.

Currently in most client-server systems, the data requested from the client side is done by human users, such as requesting news on the Internet server or filling in the order forms. When the request originates from a database or a program on the client side, i.e., a database on the client side connects to the database on the server side, a standard data interchange format is needed. At this stage, a common data format such as the XML seems to be the right choice to meet the requirement. To create the XML data file, an XML translator is built in the information infrastructure so that different database systems can achieve data interchange among themselves.

Other than the data interchange through the information infrastructure, users may intend to perform data analysis such as statistical analysis or business report. This task is normally referred as data mining. OLAP technology provides high flexibility and performance for the data mining and uses multidimensional data model for users to formulate complex queries and to arrange the query result on a report. The multidimensional data model organizes data into a hierarchy that represents levels of details on the data. Thus the data structure of multidimensional data model is clearer than the relational database which is the structure of most current databases. In the information infrastructure, a multidimensional database is implemented for the OLAP application.

Query on the large volume of data from the database by the OLAP tool is a complicated analysis and may not aggregate enough data. In the cross-platform intelligent information infrastructure, the rule-based reasoning facility is incorporated to support the OLAP tool. The tasks of the rule-based reasoning are (i) to assist the setup of a corporate database, (ii) to help the extraction of useful information from the database, and (iii) to provide suggestions of efficient OLAP query methods. Thus, rule-based OLAP provides users with the access to the knowledge hidden in the databases, thereby discovering the trends and relationships in the data to make predictions using that information.

The rule-based reasoning facility includes knowledge base and inference engine. It retrieves knowledge (stored in the knowledge base) and uses the forward and backward inference logic to produce the actions (provide suggestions). In other words, it supports decision-makers (users) to get as much useful information as they can from their valuable knowledge base. In this respect, the rule-based reasoning can be deployed to enhance the intelligence level of the OLAP application.

The knowledge base of the rule-based reasoning facility consists of declarative knowledge and procedural knowledge (Inference Corporation, 1992). The declarative knowledge contains what is currently known about the data interchange and process in the information infrastructure. The procedural knowledge is developed from repeated data interchange and process experience, and usually relate specific conditions with their likely outcomes, consequences, or indicated actions.

Conclusion

After a period of increasing professionalism in almost all areas of research and technology, the new era is to embrace the interaction of different approaches, to form multifunctional disciplines. The information infrastructures introduced above demonstrate the benefits of using combinations of technologies to form an integrated system that capitalize on the merits and at the same time offset the pitfalls of the involved technologies. Further research on the infrastructure framework for knowledge discovery, particularly the seamless integration of the technologies, is needed to ensure and sustain the benefits of the infrastructures.

REFERENCES

Berson, A., and Smith, S. J. (1997), *Data Warehousing, Data Mining, & OLAP*, McGraw-Hill, New York.

Buchanan, B. and Shortliffe, E. H. (1989). *Rule-based expert systems: the MYCIN experiments of the Stanford Heuristic Programming Project.* Addison-Wesley series in artificial intelligence. Reading, Mass.: Addison-Wesley.

Burns, R. (1997). Intelligent manufacturing. *Aircraft Engineering and Aerospace Technology*; 69(5): 440–446.

Chiueh, T. (1992). Optimization of Fuzzy Logic Inference Architecture, Computer, May; 67–71.

Driankov, D., Hellendoorn, H., and Reinfrank, M. (1996). An Introduction to Fuzzy Control. Springer; 149–163.

Erik, T., George, S., and Dick, C. (1999). *Microsoft OLAP Solutions*, John Wiley & Sons, New York.

Haykin, S. (1994). *Neural networks, a comprehensive foundation*, Macmillan College Publishing Company.

Haykin, S. (1999). *Neural network, a comprehensive foundation.* 2nd edition. Upper Saddle River, N.J.: Prentice Hall.

Herrmann, C. S. (1995). A hybrid fuzzy-neural expert system for diagnosis, *Proceedings of International Joint Conference on Artificial Intelligence*, pp. 494–500.

Inference Corporation. (1992). *ART-IM 2.5 Reference Manuals* (Los Angeles).
Kaufman, A. (1975). *Introduction to theory of fuzzy subsets.* New York, Academic.
Leung, K. S., and Lam, W. (1988). Fuzzy Concepts in Expert Systems. *IEEE,* September, 43–56.
Mamdani, E. H. (1974). Applications of fuzzy algorithms for control of a simple dynamic plant. *Proceedings of IEEE, 1974*; 121: 1585–1588.
Merwe, J. v. d., and Solms, S. H. v. (1998). Electronic commerce with secure intelligent trade agents, *Computers & Security*, Vol. 17, pp. 435–446.
Michael, L. G., and Bel, G. R. (1999). Data mining—a powerful information creating tool, *OCLC Systems & Services*, Vol. 15, No. 2, pp. 81–90.
Microsoft Corporation. (2000). *Microsoft BizTalk jumpstart kit*, Feb.
Mizumoto. M., Fukami, S., and Tanaka, K. (1979). *Some Methods of Fuzzy Reasoning. Advances in Fuzzy Set Theory and Applications.* North-Holland, Amsterdam; 117–136.
Mizumoto, M. (1981). Note on the arithmetic rule by Zedeh for fuzzy reasoning methods. *Cyben System*; 12: 247–306.
Mizumoto, M. (1990). Fuzzy controls by product-sum-gravity method. In Advancement of fuzzy theory and systems in China and Japan, *Proceeding of Sino-Japan Joint Meeting on Fuzzy Sets and Systems Oct. 15–18*, Beijing, China, International Academic; 1–4.
New Era of Networks, Inc., (2000). Powering the new economy.
Nguyen, H. T. (2000). *A first course in fuzzy logic.* 2nd edition. Boca Raton, Fla: Chapman & Hall/CRC.
Orchard, A. (1994). *FuzzyCLIPS Version 6.02A User's Guide.* National Research Council. Canada.
Peterson, T. (2000). *Microsoft OLAP unleashed*, 2nd edition, Sams Pubishing, Indianapolis.
Robert, S. C., Joseph, A. V., and David, B. (1999). *Microsoft Data Warehousing*, John Wiley & Sons.
Salminen, A., Lyytikäinen, V., and Tiitinen, P. (2000). Putting documents into their work context in document analysis, *Information Processing & Management* 36, Issue 4, July 1, 623–641.
Tandem Computers Incorporated (1997). Object Relational Data Mining Technology for a Competitive Advantage (White Paper), *Decision Support Solutions*, http://www.tandem.com/
Thomsen, E. (1999). *Microsoft OLAP solutions*, J. Wiley, New York.
Whalen, T., and Schott, B. (1983). Issues in Fuzzy Production Systems. *International Journal of Man-Machine Studies*; 19:57.
Zadeh, F. (1996). Fuzzy sets, fuzzy logic, and fuzzy systems: selected papers. Singapore, World Scientific.
Zadeh, F. (1965). Fuzzy sets. *Information and Control* 8:338–53.
Zadeh, F. (1993). *The role of fuzzy logic and soft computing in the conception and design of intelligence systems.* Klement, Slany.
Zahedi, F. (1991). An introduction to neural network and a comparison with artificial intelligence and expert systems. *Interfaces*; 21(2): 25–28.
Zahedi, F. (1993). Intelligent Systems for Business: Expert Systems with Neural Network, Wadsworth, Belmont, CA.